Endorsed by
...cel

Edexcel
Biology for A2

C J Clegg

DYNAMIC LEARNING

Innovate • Motivate • Personalise

HODDER EDUCATION

AN HACHETTE UK COMPANY

Hachette UK's policy is to use papers that are natural, renewable and recyclable products and made from wood grown in sustainable forests. The logging and manufacturing processes are expected to conform to the environmental regulations of the country of origin.

Orders: please contact Bookpoint Ltd, 130 Milton Park, Abingdon, Oxon OX14 4SB. Telephone: (44) 01235 827720. Fax: (44) 01235 400454. Lines are open 9.00–5.00, Monday to Saturday, with a 24-hour message answering service. Visit our website at www.hoddereducation.co.uk

© C.J. Clegg 2009
First published in 2009 by
Hodder Education,
An Hachette UK Company
338 Euston Road
London NW1 3BH

Impression number   5 4 3 2
Year   2012 2011 2010 2009

Cover photo STEVE GSCHMEISSNER/SCIENCE PHOTO LIBRARY
Illustrations by Oxford Designers and Illustrators
Typeset in 10pt Goudy by Fakenham Photosetting Ltd, Fakenham, Norfolk
Printed in Italy

A catalogue record for this title is available from the British Library

ISBN: 978 0 340 96780 5

Author's acknowledgements

To all the known and unknown experimental scientists, naturalists, teachers, illustrators and writers who have influenced my own understanding, I gladly acknowledge my debt.

I have had the benefit of advice and insights on the specific requirements of the new Edexcel Specification from Mr Ed Lees, previously Head of Sixth Form at The Ridgeway School, Wroughton, and Principal Examiner and Principal Moderator for Edexcel. As an experienced teacher of biology, his perceptive observations on the content and approach of the manuscript as a whole were invaluable.

On particular aspects of the Edexcel A2 Biology Specification, I have had the advantage of insights from experts whose specialist advice was much appreciated:

- Professor Chris Stringer FRS, Research Leader in Human Origins, Palaeontology Department, Natural History Museum, concerning an application of CAT scanning
- Dr Michael Dockery, Education Officer, Association for the Study of Animal Behaviour, Manchester Metropolitan University, concerning the core practicals on animal behaviour and physiology.

I am indebted to Dr Neil Millar of Heckmondwike Grammar School, Kirklees, West Yorkshire, for creating the appendix *Handling Data for A2 Biology* to meet the specific requirements of A2 Biology students (available via Dynamic Learning).

Nevertheless, any remaining inaccuracies are my sole responsibility. I hope readers will write to point out any faults they find.

At Hodder Education, the skill and patience of Katie Mackenzie Stuart (Science Publisher), Helen Townson (Designer), Andreas Schindler (Picture Research), the team who created Hodder's Dynamic Learning facility, and my Freelance Editor Gina Walker have combined to bring together text, illustrations and other materials as I have wished, and I am most grateful to them.

Dr Chris Clegg
Salisbury, Wiltshire, May, 2009

Practical work

In this text and the accompanying Dynamic Learning resources, there are suggestions for practical work which teachers might like students to perform. Detailed procedures can be found in other texts.

Since 1989, risk assessment has been required by law, initially by the Control of Substances Hazardous to Health (COSHH) Regulations but now by several sets of legislation, including the Management of Health and the Personal Protective Equipment (PPE) Regulations. All of these come under the umbrella of the Health and Safety at Work etc. Act. However, from a practical point of view, it matters little under which regulations a risk assessment is to be carried out, so that the requirement can be summed up as follows:

> A risk assessment is needed for any activity in which there is a significant hazard, whether carried out by pupils, teachers or technicians.

For those schools that subscribe to CLEAPSS (www.cleapss.org.uk) either through their Local Authority or as Independant members, they should consult CLEAPSS publications or contact CLEAPSS directly on the *Helpline*. It is advisable that a science safety policy for each establishment is written for the benefit of teachers and technicians (see Guide L196 and guide L223).

A risk assessment must be made for any work where students are the subject of an investigation (e.g. recording heartbeats), where microorganisms are involved (see section 15 of the Handbook) or where chemicals are handled (use Hazcards).

Photo credits
The Publishers would like to thank the following for permission to reproduce copyright material:

p. 2, Dr Kari Lounatmaa/Science Photo Library; **p. 3,** Dr Kenneth R. Miller/Science Photo Library; **p. 19 br,** Dr C.J. Clegg; **p. 19 tr,** Martin Harvey/NHPA; **p. 19 tl,** Rod Planck/NHPA; **p. 19 bl,** Rod Preston-Mafham/premaphotos.com All rights reserved; **p. 20,** Dr C.J. Clegg; **p. 33,** Jeremy Thomas/Natural Visions; **p. 42 both,** Dr C.J. Clegg; **p. 43,** Dr C.J. Clegg; **p. 44 l,** © Owen Franken/Corbis; **p. 44 r,** Nick Garbutt/NHPA; **p. 46,** Nina Leen/Time Life Pictures/Getty Images; **p. 54,** Dr C.J. Clegg; **p. 69,** David Parker/Science Photo Library; **p. 71,** Kwangshin Kim/Science Photo Library; **p. 73 br,** Nigel Cattlin/FLPA; **p. 73 bl,** Holt Studios/FLPA; **p. 73 tl,** Barry Dowsett/Science Photo Library; **p. 76,** Alex Rakosy/Custom Medical Sock/Science Photo Library; **p. 77 t,** Matt Meadows/ Peter Arnold/Science Photo Library; **p. 77 b,** Simon Fraser/Science Photo Library; **p. 79 b,** NIBSC/Science Photo Library; **p. 79 t,** Eye of science/Science Photo Library; **p. 81,** © Gene Cox; **p. 88,** Dr Linda Stannard, UCT/Science Photo Library; **p. 103 t,** © Gene Cox; **p. 103 b,** University of Aberdeen/Mediscan; **p. 104,** Biology Media/Science Photo Library; **p. 105 both,** Biophoto Associates; **p. 107,** Dr Gladden Willis/Getty Images; **p. 109 l,** Andrew Lambert/Science Photo Library; **p. 109 r,** Gustoimages/Science Photo Library; **p. 117 bl,** Heather Angel/Natural Visions; **p. 117 tl,** Heather Angel/Natural Visions; **p. 117 br,** A.N.T. Photo/NHPA; **p. 117 tm,** Laurie Campbell/NHPA; **p. 117 tr,** Tomas Friedman/Science Photo Library; **p. 118,** Nickel-Electro Ltd; **p. 128,** Simon Fraser Hexham General/Science Photo Library; **p. 134,** Science Photo Library; **p. 135,** Princess Margaret Rose Orthopaedic Hospital/Science Photo Library; **p. 136,** Science Photo Library; **p. 145,** Prof S. Cinti/Science Photo Library; **p. 148,** © Gene Cox; **p. 149,** © Gene Cox; **p. 152,** © Gene Cox; **p. 153,** © Gene Cox; **p. 154,** © Gene Cox; **p. 159,** Omikron/Science Photo Library; **p. 161,** Alfred Pasieka/Science Photo Library; **p. 162 both,** © Prof. Robert Turner, Department of Neurophysics; Max-Planck-Institute for Human Cognitive and Brain Sciences; **p. 168,** The Image Works/TopFoto; **p. 174,** Science Photo Library; **p. 176,** Old Man in Sorrow (On the Threshold of Eternity) 1890 (oil on canvas) by Gogh, Vincent van (1853-90); Rijksmuseum Kroller-Muller, Otterlo, Netherlands/ The Bridgeman Art Library; **p. 181,** Nigel Cattlin/FLPA; **p. 190,** CC Studio/Science Photo Library.

l = left; **r** = right; **t** = top; **b** = bottom; **m** = middle

Acknowledgements
The Publishers wish to thank the following for permission to reprint copyright material in this book, as listed below:

Figure 5.28: Autumn crocus, an historic record of changing distribution – adapted from F.H. Perring and S.M. Walters (1976) *Atlas of the British Flora*, E P Publishing Ltd; **Figure 5.31:** The temperature tolerance of four groups of bacteria – adapted from page 148, Figure 5.13, in M.T. Madigan, J.M. Martiko and J. Parker (2000) *Brock Biology of Microorganisms* (9th Edition) Prentice Hall International Inc; **Figure 5.39:** Birth weight and infant mortality, a case of stabilising selection – data from R.J. Berry (1977) *The New Naturalist Inheritance and Natural History*, HarperCollins; **page 55:** Extract from F. Crick (1988) *What Mad Pursuits – a Personal View of Scientific Discovery*, Penguin Books; **Figure 6.32:** The increasing incidence of MRSA – data from the Health Protection Agency; **Figure 6.33:** Extract taken from an article by Lois Rogers, 'Superbug deaths at 10,000 a year', appearing in *The Sunday Times*, 23 March 2008; **page 91:** Table 6.6 – data from *Clinical infectious diseases*, vol 38, p179 (as reported in *New Scientist* 29 September 2007, page 38); **Figure 6.34:** Graph of human body temperature – adapted from J.H. Green (1963) *An Introduction to Human Physiology*, Oxford University Press; **Figure 6.36:** The effect of temperature on egg development in *Calliphora vicina* – adapted from K.G.V. Smith (1986) *A Manual of Forensic Entomology*, Trustees of the British Museum (Natural History); **Figure 6.37:** The effect of temperature on larval and pupal development in *Calliphora vicina* – adapted from K.G.V. Smith (1986) *A Manual of Forensic Entomology*, Trustees of the British Museum (Natural History); **Figure 7.29:** Respiratory response to exercise – adapted from K. Weston, N. Wiggins-James, G. Thompson and S. Hartigan (2005) *Sport and PE* (3rd Edition) Hodder Arnold; **page 131:** Table 7.5 – data from page 347 in W.D. McArdle, F.I. Katch, V.L. Katch (1999) *Exercise Physiology* (5th Edition) Lippincott, Williams and Wilkins; **Figure 7.33:** The intensity of physical activity and susceptibility to URTIs – data from D.C. Nieman (1994) 'Exercise, upper respiratory track infection and the immune system', in *Med. Sci. Sports Exerc.* 26, 128; **Figure 7.39:** Drug testing and incidence of detected doping at the Olympics – adapted from an article by Owen Slot, 'The dancing entertainer Bolt runs away with his second gold', appearing in *The Times*, 21 August 2008; **Figure 8.30:** Extract taken from an article by Frances Gibb, Legal Editor, 'You can't trust a witness's memory, experts tell courts', appearing in *The Times*, 11 July 2008; **Figure 8.31:** The sea slug and the neurones serving the gills – adapted from G. Scott (2004) *Essential Animal Behaviour*, Blackwell; **Figure 8.32:** Stimulations of *Aplysia* that result in gill withdrawal – adapted from G. Scott (2004) *Essential Animal Behaviour*, Blackwell.

Every effort has been made to establish copyright and contact copyright holders prior to publication. If contacted, the Publishers will be pleased to rectify any omissions or errors at the earliest opportunity.

Contents

Topic tests and a comprehensive **glossary** are available via Dynamic Learning, along with **Activities**, **How science works** (HSW) inputs and **A* Extensions**, Answers to SAQs and two **Appendices**: *Background Chemistry for Biologists* and *Handling Data for A2 Biology*.
(To access these resources in Dynamic Learning, use the 'search' tool, whose icon appears at the left end of the task bar. Type your requirements in the box and click 'go'. The resources are also accessible via pop-up boxes on relevant pages.)

Introduction

Edexcel Biology for A2 is designed to deliver the learning outcomes of the 'concept' approach of the Edexcel Specification for GCE Biology. The intentions are to:

- extend your knowledge of Advanced Biology and develop the skills needed to use it – the structure of the Edexcel Specification emphasises how the distinctive areas of biology relate to each other
- further your understanding of scientific methods, their historic development and current application in biology – this aspect is conveniently summarised as *How science works*
- sustain and develop a life-long interest in, and enjoyment of, the study of the living world, whether or not you choose to study biology further and develop a career interest involving biological sciences
- highlight the value of biology to modern industry and the economy in general, together with the challenges that arise as society makes decisions about biologically related issues using contemporary ethical frameworks.

How does *Edexcel Biology for A2* relate to your final assessments, leading to a GCE in Advanced Biology? Let's take a look at the Edexcel A2 Assessment Requirements, summarised in this table.

Focus and method of assessment	Contribution to the A2 mark
One written examination on the learning outcomes of Unit 4 – discussed in Chapter 5 *On the wild side* and Chapter 6 *Infections, immunity and forensics,* which also cover related *How science works* issues, together with practical-related questions.	40% of the total
One written examination on the learning outcomes of Unit 5 – discussed in Chapter 7 *Run for your life* and Chapter 8 *Grey matter,* which also cover *How science works* issues, and practical-related questions. Here, one third of the marks are related to specified pre-released reading.	40% of the total
A written report on your Individual Investigation. Here, synoptic assessment is included. (Details of the Individual Investigation are given in the Edexcel Specification – you will find them in *Practical Biology and Investigative Skills – Unit 6.*)	20% of the total

Note: The total Advanced GCE mark will be the sum of 50% of the AS marks and 50% of the A2 marks awarded.

Edexcel Biology for A2 meets these assessment requirements through a host of features.

- Chapters respond to the learning objectives of the topics, more-or-less in sequence. They are written in straightforward language, building on the knowledge, skills and attitudes you have developed during your study of *Edexcel Biology for AS*.
- The text is closely complemented by the selection and positioning of photographs, electron micrographs and full-colour illustrations, linked by annotations, all designed to elaborate the context, function or application of the subject matter.
- Since biology is generally recognised as having a demanding vocabulary, essential terms are explained as they arise, and reminders are given in the **glossary**.
- Self-assessment questions that support your understanding, or guide you to research interconnecting ideas, are present throughout the chapters.
- A **topic test** (with mark scheme provided) for the contents of each chapter supports your revision. (The Edexcel website also provides sample assessment materials – www.edexcel.com/gce2008.)
- Development of your practical skills throughout the course experience is facilitated by the core practicals. In *Edexcel Biology for A2* these are integrated with theoretical issues and linked to *How science works* inputs. Your teacher will arrange for you to undertake all these practicals, and the skills you develop will underpin your Individual Investigation. (The Edexcel website details what is involved here, including the assessment criteria and exemplar materials.)

Throughout the text, additional resources are flagged, accessed via the interactive pages of the **Dynamic Learning** materials.

Activities	A selection of demonstrations, ideas for investigations, further reading sources, web references, and pencil-and-paper tasks that challenge understanding – some of the wider reading activities are adapted to provide first-hand experience of the type of longer question you will meet in Unit Test 5 on pre-released material.
How science works	These inputs focus your attention on specific HSW Criteria illustrated by issues in the text. Of course, HSW issues arise widely within the learning objectives, especially in those involving practical work.
A* Extensions	More challenging material, experience of which enhances your ability to apply knowledge and demonstrate higher-level HSW skills. Remember, A* grades are awarded on performance in the Unit Tests – no extra content is required or examined.

Available via the **Dynamic Learning** materials are the **glossary**, the four **topic tests**, and two **appendices**:

1 *Background Chemistry for Biologists*
2 *Handling Data for A2 Biology*, written by Guest Author Dr Neil Millar – here Dr Millar introduces his unique statistical package *Merlin*, created for biology students, which is made freely available for educational and non-profit use.

Other features supportive of active learning are also available via the **Dynamic Learning** facilities for *Edexcel Biology for A2*.

Using the Dynamic Learning resources

To access **Activities**, **How Science Works** resources and **A* Extension** materials, move the cursor over the yellow box in the margin, and left click. The text appears in a pop-up window – click on the PDF icon in the top left corner to open the resource.

Click on a **Figure** to enlarge it in a pop-up window. Then you can zoom into any part, and drag around the piece using the cursor. You can save **illustrations** or **photographs** to your own folders, by clicking on the icons in the top left corner.

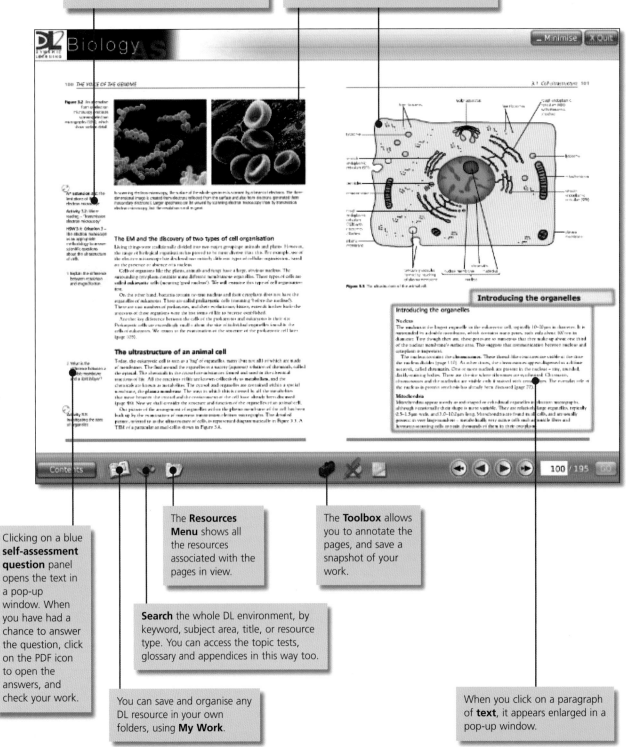

Clicking on a blue **self-assessment question** panel opens the text in a pop-up window. When you have had a chance to answer the question, click on the PDF icon to open the answers, and check your work.

The **Resources Menu** shows all the resources associated with the pages in view.

The **Toolbox** allows you to annotate the pages, and save a snapshot of your work.

Search the whole DL environment, by keyword, subject area, title, or resource type. You can access the topic tests, glossary and appendices in this way too.

You can save and organise any DL resource in your own folders, using **My Work**.

When you click on a paragraph of **text**, it appears enlarged in a pop-up window.

5 On the wild side

STARTING POINTS
- Green plants manufacture glucose by photosynthesis in their chloroplasts, using energy from sunlight.
- Organisms require energy to maintain cells and carry out their activities and functions. Cell respiration occurs in every living cell, making energy available by oxidation of glucose.
- Chemical energy stored in the biomass of green plants is transferred to other organisms during feeding, but eventually returns to the environment as heat.
- Ecology is the study of living things in their environment. Interactions with other organisms, and with the non-living parts of the environment, affect where organisms live and the sizes of their populations.
- The world human population is very large. Our lifestyles and the industries that support them cause pollution of Earth's atmosphere, land, lakes and oceans. Biodiversity is reduced as a result of the changes our numbers and activities inflict on ecosystems.
- Evolution is the development of life in geological time since its beginnings about 3500 million years ago. Evolution occurs by natural selection.

5.1 Autotrophic nutrition, the basis of plant productivity

Green plants use the energy of sunlight to produce sugars from the inorganic raw materials carbon dioxide and water, by a process called **photosynthesis**. The waste product is oxygen. Photosynthesis occurs in plant cells containing **chloroplasts** – typically, these are found mainly in the leaves of green plants. Here, light energy is trapped by the green pigment **chlorophyll**, and becomes the chemical energy in molecules such as glucose and ATP. (Note that we say light energy is *transferred* to organic compounds in photosynthesis, rather than talking of the 'conversion' of energy, although the latter term was used widely at one time.)

Sugar formed in photosynthesis may temporarily be stored as starch, but sooner or later most is used in metabolism. For example, plants manufacture other carbohydrates, together with lipids, proteins, growth factors, and all other metabolites they require. For this they need, in addition, certain mineral ions, which are absorbed from the soil solution. Figure 5.1 (overleaf) is a summary of photosynthesis and its place in plant metabolism.

Activity 5.1: The leaf as a factory for photosynthesis

Chloroplasts – site of photosynthesis

Just as the mitochondria are the site of many of the reactions of respiration (*Biology for AS*, page 102, Figure 3.5), so the chloroplasts are the organelles where the reactions of photosynthesis occur. Remember, chloroplasts are members of a group of organelles called plastids. (Amyloplasts, where starch is stored, are also plastid – *Biology for AS*, page 144.)

The chloroplast is one of the larger organelles found in plant cells, yet typically measures only 4–10 μm long and 2–3 μm wide. (A micrometre or micron, μm, is one-millionth of a millimetre.) Consequently, while chloroplasts can be seen in outline by light microscopy, for detail of fine structure (ultrastructure) electron microscopy is used. A transmission electron micrograph (TEM) showing chloroplasts can be produced from thin sections of mesophyll cells, specially prepared (Figure 5.2, overleaf).

photosynthesis: a summary

The process in the chloroplast can be summarised by the equation:

carbon dioxide	+	water	+	LIGHT ENERGY	chlorophyll in chloroplast →	organic compounds, e.g. sugars	+	oxygen
raw materials				*energy source*		*products*		*waste product*
$6CO_2$	+	$6H_2O$	+	light	chlorophyll in chloroplast →	$C_6H_{12}O_6$	+	$6O_2$

plant nutrition: a summary

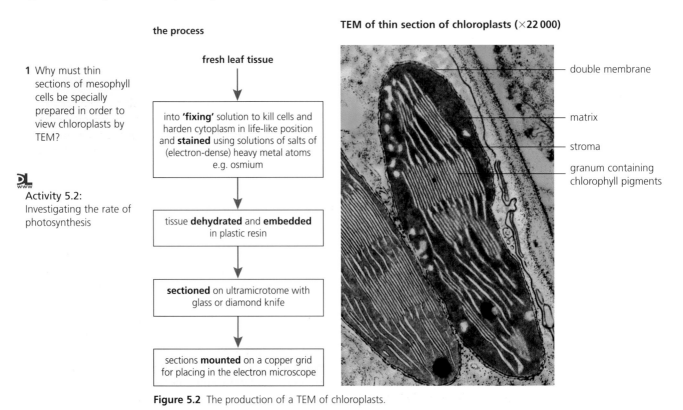

Figure 5.1 Photosynthesis and its place in plant nutrition.

the process

fresh leaf tissue

↓

into **'fixing'** solution to kill cells and harden cytoplasm in life-like position and **stained** using solutions of salts of (electron-dense) heavy metal atoms e.g. osmium

↓

tissue **dehydrated** and **embedded** in plastic resin

↓

sectioned on ultramicrotome with glass or diamond knife

↓

sections **mounted** on a copper grid for placing in the electron microscope

1 Why must thin sections of mesophyll cells be specially prepared in order to view chloroplasts by TEM?

DL
www

Activity 5.2: Investigating the rate of photosynthesis

TEM of thin section of chloroplasts ($\times 22\,000$)

- double membrane
- matrix
- stroma
- granum containing chlorophyll pigments

Figure 5.2 The production of a TEM of chloroplasts.

Ultrastructure of chloroplasts and the reactions of photosynthesis

Examine the TEM of the chloroplasts in Figure 5.2, and the diagram in Figure 5.3. You will see that the chloroplast is contained by a double membrane. The outer membrane is a continuous boundary, but the inner membrane 'intucks' to form branching membranes called lamellae or **thylakoids** within the organelle. Some of the thylakoids are arranged in circular piles called **grana**. Here, the photosynthetic pigment chlorophyll is held. Between the grana, the lamellae are loosely arranged in an aqueous matrix, forming the **stroma**.

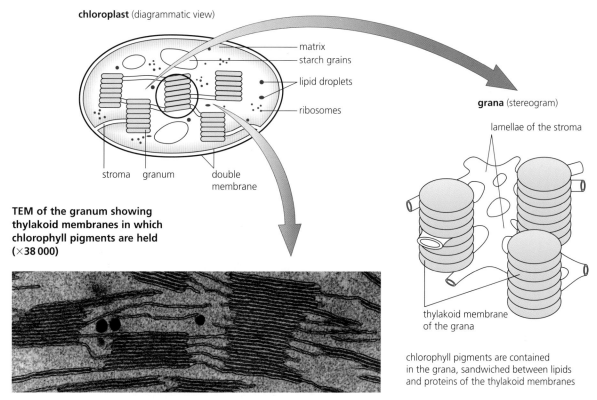

chloroplast (diagrammatic view)

- matrix
- starch grains
- lipid droplets
- ribosomes

stroma   granum   double membrane

grana (stereogram)

lamellae of the stroma

thylakoid membrane of the grana

chlorophyll pigments are contained in the grana, sandwiched between lipids and proteins of the thylakoid membranes

TEM of the granum showing thylakoid membranes in which chlorophyll pigments are held (×38 000)

Figure 5.3 The ultrastructure of a chloroplast.

It turns out that photosynthesis consists of a complex set of reactions, which take place in illuminated chloroplasts (unsurprisingly). Biochemical studies by several teams of scientists have established that the many reactions by which light energy brings about the production of sugars, using the raw materials water and carbon dioxide, fall naturally into two inter-connected stages (Figure 5.4, overleaf).

- In the **light-dependent reactions**, light energy is used directly to split water (a process known as **'photolysis'**, for obvious reasons). Hydrogen is then removed and retained by the photosynthetic-specific hydrogen acceptor, known as $NADP^+$. ($NADP^+$ is very similar to the coenzyme NAD^+ involved in respiration, but it carries an additional phosphate group, hence the abbreviation NADP – see A* Extension 5.2). At the same time, ATP is generated from ADP and phosphate, also using energy from light. This is known as photophosphorylation. Oxygen is given off as a waste product of the light-dependent reactions. This stage occurs in the grana of the chloroplasts.
- In the **light-independent reactions**, sugars are built up using carbon dioxide. This stage occurs in the stroma of the chloroplast. Of course, the light-independent reactions require a continuous supply of the products of the light-dependent reactions (ATP and reduced hydrogen acceptor $NADPH + H^+$), but do not *directly* involve light energy (hence the name). Names can be misleading, however, because sugar production is an integral part of photosynthesis, and photosynthesis is a process that is powered by transfer of light energy.

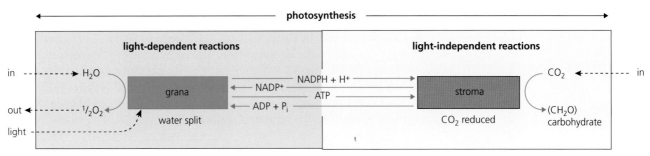

Figure 5.4 The two reactions of photosynthesis, inputs and outputs.

We shall now consider each stage in turn, in order to understand more about how these complex changes are brought about.

The light-dependent reactions

A* Extension 5.1:
Finding out more about photosynthesis

In the light-dependent stage, light energy is trapped by the photosynthetic pigment, chlorophyll. Chlorophyll molecules do not occur haphazardly in the grana. Rather, they are grouped together in structures called **photosystems**, held in the thylakoid membranes of the grana (Figure 5.5).

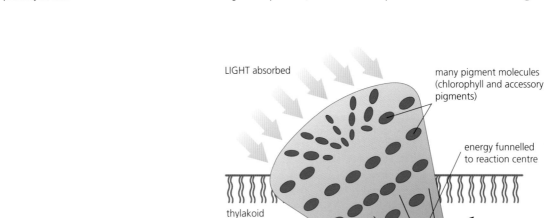

Figure 5.5 The structure of photosystems.

In each photosystem, several hundred chlorophyll molecules plus accessory pigments (carotene and xanthophylls) are arranged. All these pigment molecules harvest light energy, and they funnel the energy to a single chlorophyll molecule in the photosystem, known as the **reaction centre**. The different pigments around the reaction centres absorb light energy of slightly different wavelengths.

There are two types of photosystem present in the thylakoid membranes of the grana, identified by the wavelength of light that the chlorophyll of the reaction centre absorbs.

- **Photosystem I** has a reaction centre activated by light of wavelength 700 nm. This reaction centre is also referred to as P700.
- **Photosystem II** has a reaction centre activated by light of wavelength 680 nm. This reaction centre is also referred to as P680.

Photosystems I and II have differing roles, as we shall see shortly. However, they occur grouped together in the thylakoid membranes of the grana, along with certain proteins that function quite specifically in one of the following roles:

1 enzymes catalysing the splitting of water into hydrogen ions, electrons and oxygen atoms
2 enzymes catalysing the formation of ATP from ADP and phosphate (P_i)
3 enzymes catalysing the conversion of oxidised H-carrier ($NADP^+$) to reduced carrier ($NADPH + H^+$)
4 electron-carrier molecules (these are large proteins).

When light energy reaches a reaction centre, **'ground-state' electrons** in the key chlorophyll molecule are raised to an 'excited' state by the light energy received. As a result, **high-energy electrons** are released from this chlorophyll molecule, and these electrons bring about the biochemical changes of the light-dependent reactions (Figure 5.6). The spaces vacated by the high-energy (excited) electrons are continuously refilled by non-excited or 'ground-state' electrons. *We will examine this sequence of reactions in the two photosystems next.*

Firstly, the excited electrons from photosystem II are picked up by, and passed along, a chain of electron-carriers. As these excited electrons pass, some of the energy causes the pumping of hydrogen ions (protons) from the chloroplast's matrix into the thylakoid spaces. Here they accumulate – incidentally, causing the pH to drop. The result is a proton gradient that is created across the thylakoid membrane, and which sustains the synthesis of ATP. This is an example of chemiosmosis (HSW 5.1).

2 Construct a table that identifies the role of each of the components of photosystems I and II.

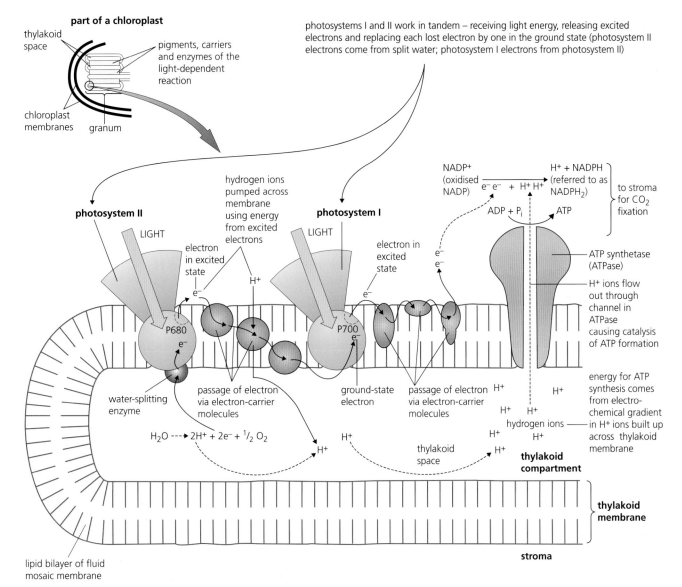

Figure 5.6 The light-dependent reactions.

As a result of these energy transfers, the excitation level of the electrons falls back to 'ground state' and they come to fill the vacancies in the reaction centre of photosystem I. Thus, electrons have been transferred from photosystem II to photosystem I.

Meanwhile the 'holes' in the reaction centre of photosystem II are filled by electrons (in their ground state) from water molecules. In fact, the positively charged 'vacancies' in photosystem II are powerful enough to cause the splitting of water (**photolysis**), in the presence of a specific enzyme. The reaction this enzyme catalyses then triggers the release of hydrogen ions and oxygen atoms, as well as ground-state electrons.

The oxygen atoms combine to form molecular oxygen, the waste product of photosynthesis. The hydrogen ions are used in the reduction of $NADP^+$ (see below).

In the grana of the chloroplasts, the synthesis of ATP is coupled to electron transport via the movement of protons by chemiosmosis. Here, the hydrogen ions trapped within the thylakoid space flow out via ATPase enzymes, down their electrochemical gradient. At the same time, ATP is synthesised from ADP and P_i. This is called **photophosphorylation**.

We have seen that the excited electrons that eventually provide the energy for ATP synthesis originate from water. They fill the vacancies in the reaction centre of photosystem II, and are subsequently moved on to the reaction centre in photosystem I. Finally, they are used to reduce $NADP^+$. The photophosphorylation reaction in which they are involved is described as non-cyclic photophosphorylation, because the pathway of electrons is linear.

Secondly, the excited electrons from photosystem I are picked up by a different electron acceptor. Two at a time, they are passed to $NADP^+$, which – with the addition of hydrogen ions from photolysis – is reduced to form $NADPH + H^+$.

By this sequence of reactions, repeated again and again at very great speed throughout every second of daylight, the products of the light-dependent reactions (ATP and $NADPH + H^+$) are formed.

ATP and reduced NADP do not normally accumulate, however, as they are immediately used in the fixation of carbon dioxide in the surrounding stroma (in the light-independent reactions). Then the ADP and $NADP^+$ diffuse back into the grana for re-use in the light-dependent reactions.

ATP – the universal energy currency

Energy made available within the cytoplasm may be transferred to a molecule called **adenosine triphosphate (ATP)**. This substance occurs in all cells at a concentration of $0.5–2.5\,mg\,cm^{-3}$. It is a relatively small, soluble organic molecule – a **nucleotide** with an unusual feature. It carries three phosphate groups linked together in a linear sequence (Figure 5.7).

ATP is formed from **adenosine diphosphate (ADP)** and phosphate ion (P_i) by transfer of energy from other reactions. ATP is referred to as 'energy currency' because, like money, it can be used in different contexts, and it is constantly recycled. ATP contains a good deal of chemical energy locked up in its structure. What makes ATP special as a reservoir of stored chemical energy is its role as a common intermediate between energy-yielding reactions and energy-requiring reactions and processes.

Energy-yielding reactions include the photophosphorylation reactions of photosynthesis discussed above, and of course many of the reactions of cell respiration.

Energy-requiring reactions include the synthesis of cellulose from glucose, the synthesis of proteins from amino acids, and the contraction of muscle fibres.

The free energy available in ATP is approximately $30–34\,kJ\,mol^{-1}$, made available in the presence of a specific enzyme. Some of this energy is lost as heat in a reaction, but much free energy is made available to do useful work, more than sufficient to drive a typical energy-requiring reaction of metabolism.

- Sometimes ATP reacts with water (a hydrolysis reaction) and is converted to ADP and P_i. Direct hydrolysis of the terminal phosphate groups like this happens in muscle contraction, for example.
- Mostly, ATP reacts with other metabolites and forms phosphorylated intermediates, making them more reactive in the process. The phosphate groups are released later, so both ADP and P_i become available for re-use as metabolism continues.

A* Extension 5.2: The source of oxygen in photosynthesis

3 In non-cyclic photophosphorylation, deduce the ultimate fate of electrons displaced from the reaction centre of photosystem II.

Activity 5.3: Studying the light-dependent reactions with isolated chloroplasts (HSW Criteria 4 and 5)

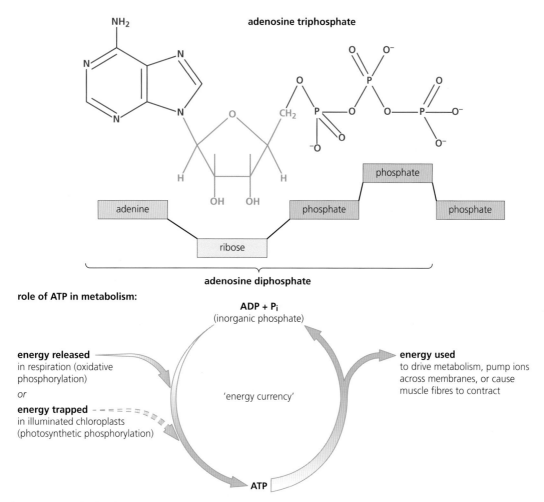

Figure 5.7 The structure and role of ATP.

Activity 5.4:
Mitochondria, and the role of ATP in protein synthesis

HSW 5.1: Criteria 1 and 11a – Chemiosmotic theory

Activity 5.5: Wider reading – 'The role of ATP in cells'

A* Extension 5.3: CO_2-limiting conditions and cyclic photophosphorylation (HSW Criterion 2c)

4 Outline why ATP is an efficient energy currency molecule.

In summary, ATP is a molecule universal to all living things; it is the source of energy for chemical change in cells, tissues and organisms. The important features of ATP are that it can:

- move easily within cells and organisms, by facilitated diffusion
- take part in many steps in cellular respiration and in very many reactions of metabolism
- transfer energy in relatively small amounts, sufficient to drive individual reactions.

The light-independent reactions

In the light-independent reactions, carbon dioxide is converted to carbohydrate. These reactions occur in the stroma of the chloroplasts, surrounding the grana. Carbon dioxide readily diffuses into the chloroplast where it is built up into sugars in a cyclic process called the **Calvin cycle**.

In the Calvin cycle, carbon dioxide is combined with an acceptor molecule in the presence of a special enzyme, ribulose bisphosphate carboxylase (**rubisco** for short). The stroma is packed full of rubisco, which easily makes up the bulk of all the protein in a green plant. In fact, it is the most abundant enzyme present in the living world.

The acceptor molecule is a five-carbon sugar, ribulose bisphosphate (referred to as RuBP) and carbon dioxide is added in a process known as **fixation** (Figure 5.8, overleaf). The product is not a six-carbon sugar, but rather two molecules of a three-carbon compound, glycerate 3-phosphate (GP). GP is then reduced to form another three-carbon compound called glyceraldehyde 3-phosphate (GALP). Some of the GALP is converted into the products of photosynthesis, such as glucose, or amino acids and fatty acids. The glucose may be immediately respired, or stored as starch until required. But the bulk of GALP is converted to more acceptor molecule, enabling fixation of carbon dioxide to continue.

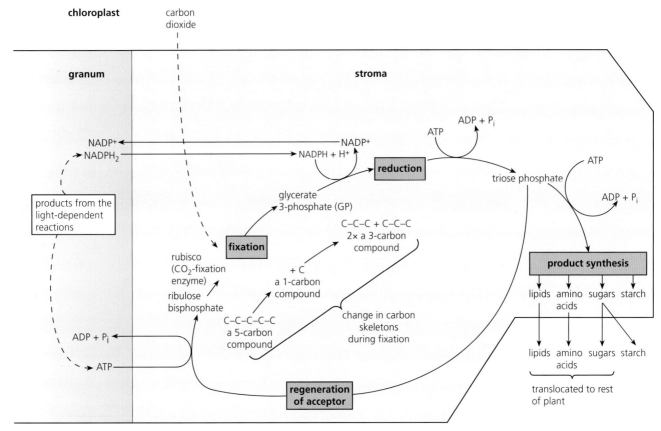

Figure 5.8 The light-independent reactions *in situ*.

Activity 5.6: Finding out about photosynthesis (HSW Criteria 1, 2, 3, 5, 6, 7 and 8)

A* Extension 5.4: Regeneration of ribulose bisphosphate – the Calvin cycle

■ Extension: Which intermediate is the acceptor molecule?

After it was established that the first product of carbon dioxide fixation in photosynthesis was GP (a three-carbon compound), a two-carbon acceptor molecule for carbon dioxide was sought by Calvin and his team. None was found, which caused some confusion. Eventually the acceptor proved to be a five-carbon molecule (ribulose bisphosphate) – when CO_2 has combined, the six-carbon product immediately splits into two three-carbon GP molecules.

Photosynthesis and plant metabolism

As we have seen, the first sugar produced in photosynthesis is a three-carbon compound, glycerate 3-phosphate (GP) (Figure 5.9). Some of this product is immediately converted into the acceptor molecule for more carbon dioxide fixation, by a pathway known as the Calvin cycle. The remainder is converted into the carbohydrate products of photosynthesis, mainly glucose and starch, or serves as intermediates that are the starting points for all the other metabolites the plant requires. By **intermediates** we mean all the substances of a metabolic pathway from which the end product is assembled.

Glucose is also the substrate for respiration. By **substrate** we mean a molecule that is the starting point for a biochemical pathway, and a substance that forms a complex with an enzyme

Figure 5.9 The path of carbon in photosynthesis – a summary.

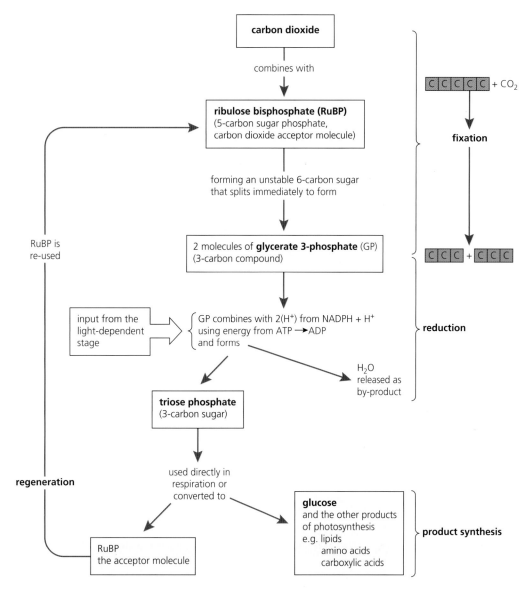

(thereby getting the pathway up and running). The intermediates of respiration are also starting points for the synthesis of other metabolites. In other words, the biochemical pathways of both photosynthesis and respiration interact to supply metabolism with the intermediates required. These include:

- specialist carbohydrates, such as sucrose for transport and cellulose for cell walls
- lipids, including those in membranes
- amino acids and proteins, including those in membranes and those that function as enzymes
- nucleic acids, growth factors, vitamins, hormones and pigments.

The fates of the products of photosynthesis are summarised in Figure 5.10 (overleaf).

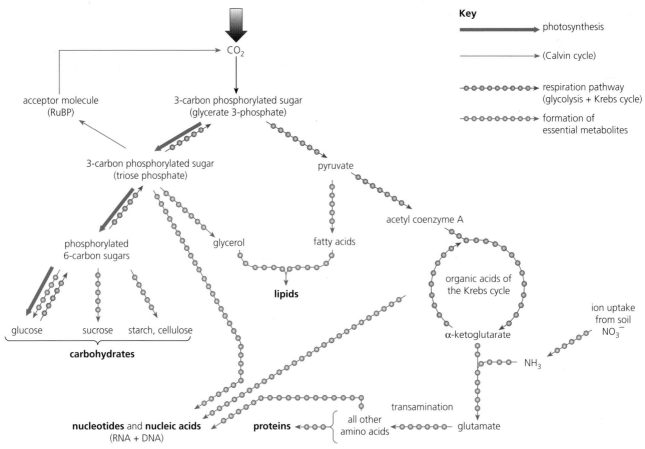

Figure 5.10 The product synthesis steps of photosynthesis.

■ Extension: Mineral ions for metabolism

While the bulk of metabolite molecules that a plant requires for its growth, development and repair activities come from photosynthesis and respiration, there are other ingredients, namely mineral ions, needed for the production of these essential metabolites (Table 5.1).

Some ions are needed in relatively large quantities, and these are called the macronutrients. An example is the nitrate ion – a form of combined nitrogen that plants absorb in quantity and use in the synthesis of amino acids. Other mineral ions are required in only tiny amounts (larger quantities might well be poisonous). These are called the micronutrients or trace elements. An example is copper(II) ion – a component of enzymes of the photosynthetic photosystems.

Table 5.1 Some mineral ions essential for plant metabolism.

Mineral ion	Uses
Examples of macronutrients	
nitrogen, as nitrate ion (NO^{3-})	required for amino acid synthesis
phosphorus, as phosphate ion (PO_4^{3-})	required for ATP, nucleic acids and phospholipids
magnesium, as magnesium ion (Mg^{2+})	required for chlorophyll, and for ATPase enzyme
Examples of micronutrients	
manganese, as manganese ion (Mn^{2+})	required for carboxylase enzymes
molybdenum, as molybdenum ion (Mo^{3+})	required for nitrate reductase enzyme

The productivity of photosynthesis

Only about half the energy emitted by the Sun and reaching the Earth's outer atmosphere gets through to soil level and to plant life – the remainder is reflected into space as light or heat energy. Of the radiation reaching green plants, about 45% is in the visible wavelength range (400–700 nm) and can be used by the plant in photosynthesis. Much of the light energy reaching the plant is reflected from the leaves or transmitted through them, however. Furthermore, of the energy absorbed by the stems and leaves of plants, much is lost in the evaporation of water (Figure 5.11).

Figure 5.11 The fate of light energy that reaches the green leaf of a crop plant (taken arbitrarily to total 1000 units per unit time).

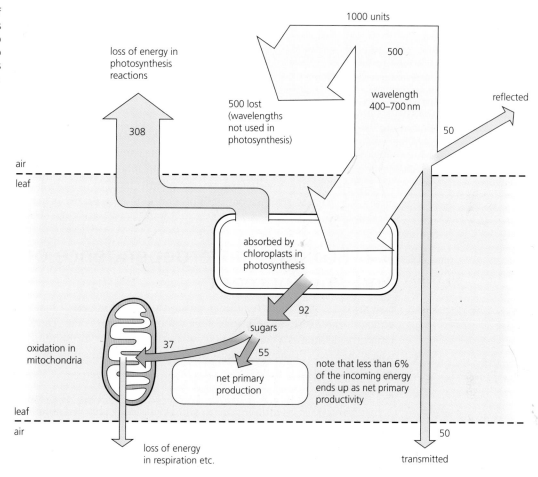

A small quantity of the energy reaching the green leaf is absorbed by the photosynthetic pigments and used in photosynthesis; only one quarter of this light energy ends up as chemical energy in molecules like glucose. The remainder is lost as heat energy in the various reactions of the light-dependent and light-independent reactions. In green plants, the total amount of light energy fixed through photosynthesis in a given period of time is known as the **gross primary productivity (GPP)**. GPP is usually expressed as units of energy per unit area per year, typically either $kJ\,m^{-2}\,y^{-1}$, or $MJ\,ha^{-1}\,y^{-1}$.

Finally, much of the energy in glucose is lost as heat energy in cellular respiration and other reactions of metabolism. The remainder is retained in new materials, either in the form of new structures (cells and tissues) or as stored food, and represents the **net primary productivity (NPP)** of the plant. The value given in Figure 5.11 for net primary productivity of about 5.5% applies to a fully grown crop plant. It is achieved for only a short period in the growth cycle of the crop plant – for a significant part of the year agricultural land is uncultivated.

Of course, in many natural habitats you might study, a part of the organic matter that makes up 'net primary productivity' is directly available to sustain browsing herbivores, and indirectly available to other organisms in the environment around the plant. We will examine energy

A* Extension 5.5:
Photosynthesis –
environmental
implications (HSW
Criterion 12)

transfer *between organisms* in a food chain, shortly. Meanwhile, the relationship between net primary productivity (NPP), gross primary productivity (GPP) and respiration (R) is summarised in the equation:

$$NPP = GPP - R$$

Applying this equation to data from a temperate ecosystem where GPP was found to be $43\,510\,$kJ $m^{-2}\,y^{-1}$, and R to be $23\,930\,$kJ $m^{-2}\,y^{-1}$, then NPP here was $9580\,$kJ $m^{-2}\,y^{-1}$.
Now carry out the calculations in SAQ 5.

5 Apply the formula
NPP = GPP – R to
complete the table.

Ecosystem	NPP (kJ $m^{-2}\,y^{-1}$)	GPP (kJ $m^{-2}\,y^{-1}$)	R (kJ $m^{-2}\,y^{-1}$)
mature rain forest (Puerto Ricoh)	?	189 000	134 400
lucerne (alfalfa) crop (USA)	63 840	?	38 640

■ Extension: Efficiency of photosynthesis

The percentage efficiency of photosynthesis is given by dividing the GPP by the estimated amount of light energy reaching the plant, multiplied by 100. We have already noted that very little of the light energy that reaches the plant is fixed in carbohydrates, and consequently figures for percentage efficiency of photosynthesis are typically below 2%.

■ 5.2 Ecology – interdependence of organism and environment

Ecology is the study of living things within their environment. One of the concepts that ecologists have introduced into biology is that of an **ecosystem** – and we have already used this term. It is defined as a community of organisms and their surroundings, the environment in which they live. Examples, such as woodland or a lake, illustrate two important features of an ecosystem, namely that it is:

- a largely self-contained unit, since most organisms of the ecosystem spend their entire lives there, and their essential nutrients will be endlessly recycled around and through them
- an interactive system, in that what organisms live there is largely decided by the physical environment, and the physical environment is constantly altered by the organisms.

Within any ecosystem, organisms are normally found in a particular part or habitat. The **habitat** is the locality in which an organism occurs. So, for example, within woodland, the canopies of trees are the habitats of some species of insects and birds, while other organisms occur in the soil. Incidentally, if the occupied area is extremely small, we call it a **microhabitat**. The insects that inhabit the crevices in the bark of a tree are in their own microhabitat. Conditions in a microhabitat are likely to be very different from conditions in the surrounding habitat.

Energy flow through ecosystems

When we describe feeding relationships and analyse food chains, the following terms are frequently used to describe and relate the roles of plants, animals and decomposers:

- autotrophs, heterotrophs
- producers, consumers
- herbivores, carnivores
- primary consumers, secondary consumers, tertiary consumers
- detritivores, decomposers
- dead organic matter, inorganic nutrients

Activity 5.7: Feeding relationship terms – a quick check

- saprotrophic nutrition
- cycling of nutrients, energy transfer from Sun, heat loss to space.

If you are not sure of the meaning of any of these terms, use the Glossary via the Dynamic Learning package, or Activity 5.7, to be sure you are able to apply them in context.

Introducing food chains

A feeding relationship in which a carnivore eats a herbivore, which itself has eaten plant matter, is called a **food chain** (Figure 5.12). Of course, light is the initial energy source. Note that in a food chain, the directions of the arrows point to the consumers, and so indicate the direction of energy transfer. A food chain tells us about the feeding relationships of organisms in an ecosystem, but they are shown as entirely qualitative relationships (we know which organisms are present as prey and as predators) rather than providing quantitative data (we do not know the numbers of organisms at each level).

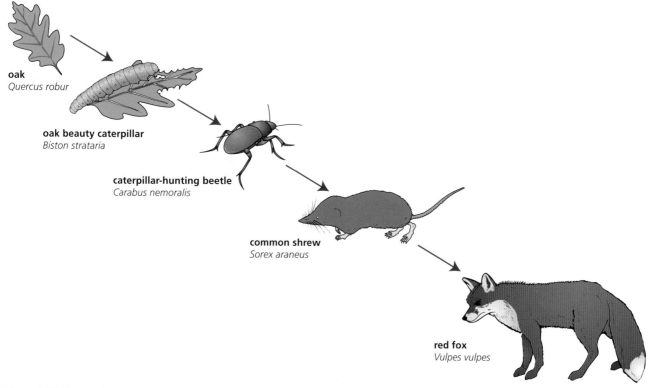

oak
Quercus robur

oak beauty caterpillar
Biston strataria

caterpillar-hunting beetle
Carabus nemoralis

common shrew
Sorex araneus

red fox
Vulpes vulpes

Figure 5.12 A food chain.

The level at which an organism feeds in a food chain is called its **trophic level**. In this way of classifying feeding relationships, the producers are designated as trophic level 1 because their energy has been transferred once, from Sun to plant. All herbivores are in level 2, because here energy has been transferred twice, and so on.

The trophic levels of some woodland organisms are classified in Table 5.2 (overleaf). Note that there is not some fixed number of trophic levels to food chains, but rather they are typically of three, four or five levels only. There is an important reason why stable food chains remain quite short. We will come back to this point, shortly.

Table 5.2 An analysis of trophic levels.

Trophic level	Woodland	
primary producer – level 1	oak	oak
primary consumer – level 2	caterpillar	caterpillar
secondary consumer – level 3	beetle	beetle
tertiary consumer – level 4	shrew	fox
quaternary consumer – level 5	fox	

6 Suggest what trophic levels humans occupy. Give examples.

Activity 5.8: Food webs and energy flow

■ **Extension: Issues with food chains**

Sometimes it can be difficult to decide at which trophic level to place an organism. For example, an omnivore feeds on both plant matter (level 2 – primary consumer) and on other consumers (level 3 – secondary consumer *or higher*). Another complication of food chains is illustrated in Table 5.2, namely that a fox more commonly feeds on beetles than shrews – simply because there are many more beetles about, and they are easier to catch! Remember also that any food chain is a snapshot of a moment in time – diet changes with season, and often very much more frequently.

The fate of energy within and between trophic levels

At the base of the food chain, green plants transfer light energy to the chemical energy of sugars, in photosynthesis. Of this, while some is transferred in the reactions of respiration that drive metabolism (and is then lost as heat energy), much is transferred to essential metabolites used in the growth and development of the plant. In these reactions, energy is locked up in the organic molecules of the plant body. Then, when parts of the plant are consumed by herbivores (or parasites), energy is transferred to other organisms. Finally, on death of the plant, the remaining energy passes to detritivores and saprotrophs when dead plant matter is broken down and decayed.

Similarly, energy is transferred in the consumer when it eats, digests and then absorbs nutrients. The consumer transfers energy in muscular movements by which it hunts and feeds, and as it seeks to escape from predators (and is then lost as heat energy). Some of the food eaten remains undigested, and is lost in the faeces. Also, heat energy – a waste product of the reactions of respiration and of the animal's metabolism – is continuously lost as the consumer grows and develops, and forms body tissues. If the consumer itself is caught and consumed by another, larger consumer, energy is again transferred. Finally, on death of the consumer, the remaining energy passes to detritivores and saprotrophs when dead matter is broken down and decayed.

Energy transfers within and between trophic levels is summarised in Figure 5.13.

So, only a limited amount of the energy transferred between trophic levels is available to be transferred to the next organism in the food chain. In fact, only about 10% of what is eaten by a consumer is built into the organism's body, and so is potentially available to be transferred on in predation. There are two consequences of this:

■ The energy loss at transfer between trophic levels is the reason why food chains are short. Few transfers can be sustained when so little of what is eaten by one consumer is potentially available to the next step in the food chain. Consequently, it is very uncommon for food chains to have more than four or five links between producer (green plant) and top carnivore.

■ Feeding relationships in a food chain may be structured like a pyramid. At the start of the chain is a very large amount of living matter (biomass) of green plants. This supports a smaller biomass of primary consumers, which in turn supports an even smaller biomass of secondary consumers. Figure 5.14 (overleaf) shows a generalised ecosystem pyramid diagram, representing the structure of an ecosystem in terms of the biomass of the organisms at each trophic level.

energy flow through a producer

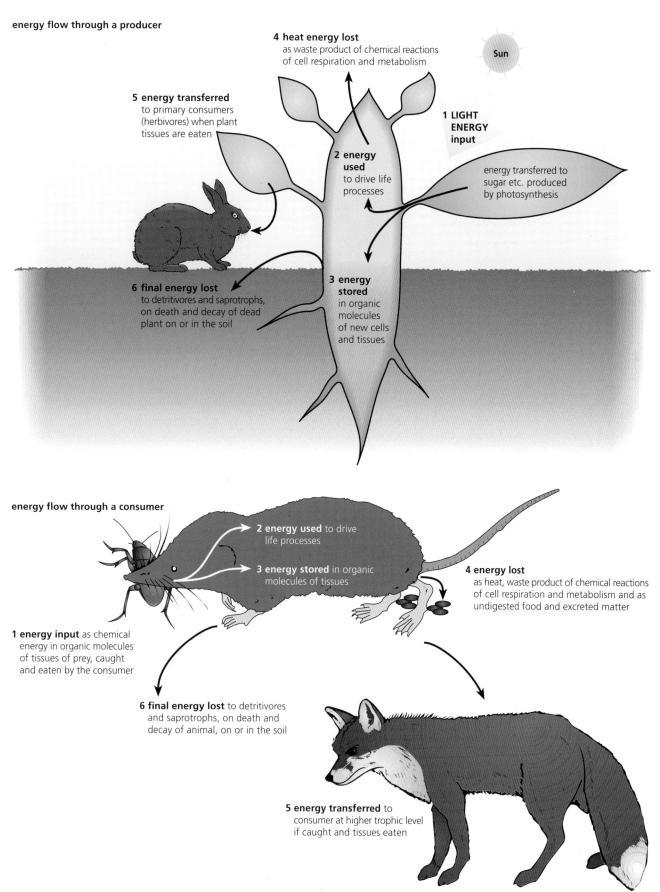

4 heat energy lost as waste product of chemical reactions of cell respiration and metabolism

Sun

5 energy transferred to primary consumers (herbivores) when plant tissues are eaten

1 LIGHT ENERGY input

2 energy used to drive life processes

energy transferred to sugar etc. produced by photosynthesis

6 final energy lost to detritivores and saprotrophs, on death and decay of dead plant on or in the soil

3 energy stored in organic molecules of new cells and tissues

energy flow through a consumer

2 energy used to drive life processes

3 energy stored in organic molecules of tissues

4 energy lost as heat, waste product of chemical reactions of cell respiration and metabolism and as undigested food and excreted matter

1 energy input as chemical energy in organic molecules of tissues of prey, caught and eaten by the consumer

6 final energy lost to detritivores and saprotrophs, on death and decay of animal, on or in the soil

5 energy transferred to consumer at higher trophic level if caught and tissues eaten

Figure 5.13 Energy flow through producers and consumers.

Only energy taken in at one trophic level and then built in as chemical energy in the molecules making up the cells and tissues is available to the next trophic level. This is about 10% of the energy.

The reasons are as follows.

- Much energy is used for cell respiration to provide energy for growth, movement, feeding, and all other essential life processes.
- Not all food eaten can be digested. Some passes out with the faeces. Indigestible matter includes bones, hair, feathers, and lignified fibres in plants.
- Not all organisms at each trophic level are eaten. Some escape predation.

Figure 5.14 A generalised pyramid of energy.

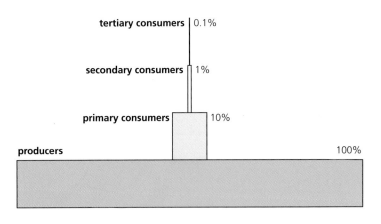

tertiary consumers 0.1%

secondary consumers 1%

primary consumers 10%

producers 100%

Calculating the efficiency of energy transfers

Figure 5.15 shows a pyramid of energy produced by an American ecologist, working on a river system in Florida, USA, over 50 years ago. Here is recorded the energy in each of four trophic levels. So, we can calculate the percentage energy transfer from producers (green aquatic plants) to the primary consumers:

$$\frac{14\,000}{87\,000} \times 100\% = 16.1\%$$

This is significantly more than might be anticipated. Are we to assume that the figure of about 10% of energy transferred at each trophic level is an inaccurate, sweeping generalisation? Probably not – in this river, significantly more of the energy of these particular primary producers was transferred to primary consumers because the plants concerned were almost entirely of highly digestible matter. They lacked any woody tissues common to most terrestrial plant matter. *Now complete the calculation in SAQ 7.*

Figure 5.15 also records energy transfer from grass (the producers) to a cow (primary consumer), but the value obtained for secondary production (the new biomass produced) in this study has been omitted. *Complete the calculations in SAQ 8.*

7 What is the percentage energy transfer between primary and secondary consumers in the data from the river system in Florida (Figure 5.15).
8 From the data in Figure 5.15, calculate:
  a the energy value of the new biomass of the cow, and then express this as a percentage of the energy consumed by the cow
  b the percentage energy transfer between primary and secondary consumer.

Ecosystems – abiotic and biotic factors

We have defined an ecosystem as a stable unit of nature consisting of a community of organisms interacting between themselves and the physical and chemical environment. The living things are known as the **biota**, and their physical environment as the **abiotic environment**. These aspects of ecosystems are so closely related as to be almost inseparable, as we shall shortly see. To learn about the working of the ecosystem, however, we need to look at both aspects in more detail. While we do, keep in mind examples of ecosystems you are familiar with, such as woodland or seashore, or perhaps a laboratory model (Activity 5.9).

Activity 5.9: Setting up a 'bottle' ecosystem

pyramid of energy from a river system in Florida

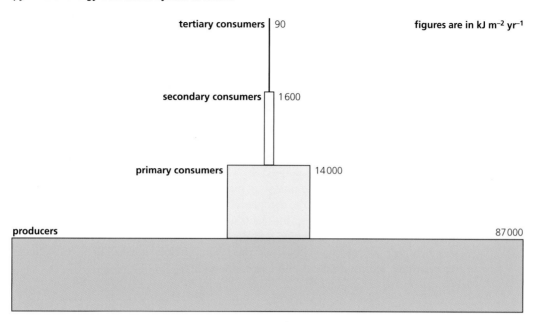

tertiary consumers | 90

figures are in kJ m⁻² yr⁻¹

secondary consumers | 1600

primary consumers | 14000

producers | 87000

energy transfer from grass (producer) to cow (primary consumer)

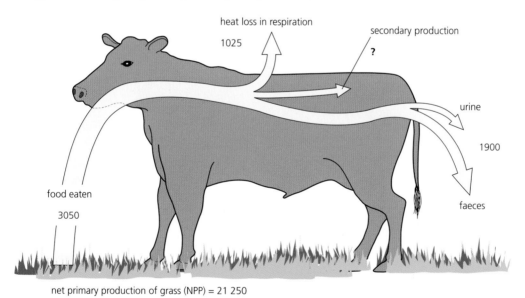

heat loss in respiration
1025

secondary production
?

urine

food eaten
3050

1900

faeces

net primary production of grass (NPP) = 21 250

Figure 5.15 Energy transfer studies in a river ecosystem and in an agricultural context.

Introducing abiotic factors

The physical and chemical components of an ecosystem more-or-less decide the physical conditions in which populations live (Figure 5.16, overleaf). Abiotic factors of a terrestrial habitat are of three types, relating to:

- climate – factors such as solar radiation, temperature, rainfall and wind
- soil – factors such as the parent rock, soil water and soil chemistry, and the mineral nutrients available (**edaphic** factors)
- topography – factors such as slope and aspect of the land, and altitude.

We can illustrate the far-reaching impact of abiotic factors by looking at the effects of solar radiation. Light is the ultimate source of energy for the ecosystem; green plants grow only where there is sufficient light for their autotrophic nutrition. This need for light by green plants has an effect on the structure of plant communities. For example, a woodland is stratified into layers from the canopy above, to the shrub layer below, the field layer (herbaceous plants) and ground layer (mosses). Each layer has particular plant life adapted to the light regime, and its own fauna. In aquatic habitats, plant life is largely confined to a region close to the surface.

The duration of illumination is the environmental trigger for inducing flowering of many plants, and in the timing of reproduction, migration and hibernation of animals. Light enables animals to see and be seen.

Sunlight is the major source of heat. Very few organisms grow if the temperature of their environment falls outside the range 0–40 °C. The effect of temperature on organisms is direct, for temperature influences the rate of all biochemical reactions. At low temperatures, ice crystals may form in cells, disrupting the cytoplasm. High temperatures denature enzymes, although certain bacteria found in hot springs have evolved tolerance of temperatures above 100 °C.

The length of daily illumination and the intensity of the light is determined by latitude, season, aspect (slope), time of day, and the extent of cloud cover. Through its effects on temperature, light intensity also influences humidity.

Figure 5.16 Interaction of climate, soil and topography in terrestrial ecosystems.

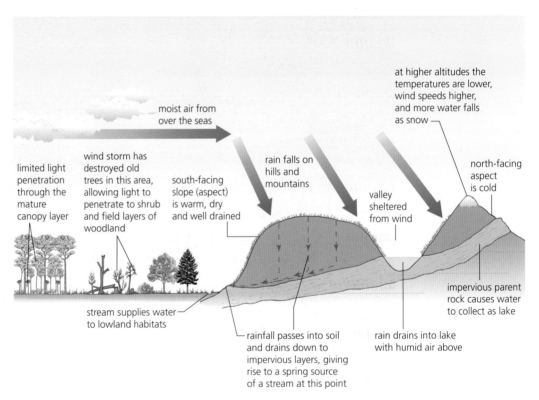

Introducing biotic factors

The organisms of an ecosystem affect each other (Figure 5.17). Interactions between organisms, known as biotic factors, are between members of the same species (**intraspecific competition**) and between members of different species (**interspecific competition**).

Of course, the impact of biotic factors depends upon the numbers of organisms present in relation to resources available, within a given environment. So we say that biotic factors are **density dependent**. Furthermore, we can recognise that biotic factors must be highly influential since most species occupy only a small part of the environment in which they are equipped to live.

A* Extension 5.6: Prey – predator oscillations

Competition

Plants compete for space, light and mineral nutrients. Animals compete for food, shelter and a mate. To loose out in competition for resources means the individual grows and reproduces more slowly or, in extreme cases, dies. When the fastest growing competitor eliminates a slower growing competitor, it takes over the area completely. This is known as the principle of **competitive exclusion**.

Predation, grazing and symbiotic relations

Interactions between individuals of different species may also take the form of predation, grazing or symbiosis.

A predator is an organism that feeds on other living species. Predators are normally larger than their prey, and they tend to kill before they eat. The predator's prey is another animal – the eating of plants by herbivorous animals is a very similar process, but is referred to as grazing or browsing. All food webs show numerous examples of both predation and grazing.

Symbiosis is the name we give to a relationship between two or more organisms living in intimate association. It simply means 'living together'. Parasitism is one form of symbiosis, in

Figure 5.17 Interactions between species.

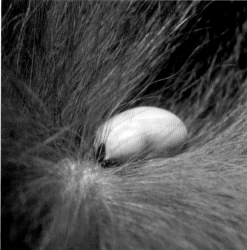

Top left: Herbivory – caterpillars of the monarch butterfly feeding on milkweed leaves
Top right: Predation – African lion at the moment of capture of prey (kudo – a savannah herbivore)
Bottom left: Parasitism – sheep tick (an ectoparasite) attached to the skin of a cat where it has fed on a blood meal
Bottom right: Mutualism – mushroom of fly agaric fungus takes sugars and amino acids from a tree's roots in return for essential ions, via its hyphae attached below ground

9 For an ecosystem you are familiar with, identify:
a two abiotic factors
b two biotic factors that will be operating.

A* Extension 5.7: Interactions of biotic and abiotic factors

Activity 5.10: Checking definitions

which the parasite lives on or in another organism, the host, for all or much of its life cycle. The parasite depends on the host for food and the host receives no benefit at all. **Endoparasites** live *in* the body of their host, like the human tapeworm and the malarial parasite. **Ectoparasites** live *on* the body of their host, like the aphids that tap the phloem sieve tubes of plants.

A parasite may affect the growth and reproduction of its host and in these cases the parasite is a limiting factor for the host species. In fact, parasitic associations show a gradation from those that normally kill the host (like the myxoma virus on the rabbit, causing the fatal myxomatosis disease), to associations so bland that the parasite virtually leaves its host unharmed.

Field ecology

Ecological investigations are often more complex than laboratory investigations because there are numerous variables involved that are frequently difficult or impossible to control.

For example, you might put out some pitfall traps at noon one day and examine them at dusk, and again the following morning, looking for correlations between patterns of activity in small, non-vertebrate animal populations and the time of day or night. However, during the course of a 24-hour period there might be abrupt changes in temperature, humidity or rainfall, over which you have no control. It is essential, therefore, to combine selected measurements of abiotic factors with measurements of biotic factors.

Even then, the handling of the data produced by ecological investigations almost invariably presents challenges. Statistical tests should be used to confirm the significance of numerical relationships. (The selection and application of appropriate statistical steps is described in the appendix *Handling Data for A2 Biology*, in the accompanying Dynamic Learning materials.)

Careful planning is the essential first step in any investigation. This is illustrated if you think about the planning that was required for the student investigation reported in Figure 5.18, for example.

Look at the range and quantity of data recorded in the table in Figure 5.18, now.

The ecological techniques you select will vary according to the issues you are investigating, the accuracy needed, and the ability of the technique to 'work' in the demanding experimental situation of the environment. For example, rain can ruin delicate electronic equipment, and so the apparatus or approach adopted must fit the particular circumstances. Accurate measurements from carefully calibrated equipment are vital. However, if you are comparing two or more habitats or microhabitats then accurate *comparisons*, using identical techniques, may be more important. Of course, whatever the field study situation you plan to be involved in, the issues of safety take priority (HSW 5.2).

HSW 5.2: Safety in fieldwork – Criterion 4

Figure 5.18 A sand dune community – a student field study exercise.

Sand deposited by the sea and blown by the wind builds into small heaps around pioneer xerophytic plants, such as marram and couch grass, at coasts where the prevailing wind is on-shore. The tufts of leaves growing through the sand accelerate deposition, and gradually drifting sands gather a dense cover of vegetation. Fixed sand dunes are formed.

point frame quadrat in use

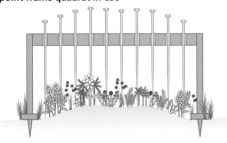

The frame is randomly placed a large number of times, the 10 pins lowered in turn onto vegetation and the species (or bare ground) recorded.

Behind the foredune, the fixed dunes can be seen.

Study of a sand dune succession from embryo state to fixed dune

	Site 1	Site 2	Site 3	Site 4
Stage in succession	Embryo dune	Fore dune	Semi-fixed dune	Fixed dune
Number of pins dropped	220	220	220	220
sea couch grass	169	9	0	0
marram grass	1	123	19	0
fescue grass	0	0	126	182
spear-leaved orache	4	0	0	0
prickly saltwort	2	0	0	0
bindweed	1	44	0	0
bird's foot trefoil	0	0	0	6
biting stonecrop	0	0	0	1
buttercup	0	0	0	1
cat's ear	0	0	5	2
clover	0	0	0	68
common stork's bill	0	0	0	11
daisy	0	0	2	8
dandelion (common)	0	0	5	1
eyebright	0	0	0	4
hawkbit	0	0	20	1
ladies bedstraw	0	0	86	35
medick	0	0	0	62
mouse-ear chickweed	0	0	0	2
ragwort	0	0	8	1
restharrow	0	0	25	15
ribwort plantain	0	0	0	37
sand sedge	0	0	32	17
stagshorn plantain	0	0	0	36
tufted moss	0	0	0	119
yellow clover	0	0	0	5
Yorkshire fog	0	0	2	0
wild thyme	0	0	0	82
Total live hits	**177**	**176**	**330**	**706**
Bare ground hits	**48**	**68**	**6**	**0**
% bare ground	27	38	3	0
soil moisture (%)	5.0	8.5	16.0	14.3
soil density (g cm^{-3})	1.6	0.9	0.6	0.5
soil pH	8.0	7.5	7.0	7.0
wind speed (m s^{-1})	10.0	9.3	2.4	1.3

Estimating population size and distribution in a habitat

An essential step in the study of a habitat may be the collection of accurate information on the sizes of populations present. A total count of all the members of a population is called a **census**, but this is almost always impractical – for example, because the size of the ecosystem is too large, or because of movements of animals, or because some species are only active at dusk or after dark. With plants, the numbers of individual plants typically involved is far too great. Instead, population sizes are investigated in representative, **random sample** areas. By means of random sampling, every individual of the population has an equal chance of being selected, and so a representative sample is assured.

Activity 5.11: Random sampling of plant populations, using quadrats

1 Quadrats

A quadrat is a frame that outlines a known area for the purpose of sampling (Figure 5.19). Quadrats are particularly appropriate where communities appear relatively uniform over a given area. The practical use of quadrats in making quantitative assessments of populations is discussed in Activity 5.11.

Activity 5.12: Estimating species distribution by means of a transect

2 Transects

Some communities show a trend of variation in a particular direction. Examples include a seashore, pond margin, salt marsh or even land with a simple change from dry to wet soil. Transects are a means of sampling biotic (and abiotic) data at right angles to the impact of unidirectional physical forces. The practical steps in the use of transects are discussed in Activity 5.12.

Figure 5.19 Random locating of quadrats.

1 A map of the habitat (e.g. meadowland) is marked out with gridlines along two edges of the area to be analysed.

2 Co-ordinates for placing quadrats are obtained as sequences of random numbers, using computer software, or a calculator, or published tables.

3 Within each quadrat, the individual species are identified, and then the density, frequency, cover or abundance of each species is estimated.

4 Density, frequency, cover, or abundance estimates are then quantified by measuring the total area of the habitat (the area occupied by the population) in square metres. The mean density, frequency, cover or abundance can be calculated, using the equation:

$$\text{population size} = \frac{\text{mean density (etc.) per quadrat} \times \text{total area}}{\text{area of each quadrat}}$$

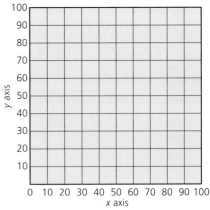

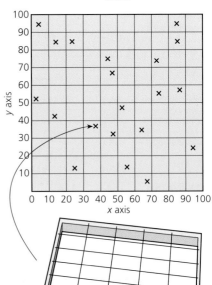

quadrat

10 From the data in the illustration in Activity 5.12, deduce a plant and an animal species that appear to be well adapted to the degree of exposure experienced at:
  a a high-water location   **b** a low-water location of the rocky shore.

Activity 5.13: Nets and traps for sampling animal communities

Activity 5.14: Estimating animal populations using MRR

3 Techniques for estimating animal population size

The sizes of animal populations present in a habitat may be estimated from sampling of particular communities. Techniques include the use of various types of nets or traps (Activity 5.13). The capture, **mark, release and recapture (MRR)** technique – a practical method of estimating population size for mobile animals, such as small mammals, woodlice or insects – is discussed in Activity 5.14.

11 Using MRR, relatively large samples must be caught for significant results. Calculate the estimated size of the population illustrated in Activity 5.14 if the second sample had included *two* marked woodlice, not one.

The measurement of abiotic factors

Which abiotic factors will most strongly influence distribution of particular organisms within a habitat under investigation? We have already noted that the important abiotic factors are climate factors (light, temperature, water availability and wind) and **edaphic** factors (the soil, its texture, nutrient status, acidity and moisture content). Topographic factors (angle and aspect of slope, and altitude) operate by their influence on local climate and edaphic factors. In fact, all factors interact to varying degrees. Table 5.3 lists a selection of these factors, their chief influences on the biota, and how they may be measured in a terrestrial habitat, such as a woodland, or in a pond. In Activity 5.15 the appropriate fieldwork resources are reviewed.

Activity 5.15: Field apparatus for the measurement of selected abiotic factors

Factor		Chief influence on biota	Measurement
climatic	*light*	the ultimate source of energy	dedicated digital sensor linked to a sensor meter
	temperature	directly influences rates of biochemical reactions, and has indirect effects on other factors e.g. evaporation	dedicated digital sensor linked to a sensor meter, or a permanently mounted maximum and minimum thermometer
	relative humidity	influences rate of water loss by evaporation, and rate of transpiration in plants	dedicated digital sensor linked to a sensor meter, or a whirling hygrometer
edaphic	*pH*	affects availability of nutrient ions that otherwise exist in unavailable forms	dedicated digital sensor linked to a sensor meter, or colorimetrical measurement using a soil test kit
	temperature	affects root growth, micro-organism activity, and seed germination	dedicated digital sensor linked to a sensor meter
	texture	relative proportions of different-sized particles affect, among other things, aeration and drainage	hand assessment of soil (using table in Activity 5.15)
topographical – terrestrial	*slope*	indirect effects on illumination, temperature, drainage and so on	survey methods, as in profile transect
	aspect		
topographical – pond	*water supply, or flow*	ponds with 'spring' source are permanent with relatively stable communities, whereas ponds raised by surface drainage tend to have ephemeral communities	direct observation and measurements of seasonal changes in water levels
	O_2 *availability*	low or non-existent concentrations of O_2 trigger anaerobic respiration, and favour obligate anaerobic organisms – otherwise, small changes in percentage O_2 concentration in an environment may have little impact on life under generally aerobic conditions	dedicated digital sensor linked to a sensor meter

Note: Digital sensors are available from several suppliers, including those listed in Activity 5.15. Data harvested is then processed using dedicated software.

Table 5.3 Introducing key abiotic factors and their measurement.

Distribution, abundance and succession

Activity 5.16: The concept of niche (AS revision)

Niche is a comprehensive ecological term that defines how an organism feeds, where it lives, and how it behaves in relation to other organisms in its habitat. This term was introduced in your AS programme, where the principle of distinct niches was illustrated by the two common and rather similar sea birds of UK coastal habitats, the cormorant and the shag.

Remind yourself how those two sea birds illustrate the concept of 'niche', now (Activity 5.16).

The 'niche' concept is useful because it identifies the precise conditions a species needs. We can imagine that similar (and obviously once closely related) organisms like the cormorant and shag have competed for similar resources, at least at some stage. For competing organisms, the more their niches overlap, the more that both will strive to secure a finite resource. Hence, these potential competitors have evolved different niches.

■ Extension: Competitive exclusion principle

Competition between organisms of two different species that persists may result in one competitor taking the resource exclusively, and the other being driven out or even dying out. In such cases – where two species fail to adapt, evolve separate niches, and come to co-exist – the situation is described as competitive exclusion. This principle was first suggested by a Russian biologist G.F. Gause in 1934, based on his experiments culturing different species of *Paramecium* in the laboratory (Figure 5.20).

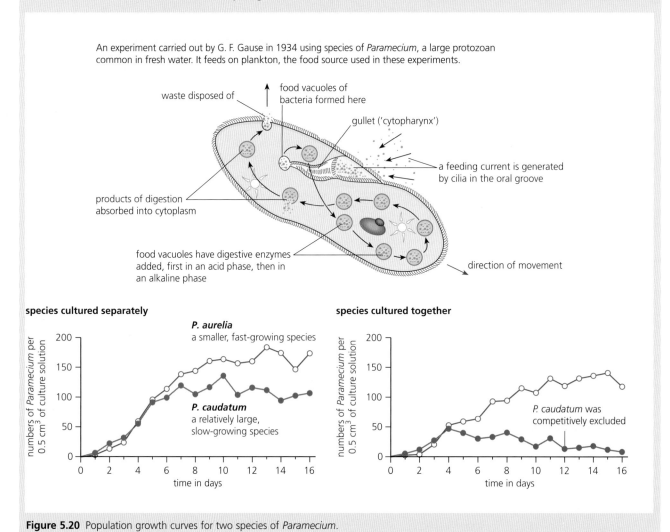

An experiment carried out by G. F. Gause in 1934 using species of *Paramecium*, a large protozoan common in fresh water. It feeds on plankton, the food source used in these experiments.

waste disposed of

food vacuoles of bacteria formed here

gullet ('cytopharynx')

a feeding current is generated by cilia in the oral groove

products of digestion absorbed into cytoplasm

food vacuoles have digestive enzymes added, first in an acid phase, then in an alkaline phase

direction of movement

species cultured separately

P. aurelia a smaller, fast-growing species

P. caudatum a relatively large, slow-growing species

species cultured together

P. caudatum was competitively excluded

numbers of *Paramecium* per 0.5 cm³ of culture solution

time in days

Figure 5.20 Population growth curves for two species of *Paramecium*.

Niche – distribution and abundance of species

Competition between organisms is an ecological 'force' resulting in the establishment of distinct niches, and distinct differences in distribution and abundance of related species in particular habitats. We can illustrate this with two examples.

1 Barnacle distribution

Two species of marine crustaceans, the barnacles *Chthamalus* and *Semibalanus*, are common creatures of seashore habitats (Figure 5.21). These sedentary animals release their gametes into sea water, where fertilisation occurs. From the fertilised eggs free-living larvae emerge, which feed and grow before attaching to a surface, thereby adopting the sessile mode of life of the adults. Attachment occurs randomly, on firm, submerged surfaces (typically rocks) of the intertidal region of the shore. However, one species (*Chthamalus*) is able to withstand prolonged exposure when the tides recede, whereas these same conditions slows the growth or actually kill off the other species (*Semibalanus*). As a result, as the degree of exposure is experienced by the growing barnacles, *Chthamalus* barnacles become less abundant in lower zones of the shore, and *Semibalanus* barnacles are similarly crowded out from upper (exposed) zones (Figure 5.21).

the degree of exposure determines the distinctive distribution pattern of these two species of barnacle

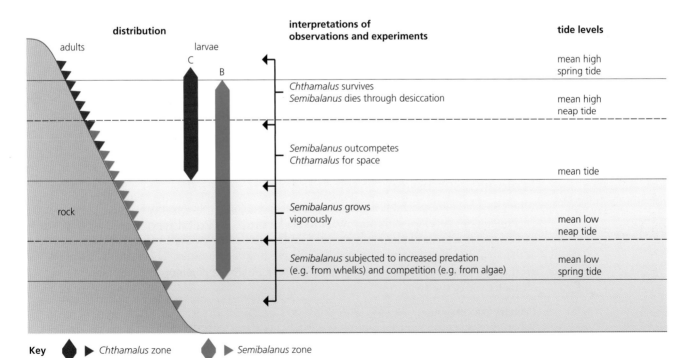

Figure 5.21 The growth of two species of barnacle on the seashore.

So the distribution of *Chthamalus* in the upper intertidal zones, and of *Semibalanus* in the lower intertidal zones, is a function of differences in their respective niches. That is, behavioural and structural differences in resistance to periodic desiccation and endurance of prolonged submersion have determined where each species survives best.

2 Marine alga distribution

Another illustration of the evolution of distinctive niches between related species that has lead to differences in distribution and abundance is found on the rocky shore among common species of brown algae (Figure 5.22). All seaweeds have a covering of mucilage over their plant 'body' (thallus), and this acts as a reservoir of water. Differences in mucilage production and other differences appear to account for differences in species distribution. The algal species of the upper shore are shown to be better able than others to withstand desiccation – they contain more water when hydrated and they loose it more slowly when exposed.

Figure 5.22 The resistance to desiccation of related species of brown algae.

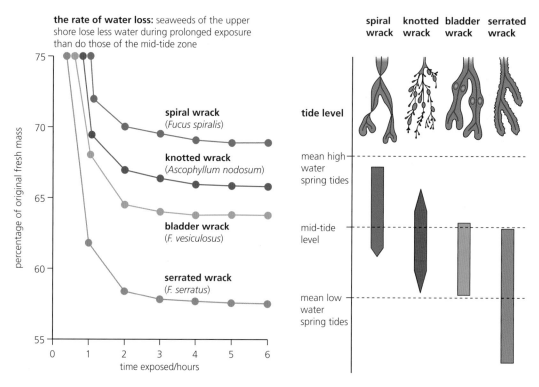

Ecological succession

When new land is exposed, it is quickly invaded and colonised by organisms. In fact, a sequence of communities develops with time by a process known as **ecological succession**. The stages in a succession are a series of plant and animal communities of increasing complexity, which develop as the abiotic factors operating change with succeeding communities. These stages are called **seral stages**, and the whole process is termed a **sere**. A **climax community** finally results, characteristic of the area.

Primary succession

When the succession sequence starts on entirely new land without soil, the process is known as a **primary succession**. New land is formed on the Earth's surface at river deltas, at sand dunes, and from cooled volcanic lava, for example. Primary successions also develop in aquatic habitats, such as in a pond formed and fed by a spring.

In all cases, the first significant development is the formation of soil, for at the initial site of a primary succession all that may be present is parent rock, from which the bulk of the soil is formed by erosion. However, mineral particles may also be blown or washed in from elsewhere, and the resulting mineral skeleton is of particles of a wide range of sizes (Activity 5.15).

Soil, when fully formed, has organic matter called **humus**, wrapped around the particles of the mineral skeleton. Humus is a substance derived from dead plant and animal remains, together with animal faeces, that have been decomposed by the actions of micro-organisms. Humus contributes mineral nutrients as it continues to be decayed, and it also helps soil to hold water and to retain heat. Between mineral particles and humus linings are innumerable pockets of air.

Humus is first added by plant invaders of the primary succession, known as pioneer plants, as shown in Figure 5.23. Since the first-formed soil retains little water, plants able to survive there (called xerophytes) have drought-resistant features. When a sere starts from dry conditions, then the sere is called a **xerosere**.

A **xerosere** = succession under dry, exposed conditions where water supply is an abiotic factor limiting growth of plants, at least initially.

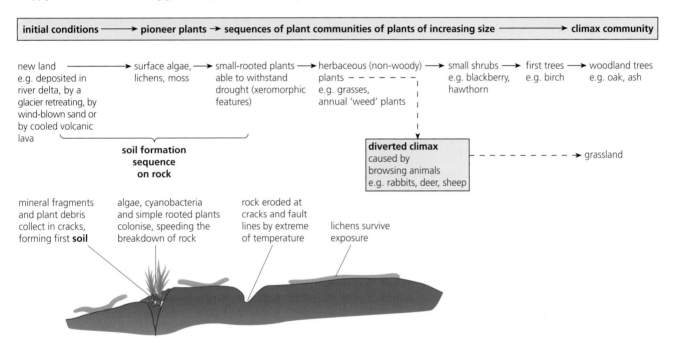

Figure 5.23 A primary succession on dry land – a xerosere.

The growth and death of the early plant communities continue to add humus, and so more soil water is retained. Nutrients are added to the soil when organisms die, and the range of nutrients available to plants increases steadily. Different plants now grow – various herbaceous weeds, for example, may start to shade out the pioneers. Herbaceous plants are followed by shrubs and small trees, all growing from seeds carried in by wind, water or the activities of animals. If the site remains undisturbed, a climax community such as a stable woodland will result.

So, succession can be seen as a directional change in a community with time. Initially abiotic factors have the greater influence on the survival and growth of organisms. Later, as the numbers of living organisms build up, biotic factors increasingly affect survival too, especially as they come to modify the abiotic factors operating.

An important feature of a succession is the progressive increase in the number of species present. As more species occur in a habitat, the food webs diversify. Now, in the event that one population crashes (such as when a disease sweeps through, or predators have a temporary population explosion), then alternative food chains may be sufficient to supply the higher trophic levels.

■ Extension: A hydrosere

If a primary succession develops in an aquatic habitat, then the sequence of pioneer plants differs from that in a dry land primary succession, but the result may well be a woodland climax community, too. The succession is called a **hydrosere** – the pioneer plants are adapted to aquatic or permanent swamp conditions, and are known as hydrophytes.

Secondary succession

Sometimes established communities are suddenly disrupted and totally destroyed. This occurs, for example, when fire destroys a large area of vegetation; occasionally it occurs as a result of human activities. In these situations, soil is already formed and present – it is just the existing biota that has been abruptly removed. A succession that starts from existing soil is known as a **secondary succession**.

Secondary successions normally happen quite quickly, since the necessary soil for plant life is already present. Plant communities are established in succession, as spores and seeds are blown in, or carried in by visiting animal life, or as they grow in from the surrounding, unharmed climax communities. After forest fires, for example, the soil is quickly covered by moss species that favour scorched soil habitats. The carpet of moss reduces soil erosion, starts to contribute to the supply of humus to the soil, and provides conditions favourable to the lodging and germination of seeds of higher plants.

Activity 5.17: Features
of a xerophyte

12 Examine the data displayed in Figure 5.18 (page 21).
 a What sort of succession is illustrated there?
 b What evidence indicates that the succession of plant communities is changing the habitat at the four sites, and why are the plants having this effect?

■ 5.3 Humans and the environment – the global warming issue

Carbon dioxide is present in the atmosphere at about 0.038% by volume (which represents 0.057% by mass). Atmospheric carbon dioxide is added as a waste product of respiration by all living things, by combustion, and from the decay of organic matter by micro-organisms. Much carbon dioxide is removed by fixation during photosynthesis – an interrelationship illustrated in the **carbon cycle** (Figure 5.24). About as much carbon dioxide is withdrawn from the atmosphere during the daylight each day as is released into the air by all the other processes, day and night – *or nearly so*.

13 In what forms does inorganic carbon exist, in:
 a the atmosphere
 b the hydrosphere
 c the lithosphere?

The effect of a low level of atmospheric carbon dioxide is to maintain a favourable environmental temperature on Earth – a phenomenon known as the **greenhouse effect**. Actually, the level of atmospheric carbon dioxide is now rising, for reasons we will investigate shortly.

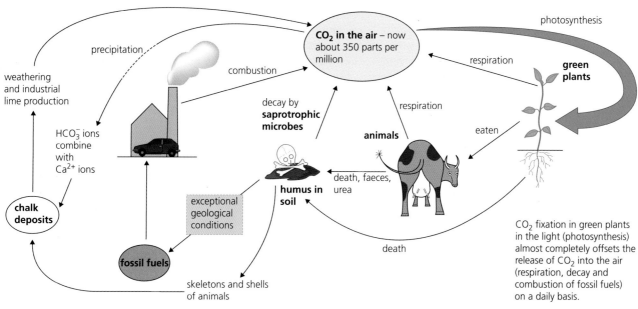

Figure 5.24 The carbon cycle.

The mechanism of the greenhouse effect

The radiant energy reaching the Earth from the Sun includes visible light (short wave radiation), and infra-red radiation (longer wave radiation – heat), which warms up the sea and land. As it is warmed, the Earth radiates infra-red radiation back towards space. However, much of this heat does not escape from our atmosphere. Some is reflected back by clouds and much is absorbed by gases in the atmosphere, which are warmed. In this respect, the atmosphere is working like the glass in a greenhouse, which is why this phenomenon is called a 'greenhouse effect' (Figure 5.25). It is vitally important – without it, surface temperatures would be too cold for life to exist on Earth.

Any gas in the atmosphere that absorbs infra-red radiation is referred to as a **greenhouse gas**. Carbon dioxide is neither the only component of our atmosphere with this effect, nor the most 'powerful'. Both water vapour and methane are also naturally occurring greenhouse gases, and the latter is much more efficient at heat retention than carbon dioxide, although not present in the same proportions (so far).

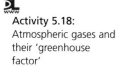

Activity 5.18: Atmospheric gases and their 'greenhouse factor'

Figure 5.25 The greenhouse effect.

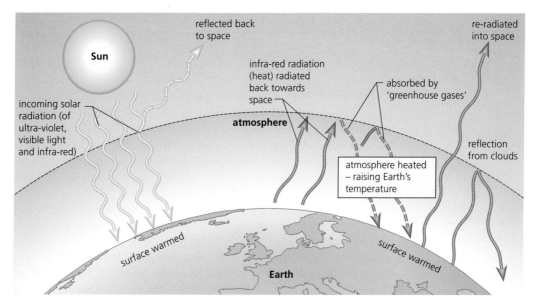

In addition, purely anthropogenic atmospheric pollutants – such as oxides of nitrogen (particularly nitrous oxide), and chlorofluorocarbons (CFCs) – have 'greenhouse' properties, too. Oxides of nitrogen are waste products of the combustion of fossil fuels (oil and coal), and so occur in the exhaust fumes of vehicles. CFCs, on the other hand, are unreactive molecules that were deliberately manufactured by the chemical industry to use as propellants in aerosol cans and as the coolant in refrigerators. With the passage of time these gases have escaped into the atmosphere, and have slowly carried up to the stratosphere.

14 What are the sources of atmospheric methane?

An enhanced greenhouse effect leading to global warming?

Increases in the atmospheric concentrations of greenhouse gases will have inevitably enhanced the greenhouse effect. In order to assess how the composition of the atmosphere has changed over time, current and historic levels of atmospheric carbon dioxide and methane must be known. *How are such records obtained?*

The best long-term records of changing levels of these greenhouse gases (and associated climate change) are based on evidence obtained from ice cores drilled in the Antarctic and Greenland ice sheets. As water freezes, bubbles of air from the surrounding atmosphere become trapped within the ice. For example, data from the Vostok ice core in East Antarctica (that is, the composition of the bubbles of gas obtained from these cores) show us how methane and carbon dioxide levels have varied over no less than 400 000 years. Similarly, variations in the concentration of oxygen isotopes from the same source indicate how temperature has changed during the same period (Figure 5.26).

Figure 5.26 Three types of data recovered from the Vostok ice cores over 400 000 years of Earth history.

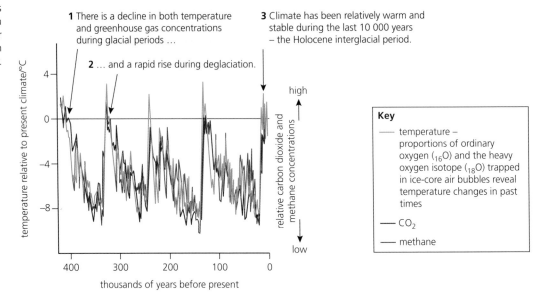

Clearly, here the levels of greenhouse gas in the atmosphere can be closely correlated with global temperature. Environmental conditions on Earth have changed as a consequence. In fact, the Earth's climate has varied very greatly over its billions of years of existence. Even over the 100 000 years of human presence, ice ages have come and gone! However, since the beginning of agriculture and the formation of city communities (about 8000 years ago) Earth conditions have been atypically steady. This stability can be correlated with steady atmospheric levels of carbon dioxide and methane (Figure 5.27).

Since the Industrial Revolution in the developed countries of the world (about 200 years ago), there have been sharp rises in the levels of greenhouse gases, attributed to the burning of coal and oil (Table 5.4). These 'fossil fuels' were mostly laid down in the Carboniferous Period. So, we are now adding to our atmosphere carbon that has been locked away for about 350 million years. This is an entirely new development in geological history. The effect has been a recent, accelerating rate of global warming. Many climate scientists argue that this development poses a major environmental threat to life as we know it.

Figure 5.27 Greenhouse gas levels in the Holocene (from 10 000 years ago).

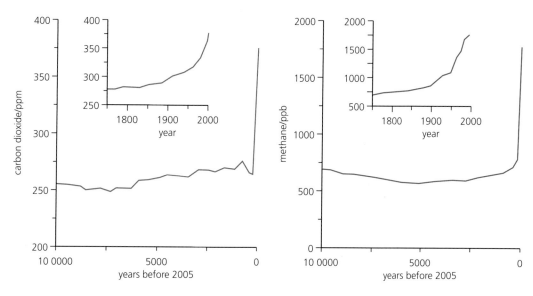

Table 5.4 Changing levels of atmospheric CO_2.

	CO₂ (in ppm)
pre-Industrial Revolution level	280 (±10)
by mid 1970s	330
by 1990	360
by 2007	380
by 2050 (if current rate maintained)	**500**

The evidence for global warming – environmental change

The report of the Intergovernmental Panel on Climate Change (IPCC) of 2007 estimated global warming would be in the range 2.4–6.4 °C by 2100. This would generate the warmest period on Earth for at least 100 000 years, with highly significant environmental impacts. The paragraphs that follow describe in outline various theatres of environmental change attributed to global warming. These changes (and others) are already evident in part, and will have disastrous consequences if they continue unabated.

Polar ice melt

The Arctic is a highly sensitive region – ice cover varies naturally. However, since 1979 the size of the summer polar ice cap has shrunk more than 20%. In this period, the decline in the ice has been, on average, more than 8% per decade. At this rate, there may be no ice in the summer of 2060. The associated Greenland ice is similarly in decline.

In Antarctica the picture is less clear. The Antarctic Peninsular has warmed, and 13 000 km² of ice have been lost in the past 50 years. Also, major sections of the Antarctic ice shelf have broken off. Meanwhile, at times the interior ice has become cooler and thicker – due to circular winds around the land mass preventing warmer air reaching the interior. Warmer seas may be eroding the ice from underneath, but IPCC predicts that the Antarctic's contribution to rising sea levels will be small.

Glacier retreats

Retreat by glaciers is worldwide and rapid – since 1980, glacier retreat has become ubiquitous. Mid-latitude mountain ranges such as the Himalayas, the Tibetan plateau, Alps, Rockies, and the southern Andes, plus the tropical summit of Kilimanjaro, show the greatest losses of glacier ice. Rivers below these mountain ranges are glacier-fed, and so the melting of glaciers will have increasing impact on the water supplies for a great many people.

Rising sea levels

The impact of global warming on sea levels is due to thermal expansion of sea water and the widespread melting of ice. The global average sea level rose at an average rate of 1.8 mm per year in the period 1960–2003, but during the later part of that period the rate was far higher than at the beginning. If this acceleration continues at the current rate, sea levels could rise by at least 30 cm in this century. This phenomenon will threaten low-lying islands and countries (including Bangladesh), and major city communities such as London, Shanghai, New York and Tokyo.

Changing weather and ocean current patterns

At the poles, cold, salty water sinks and is replaced by surface water warmed in the tropics. Now, melting ice decreases ocean salinity, which then slows the great ocean currents that convey heat energy from warmer to colder regions through their pattern of convection. So, for example, as the Gulf stream (which to date, keeps temperatures in Europe relatively warmer than in Canada) slows down, more heat is retained in the Gulf of Mexico. Here, hurricanes get their energy from hot water, and become more frequent and more severe.

Also, alteration in the patterns of heat and rainfall distribution over continental land masses are predicted to cause Russia and Canada to experience the largest mean temperature rises, followed by several Asian countries and already drought-ridden countries in West Africa. Least warming is anticipated in Ireland and Britain in the northern hemisphere, and New Zealand, Chile, Uruguay and Argentina in the south. The most immediately vulnerable populations are already impoverished communities in parts of Africa; the least vulnerable is the wealthy population of Luxembourg.

Coral bleaching

Microscopic algae live symbiotically in the cells of corals, giving them their distinctive colouration, but when under environmental stress (for example, high water temperature), the algae are expelled (causing loss of colour). The coral starts to die. Mass bleaching events occurred in the Great Barrier Reef in 1999 and 2002. The effects from thermal stress are likely to be exacerbated under future climate scenarios, threatening biodiversity in coral communities.

Other bio-indicators of climate change

Evidence of past climate changes may also be deduced from the remains of organisms that survived in habitats in the past. For example, in ancient peat deposits are found the 'fossilised' pollen grains of the once dominant vegetation. Alternatively, the study of tree rings (known as dendrochronology) indicates climatically favourable and less favourable years for tree growth, for as far back as preserved ancient timbers go. Information on these sources is given in Activity 5.19.

Temperature change and organisms, diversity, behaviour and development

Global warming, in the form of rising temperatures, changing rainfall patterns and other seasonal cycles can be expected to trigger changes in the behaviour and diversity of the biota in habitats affected. After all, the importance of 'climate' as an abiotic factor has already been highlighted (Table 5.3, page 23). What sorts of changes may be expected?

Changes in the distribution of organisms

Ecologists and naturalists in the UK have maintained records of the locations of species, using the Ordnance Survey six-figure grid reference system, since early in the twentieth century. The results are national and local distribution atlases, recording presence and sightings using dots of equal size. Scales vary, but are typically 10 km by 10 km (OS grid squares) or 2 km by 2 km squares (Figure 5.28). You can learn more about these records from published county, country and international records and databases in Activity 5.20. Now, current and future changes in distribution, possibly arising in response to climate change, may be detected by comparisons with these records of previous occurrences.

DL
www
Activity 5.19: Bio-indicators of past climate change

A* Extension 5.8: Raised heat levels, permafrost and peat (HSW Criterion 10)

Figure 5.28 Autumn crocus, an historic record of changing distribution.

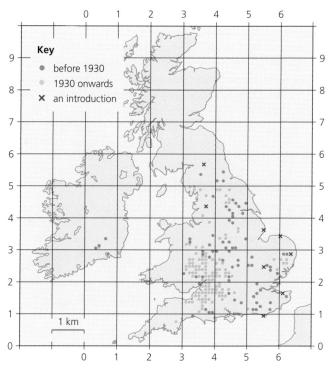

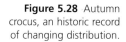

Activity 5.20: Biological recording sources

Recognising correlations and causal relationships

The Large Blue butterfly (*Maculinea arion L.*) is widespread in central and southern Europe. It was once common in the south west of the British Isles, but was reported as extinct here by 1979. But in June 2000, numbers of these butterflies were again recorded in Somerset, and later the laying of large numbers of eggs was observed during the summer season of 2007. Incidentally, the life cycle is unusual: caterpillars that form from the eggs in late spring first feed on the wild thyme plant, but are later carried by ants to their nests (mistakenly attracted by a secretion from the caterpillar's 'honey gland'). Here, the caterpillars feed on ant larvae before pupating, later to emerge from the ants' nests as butterflies.

Figure 5.29 A Large Blue (*Maculinea arion L.*) in it's natural surroundings.

15 What does the '*L.*' in *Maculinea arion L.* establish? You may need to revise this issue (*Biology for AS*, pages 171–3).

The reappearance of the Large Blue in southern England is clearly **correlated** with a period of increasing average temperature. The question is, can it be established as a **causal relationship** (dependent on elevated ambient temperatures, for example)? Alternatively, is it a coincidence, or due to another environmental change – such as some change in land husbandry. In this case, we should await the reporting of similar re-colonisations in other parts of Europe also experiencing warmer climates, and the examination of associated changes there, before being more confident of a causal relationship.

16 Look out for news items during this year, reporting evidence of changed distributions among plants and animals (including vertebrates and non-vertebrates) and other groups of organisms. Record and report these events to peers (a 'wall newspaper' is one possibility). Discuss what evidence is needed to confirm a causal relationship with permanent climate change.

Activity 5.21:
Temperature and enzyme action – a study using amylase (HSW Criteria 2 and 4)

Parasites

The distributions of parasites causing diseases may also be affected by climate change. For example, the dangerous human disease of malaria is currently described as 'marching north' as the mosquito begins to re-colonise areas of Europe and the USA. Incidentally, malaria was widespread in Europe and North America well into the nineteenth century. Climate change may establish conditions in which the mosquito can breed and complete their life cycles in the UK, for example. Whether or not this occurs, certainly some pest and disease organisms may benefit from climate change in the UK and so take a toll on health or agricultural productivity and food supplies. You can read an update on this issue via the Department for the Environment, Food and Rural Affairs (www.defra.gov.uk).

Changes in metabolism and development

The effect of temperature on organisms is direct, for temperature influences the rate of all biochemical reactions. As temperature rises, molecules have increased active energy, and reactions between them go faster. In chemical reactions, for every 10 °C rise in temperature, the rate of the reaction approximately doubles. This property is known as the **temperature coefficient** (Q_{10}) of a reaction.

$$Q_{10} = \frac{\text{rate of reaction at } (x + 10\,°C)}{\text{rate of reaction at } x\,°C} = 2 \text{ (for most chemical reactions)}$$

In enzyme-catalysed reactions, the effect of temperature is more complex. As the temperature rises, the substrate and the enzyme molecules are moving more rapidly and are more likely to collide. The rate of reaction rises. However, proteins are denatured by heat, and the rate of denaturation increases at higher temperatures. Heat denaturation is an irreversible change in the enzyme, due to the destruction of the active site. So as the temperature rises, the amount of active enzyme progressively decreases, and the rate is slowed. As a result of these two effects of heat on enzyme-catalysed reactions, each enzyme has an apparent 'optimum temperature'.

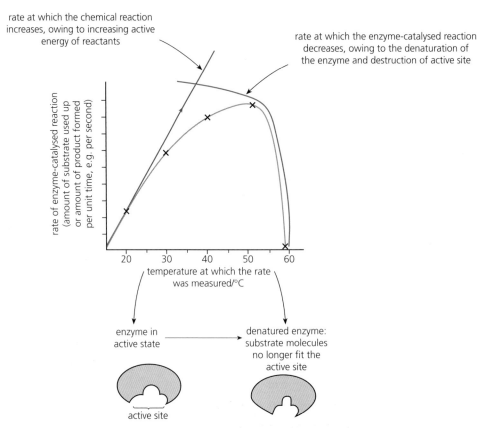

Figure 5.30 Temperature and the rate of an enzyme catalysed reaction.

Not all enzymes have the same optimum temperature (Figure 5.30). For example, the bacteria in hot thermal springs have enzymes with optima between 80 and 100 °C or higher, whereas seaweeds of northern seas and the plants of the tundra have optima closer to 0 °C. Humans have enzymes with optima at or about normal body temperature. This feature of enzymes is often exploited in the commercial and industrial uses of enzymes.

17 How would you anticipate the optimum temperatures of the enzymes of basic metabolism (for example, of respiratory pathways) to differ in a marine plankton organism and an endothermic marine mammal, such as a whale?

Temperature and sex determination in reptiles

The sex of organisms such as mammals is genetically determined by sex chromosomes. In contrast to this, in many species of reptiles (but not all) it is the temperature of incubation of fertilised eggs that determines whether they are male or female.

Temperature sex determination (TSD) came to light when it was noticed that the ratio of the sexes varied erratically in many species of reptile. Experimentally, when the eggs of alligators were artificially incubated at various temperatures, this mechanism was confirmed. Typical of most reptiles, the alligator deposits its eggs in warm conditions (such as piles of rotting vegetation), rather than incubating them in nests, as birds do. In the alligator, relatively low temperatures give females; higher temperatures give males (Table 5.5). Lizards show this same pattern, turtles the reverse pattern. And the temperature at which a shift in sex ratio occurs varies with species, too.

18 Today, relatively few organisms exhibit TSD; most have evolved some form of genetic sex determination. Speculate on the possible influences of TSD in the extinction of the dinosaurs, assuming earlier reptiles did exhibit this type of gender control.

Temperature and plant growth

Plant metabolism and growth is dependent upon photosynthesis. Perhaps you will have already noted that the effect of temperature on photosynthesis depends upon other critical factors – and in particular, light intensity (A* Extension 5.1)?

Photosynthesis is a biochemical process involving a series of interconnected reactions. All these reactions contribute to the overall rate of the process. At any one time, the rate of photosynthesis will be limited by the slowest of these reactions. In fact, the rate of photosynthesis will be limited by the factor that is in shortest supply (whether it be CO_2 concentration, light intensity or the temperature). This factor, whichever one it is, is known as the **limiting factor** (Activity 5.22).

Impact of heat on growth and development – experimental approaches

Elevated temperatures may enhance the rate of photosynthesis, but higher temperatures may quickly have an adverse effect. So it is with biochemical reactions in all organisms. Adapted as they are to environmental conditions in a particular habitat, consistently raised temperatures there may well have a complex effect on organisms' growth and development. In Activities 5.23 and 5.24 there is the opportunity to plan investigations into the effects of temperature on seedling growth and on brine shrimp hatching rates.

DL
www
Activity 5.22:
Understanding limiting factors in photosynthesis

Activity 5.23:
Investigating the effects of temperature on seedling growth rate (HSW Criteria 2, 3, 4, 5 and 8)

Activity 5.24:
Investigating the effects of temperature on brine shrimp hatch rates (HSW Criteria 2, 3, 4, 5 and 8)

Table 5.5 The effects of incubation temperature on sex determination in the alligator.

	Temperature of egg incubation (°C)					
	26	**28**	**30**	**32**	**34**	**36**
Number of eggs at start	50	100	100	100	100	50
% of total that died	86	4	3	2	6	86
Females (% of living offspring)	100	100	100	86.7	0	0
Males (% of living offspring)	0	0	0	13.3	100	100

■ **Extension:** Bacterial ecology – impact of ambient temperatures.

Temperature is perhaps the most important environmental factor affecting growth and survival of bacteria (of which there are vast numbers of different species). As with other organisms, there are minimum, optimum and maximum temperatures for each species or strain. However, the range of temperatures over which bacteria can survive is extraordinarily wide. It has been possible to distinguish four groups within the bacteria in relation to their temperature optima (Figure 5.31).

Psychrophiles exist in extremely cold habitats, and may also be found to contaminate deep-freeze facilities. Mesophiles occur in 'warm blooded' animals, and in temperate and tropical habitats, and thermophiles occur in unusually hot environments. Hyperthermophiles occur in extremely hot thermal vents and deep-sea hydrothermal vents.

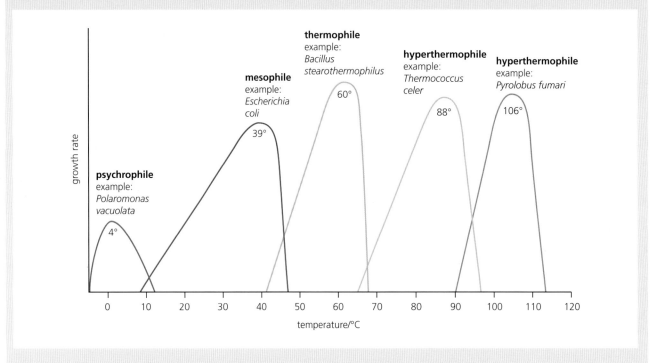

Figure 5.31 The temperature tolerance of four groups of bacteria.

■ **Extension:** Climate change – daily variation versus a rising global average?

Since the end of the last ice age (about 10 000 years ago), the average global temperature has risen by only about 5 °C. Now, climate scientists variously estimate that further global warming will be of the order 2.4–6.4 °C by the year 2100. Given that we commonly experience daily ambient temperature variations of 10 °C or more, the predicted consequences from a relatively small rise in global average temperature may be hard to understand. Nevertheless, both phenomena are highly significant for all living things.

The enhanced greenhouse effect – the future

Powerful computer models are used to predict both day-to-day weather patterns, and changes to the climate over longer time scales. The climate system is highly complex and it is impossible to represent all components fully. Consequently, approximations have to be made, based on value judgements, but these are then continually modified in the light of experiences. Certainly, current models take account of:

1 impact of clouds on heating and cooling – cloud reduces incoming heat energy, but traps heat radiating from the Earth's surface; different types and heights of clouds have contrasting effects on climate, too
2 heating of oceans and their circulations – water heats slowly, but then retains heat, and transports and circulates it according to particular current patterns
3 absorption of heat by land – 'dark' land (such as that covered by trees) absorbs more heat than desserts or ice sheets
4 aerosols and atmospheric pollutants – pollutants come from volcanoes, forest fires, and from burning of fossil fuels; they generally have a cooling effect
5 chemistry of the atmosphere, and the carbon cycle – greenhouse gases differ in their heat retention, and on how long they remain; half the human-generated CO_2 is removed by green plants; and if land continues to heat up it will release even more greenhouse gases.

Long-term climate predictions depend upon the accurate estimation of the impact of these factors, and on how they interact with time. Owing to the complexity of this situation, it is wise to regard all predictions, whether pessimistic or optimistic, with a fair measure of scepticism.

Another important feature of climate change prediction is the distinctive schools of thought that are engaged. These include:

- profoundly committed environmentalists, who pay the greatest attention to anthropogenic factors, for example – their views of the future are most accessible in the writings of James Lovelock (2006) *The Revenge of Gaia*, Allan Lane / Penguin Books, and Al Gore (2005) *An Inconvenient Truth*, Bloomsbury Paperback
- students of the long-term geological records of past climates and Earth conditions, who have focused on the profound changes that have occurred and re-occurred in Earth history, including through the bulk of time when humans were not present
- atmospheric chemists who, among other things, draw attention to the contribution of water vapour as the most influential greenhouse gas (accounting for about 95% of the Earth's greenhouse effect), ignorance of which, they say, contributes to overestimations of human impact – some have argued that human greenhouse gases contribute only about 0.3% of the greenhouse effect, although unfortunately this school of thought is sometimes also supported by people associated with fossil fuel industries who may be keen to maintain 'business as usual'.

HSW 5.3: Criteria 10a, 11a and 12 – Issues in the global warming crisis

Global warming – international and individual responses

What are the most likely consequences that may result from failure to halt the rising level of atmospheric carbon dioxide, and reduce it to earlier values? What actions are needed to enable us to achieve these things? In Table 5.6 (overleaf), responses to these questions are summarised.

To be effective, 'strong' actions taken in response to these challenges need to:

- be agreed internationally by being acceptable to all nations, and be acted on by each and everyone, simultaneously
- recognise that existing developed countries have already experienced their industrial revolutions (which largely initiated these processes of environmental damage), and surely need to fully share the benefits thus accrued with less developed countries that would be required to otherwise forgo some of the benefits of development.

Is effective international agreement possible?

The need is for drastic cuts in global emissions of carbon dioxide and other greenhouse gasses. An international agreement to limit release of greenhouse gases by all industrial countries and emerging industrial countries was first agreed at the Earth Summit in Rio de Janeiro in 1992.

Table 5.6 Global warming – likely consequences and appropriate actions?

Likely consequences of unchecked, enhanced global warming	Effective 'strong' actions that may combat these threats
■ Complete meltdown of the polar ice caps and the glaciers of mountain regions, releasing vast amounts of water into the seas, so raising sea levels ■ Warming of sea waters, causing them to expand in volume, so further raising sea levels ■ Permanent flooding of much lowland territory where currently vast numbers of the human population live and where the most agriculturally productive land occurs ■ Raising of sea temperature to levels where surface waters (where algae flourish) are no longer ion-enriched by natural mixing with colder deep water, causing failure of algal photosynthesis (a major CO_2 sump) – so leading to further increases in atmospheric CO_2 levels ■ Destruction of forests by global temperatures that, in many parts of the world, are too high to support the survival and natural growth of trees ■ Interruption of ocean current systems that distribute warm waters from the tropical regions of the globe northwards, thereby disrupting agricultural production levels that sustain the human food chain for many human populations	■ Conserve fossil fuel stocks, using them only sparingly, and only where there are no apparent alternatives (such as oils from biofuel sources) ■ Develop nuclear power sources to supply electricity for industrial, commercial and domestic needs ■ Develop so-called renewable sources of power, exploiting environmental energy sources, such as wave energy and wind power ■ Develop biofuel sources of energy, exploiting organic waste matter that will naturally decay anyway, and biofuel crops that are renewable sources of energy using current photosynthesis products ■ Reduce use of fuels for heating of homes, where necessary, to minimum levels by economical (well insulated) designs of housing ■ Reduce use of fuels for transport systems through efficient design ■ Terminating the destruction of forests in general, and of rainforest all around the tropical regions of the Earth in particular, since these are a major CO_2 sumps

The initiative known as Agenda 21 was launched. Subsequently, at the Kyoto Conference in Japan a first attempt was made to meet the pledges made at Rio. Carbon dioxide emission targets for the industrial nations were set for the period 2009–2012.

However, nations were allowed to offset emissions with devices such as 'carbon sinks' – mechanisms by which atmospheric carbon dioxide is removed from the air either permanently, or on a long-term basis. An example is when it is absorbed by *additional* forest trees and becomes the carbon of wood that is not harvested and burnt. By and large, many of the arrangements are so complex as to be difficult to enforce. Real progress is extremely slow.

Activity 5.25: Biofuels and re-forestation – a research task

Individual responses – 'Think globally, act locally'?

A point for everyone to consider is what practical actions they as individuals can take to reduce their 'carbon footprint'. Like all resolutions, ideas may be easier to espouse than to carry through, consistently. Perhaps this is an issue to work at with a group of peers, within the context of your own environment, spheres of influence, and evaluations of the global crisis?

■ 5.4 Evolution and speciation – modern evidence

By **evolution**, we mean the gradual development of life in geological time. The word 'evolution' is used very widely, but in biology it means specifically the processes by which life has been changed from its earliest beginnings to the diversity of organisms we know about today, living and extinct. It is the development of new types of living organisms from pre-existing types by the accumulation of genetic differences over long periods of time.

A* Extension 5.9: Charles Darwin and the origins of the *Origin* (HSW Criterion 5b)

The idea of evolution is most closely associated with Charles Darwin (1809–1882). Darwin, and the arguments he presented for the origin of species by natural selection, were introduced in *Biology for AS*, pages 181–3.

Revise this section now, if you are not fully familiar with the ideas and origins of natural selection.

19 Tabulate the points of the argument that Darwin advanced for the origin of species by natural selection.

Neo-Darwinism

Charles Darwin, together with almost everyone else working in the science at that time, knew nothing of Mendel's discovery of the principles of modern genetics. Chromosomes had not been reported, and the existence of genes, alleles and DNA were unknown.

Instead, biologists then believed in 'blending inheritance' to account for the similarities and differences between parents and offspring. According to this explanation, an offspring was a 'blend' or average of the characteristics of the parents. The outcome of the blending of parental characteristics in offspring, if it happened, would be increasing uniformity. That is, genetic variation (which is essential for natural selection) would actually be reduced.

Today, modern genetics has shown us that blending generally does not occur, and that there are several ways by which genetic variations arise in gamete formation and fertilisation. Neo-Darwinism is a restatement of the ideas of evolution by natural selection in terms of modern genetics. Table 5.7 summarises the ideas of neo-Darwinism.

HSW 5.4: Criteria 1 and 2 – Models and creative thinking in science

A* Extension 5.10: Alternative explanations of the origin of species (HSW Criterion 7)

Table 5.7 The ideas of neo-Darwinism.

Genetic variations arise via:
- **mutations**, including chromosome mutations and gene mutations
- **random assortment** of paternal and maternal chromosomes in meiosis – this occurs in the process of gamete formation
- **recombination of segments** of maternal and paternal homologous chromosomes – during crossing-over that occurs at meiosis in gamete formation
- the **random fusion of male and female gametes** in sexual reproduction – this was understood in Darwin's time

Then, when genetic variation has arisen in organisms:
- it is expressed in their phenotypes
- some phenotypes are better able to survive and reproduce in a particular environment
- natural selection operates, determining the survivors and the genes that are perpetuated

In time, this process may lead to new varieties and new species.

Population genetics

Population genetics is the study of genes in populations (Figure 5.32). Populations are important to our discussion at this stage because they are where evolution may occur.

A **population** is a group of individuals of a species, living close together, and able to interbreed.

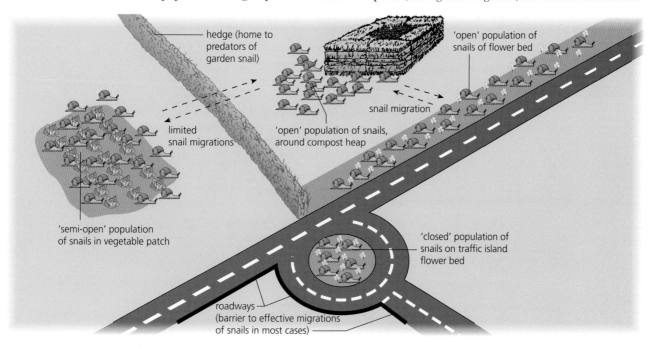

Figure 5.32 The concept of 'population'.

So a population of garden snails might occupy a small part of a garden – say, around a compost heap. A population of thrushes might occupy some gardens and surrounding fields. In other words, the area occupied by a population depends on the size of the organism and on how mobile it is, for example, as well as on environmental factors (such as food supply, predation, and so on).

The boundaries of a population may be hard to define, too. Some populations are fully 'open', with individuals moving in or out, from nearby populations. Alternatively, some populations are more-or-less 'closed' – that is, isolated communities, almost completely cut off from neighbours of the same species.

Populations and gene pools

A **gene pool** consists of all the genes, and their different alleles, present in the reproductive cells of the individuals in an interbreeding population.

When breeding occurs between members of a population, a sample of the alleles of the gene pool will form the genomes (gene sets of individuals) of the next generation – and so on, from generation to generation. Remember, an allele is one of a number of alternative forms of a gene that can occupy a given locus on a chromosome.

The frequency with which any particular allele occurs in a given population is called the **allele frequency**. When allele frequencies of a particular population are investigated, they may turn out to be static and unchanging. Alternatively, we may find allele frequencies changing. They might do so quite rapidly with succeeding generations, for example.

When the allele frequencies of a gene pool remain more-or-less unchanged, then we know that population is static as regards its inherited characteristics. We can say that the population is not evolving.

However, if the allele frequencies of a gene pool are changing (that is, the proportions of particular alleles are altered, or 'disturbed', in some way), then we may assume that evolution is going on. Indeed, evolution can be defined as a change in allele frequency.

Figure 5.33 Deriving the Hardy–Weinberg formula.

Let the frequency of the dominant allele (**G**) be p, and the frequency of the recessive allele (**g**) be q.

The frequency of alleles must add up to 1, so $p + q = 1$.

This means in a cross, a proportion (p) of the gametes carries the **G** allele, and a proportion (q) of the gametes carries the **g** allele.

The offspring of each generation are given by the Punnett grid.

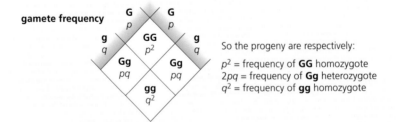

gamete frequency

So the progeny are respectively:

p^2 = frequency of **GG** homozygote
$2pq$ = frequency of **Gg** heterozygote
q^2 = frequency of **gg** homozygote

Hardy–Weinberg formula

If the frequency of one allele (**G**) is p, and the frequency of the other allele (**g**) is q then the frequencies of the three possible genotypes **GG**, **Gg** and **gg** are respectively p^2, $2pq$ and q^2.

In this way, Hardy and Weinberg developed the following equation to describe stable gene pools:

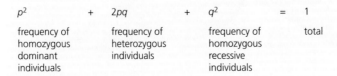

p^2	+	$2pq$	+	q^2	=	1
frequency of homozygous dominant individuals		frequency of heterozygous individuals		frequency of homozygous recessive individuals		total

For example, some alleles may be increasing in frequency because of an advantage they confer to the individuals carrying them. With possession of those alleles, the organism is more successful. It may produce more offspring, for example. If we can detect change in a gene pool, we may detect evolution happening, possibly even well before a new species is observed.

How can we detect change or constancy in gene pools?
The answer is, by a mathematical formula called the **Hardy–Weinberg formula** (Figure 5.33). This principle was discovered independently by two people, in the process of their explaining why dominant characteristics don't take over in populations, driving out the recessive form of that characteristic. (For example, at the time, people thought – wrongly – that human eye colour was controlled by a single gene, and that an allele for blue eyes was dominant to the allele for brown eyes. They were trying to explain why the whole population hasn't become blue-eyed.)

The main problem in finding gene frequencies is that it is not possible to distinguish between homozygous dominants and heterozygotes based on their appearance or phenotypes. However, using the Hardy–Weinberg equation, it is possible to calculate gene frequency from the number of homozygous recessive individuals in the population. This is q^2. We can find q – the frequency of the recessive allele – by finding the square root, and this can then be substituted into the initial equation $p + q = 1$, to find the frequency of the dominant allele.

■ Extension: Using the Hardy–Weinberg formula

The absence of the skin pigment, melanin, is a condition called **albinism**, and is a genetically controlled characteristic. An albino has the genotype **pp** (homozygous recessive), whereas people with normal pigmentation are homozygous (**PP**) or heterozygous (**Pp**). In a typical large human population, only one person in 10 000 is albino.
From the Hardy–Weinberg equation, homozygous recessives (**pp**) = q^2.

Thus $q^2 = 0.0001$, so $q = \sqrt{0.0001} = 0.01$.

So substituting into the initial equation $p + q = 1$,

$p + 0.01 = 1$, therefore $p = 0.99$.

Thus the Hardy–Weinberg formula has allowed us find the frequencies of alleles **P** and **p** in a population.
  Incidentally, it has also been shown that the frequency of 'carriers' of an allele for albinism in the population (**Pp**) is quite high (about 1 in 50 of the population) despite the fact that albinos make up only 1 in 10 000. In other words, very many more people unknowingly carry around an allele for 'albinism' than those who know they may do so.

The Hardy–Weinberg principle and disturbing factors

The Hardy–Weinberg principle predicts that the gene pool in a population does not change in succeeding generations. That is, genes and genotype frequencies normally remain constant in a breeding population, *provided that*:

- the breeding population under investigation is a large one
- there is random mating, with individuals of any genotype all equally likely to mate with individuals of any other genotype (for example, no one genotype is being selectively predated)
- there is no introduction of new alleles into the population, either by mutations or by immigration of new breeding individuals.

But sometimes, in some populations, the composition of the gene pool does change. This may be due to a range of factors, known as **disturbing factors** because they operate to alter the proportions of some alleles. Disturbing factors include the following.

1 **Mutation** – random, rare, spontaneous change in the genes occurs in gonads. This leads to the possibility of new characteristics in the offspring – for example, the ability to inactivate a pesticide molecule or to inactivate heavy metal ions and so thrive in a particularly polluted environment.

2 **Selective predation** of members of the population with certain characteristics that are genetically controlled will lead to changing frequencies of certain alleles – for example, selective predation of snails with a particular shell coloration that makes them visible in (say) a woodland habitat, but effectively camouflaged in a grassland habitat (Figure 5.34).

3 **Emigration** and **immigration** – snails with superior locomotory musculature, for example, or better able to withstand moisture loss during journeys are more likely to survive a migration than others.

4 **Random genetic drift** – a sudden hostile physical condition (for example, cold, flooding or drought) may sharply reduce a natural population to very few survivors. On the return of a favourable environment, numbers of the affected species may quickly return to normal (because of reduced competition for food sources, for example). However, the new population has been built from a very small sample of the original population, with numerous 'first cousin' and backcross matings (causing fewer heterozygotes and more homozygotes) and with some alleles lost altogether.

5 **Founder effect** – a barrier may arise within a population, instantly isolating a small sample of the original population, which may carry an unrepresentative selection of the gene pool, yet be the basis of a new population. This is another form of genetic drift.

20 What factors may cause the composition of a gene pool to change?

Figure 5.34 Selective predation of snails.

woodland leaf litter

the **thrush** (*Turdus ericetorum*) selectively predates local populations of snails, using a stone as an 'anvil'

grass sward

The banded, coloured shells of the snail *Cepaea nemoralis* are common sights in woods, hedges and grasslands. The shells may be brown, pink or yellow, and possess up to five dark bands. In woodland leaf litter the shells that are camouflaged are darker and more banded than those camouflaged among grasses.

How changing gene pools may lead to speciation

We have seen that species exist almost exclusively as local populations, even though the boundaries to these populations are often rather open and ill-defined. Individuals of local populations tend to resemble each other more closely than they resemble members of other populations. Local populations are very important as they are potential starting points for speciation.

Speciation is the name given to the process by which one species may evolve from another. A first step to speciation may be when part of a local population becomes completely cut off in some way. Even then, many generations may elapse before the composition of the gene pool has changed sufficiently to allow us to call the new individuals a different species. Such changes in local gene pools may be detected at an early stage by application of the Hardy–Weinberg formula.

Speciation by isolation

Occasionally a population is suddenly divided by the appearance of a barrier, resulting in two populations, isolated from each other. Before separation, individuals shared a common gene pool, but after isolation, 'disturbing processes' like natural selection, mutation and random genetic drift may occur independently in both populations, causing them to diverge in their features and characteristics.

Geographic isolation between populations occurs when natural, or human-imposed, barriers arise and sharply restrict movement of individuals (and their spores and gametes, in the case of plants) between the divided populations (Figure 5.35).

1 isolation by a new, natural physical barrier
A natural habitat became divided when a river broke its banks and took a new route:

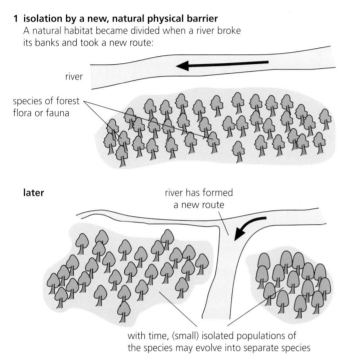

2 Isolation by a human-imposed barrier
The by-pass at Newbury cuts through established habitats, separating local populations.

Figure 5.35 Geographical barriers.

Geographic isolation also arises when motile or mobile species are dispersed to isolated habitats – as, for example, when organisms are accidentally rafted from mainland territories to distant islands. The 2004 tsunami generated examples of this in South East Asia. Violent events of this type have punctuated world geological history surprisingly frequently.

Charles Darwin visited the isolated islands of Galapagos, off the coast of South America, during his voyage with *The Beagle* in 1831–36. The islands are 600 miles (970 km) from the South American mainland (Figure 5.36), and their origin is volcanic – they appeared out of the sea about 16 million years ago, at which point they were of course uninhabited. Today, they have a flora and fauna that relates to mainland species.

Darwin encountered examples of population divergence on the Galapagos Islands. For example, the tortoises found on these islands had distinctive shells. With experience, an observer could tell which individual island an animal came from by its appearance, so markedly had the local, isolated populations diverged since their arrival from the mainland.

The iguana lizard here had no mammal competition when it arrived on the Galapagos Islands. It became the dominant form of vertebrate life, and was extremely abundant when Darwin visited. By then, two species were present, one terrestrial and the other fully adapted to marine life (Figure 5.36, overleaf). The latter is assumed to have evolved locally as a result of pressure from overcrowding and competition for food on the islands (both species are vegetarian), which drove some members of the population out of the terrestrial habitat.

Figure 5.36 The Galapagos Islands and species divergence there.

Many organisms (e.g. insects and birds) may have flown or been carried on wind currents to the Galapagos from the mainland. Mammals are most unlikely to have survived drifting there on a natural raft over this distance, but many large reptiles can survive long periods without food or water.

immigrant travel to the Galapagos

The Galapagos Islands

Today the tortoise population of each island is distinctive and identifiable.

The **giant iguana lizards** on the Galapagos Islands became dominant vertebrates, and today are two distinct species, one still terrestrial, the other marine, with webbed feet and a laterally flattened tail (like the caudal fin of a fish).

terrestrial iguana

marine iguana

Reproductive isolation mechanisms occasionally develop that are strong enough to prevent interbreeding between members of small, isolated populations that have diverged genetically, if only slightly, as a result of their isolation. Cases of reproductive isolation are likely to be less consistently effective than geographic separation in bringing about complete isolation in the early stages. This is especially true if the isolation is based on slight, physiological differences, as is the case in some incompatibility mechanisms in flowering plants (Figure 5.37). Nevertheless, if members of a population become further isolated in this way, their gene pools may diverge significantly as a result.

Figure 5.37 An example of reproductive isolation in a flowering plant.

Incompatibility in flowering plants is the name given to physiological mechanisms that may make fertilisation impossible by preventing the growth of pollen tubes on the stigma or through the style.

Pollen that lodges on a stigma 'germinates' and attempts to send out a pollen tube that may eventually reach the embryo sac. Growth of pollen tubes that are opposed or unsupported by the stigma tissue fails.

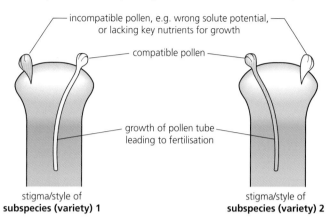

performance of pollen grains on different varieties of plant

incompatible pollen, e.g. wrong solute potential, or lacking key nutrients for growth

compatible pollen

growth of pollen tube leading to fertilisation

stigma/style of **subspecies (variety) 1**

stigma/style of **subspecies (variety) 2**

Speciation by polyploidy, a form of mutation

A mutation is a sudden change in the genetic information of an organism that may be heritable, arising by change in structure, arrangement or quantity of the DNA of the chromosomes. These events occur randomly and spontaneously, and usually result in a marked difference in the characteristics of an organism.

Chromosome mutations involve a change in the structure or number of chromosomes. In plants, polyploidy is a rare occurrence, but one which more-or-less instantly creates a new species (provided the polyploid survives the early period when its numbers are incredibly low).

The types of chromosome mutation that may lead to a new species generally involve an alteration in the number of whole sets of chromosomes (known as euploidy). An organism with more than two sets of chromosomes is called a **polyploid**. Polyploids are largely restricted to plants and (some) animals that reproduce asexually (the sex determination mechanism of vertebrates prevents polyploidy).

In polyploids, the additional set or sets of chromosomes may come from a member of the same species. Typically, this occurs if the spindle fails in meiosis, causing diploid gametes to be formed. A well-known and economically very important example is the origin of the cultivated potato *Solanum tuberosum* ($2n = 48$), a polyploid of the smaller, wild *Solanum brevidens* ($2n = 24$).

Alternatively, additional sets of chromosomes may come from a different species. The additional sets are most likely not to be homologous, so pairing cannot occur early in meiosis, and the new individual is sterile. However, if the chromosome number is accidentally doubled by mitosis in the polyploid cell, immediately the polyploid is formed, then pairing *is* possible. The origin of modern bread wheat is an example, but there are several steps to this complex mutation story.

The total of other mechanisms or changes leading to reproductive isolation are summarised in Table 5.8.

Table 5.8 A summary of isolating mechanisms.

Ecological	occupation of different parts of the habitat, leading to effective separation and therefore reproductive isolation e.g. terrestrial and marine iguana lizards of the Galapagos Islands
Temporal	occupation of the same habitat but developing a permanent difference in time of year when gametes are formed and reproduction occurs e.g. Monterey and Knobcorn pines of the Californian forests
Behavioural	members of a population develop distinctive behaviour routines in their development, courtship or mating processes e.g. imprinting behaviour of geese and swans discovered by Konrad Lorenz (Figure 5.38, overleaf) – swans and geese are related species that have evolved apart for long enough for their progeny (the hybrid 'gwan') to be infertile

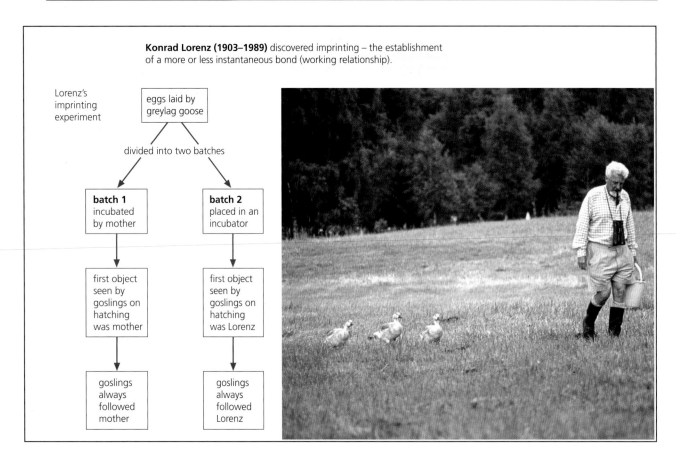

Konrad Lorenz (1903–1989) discovered imprinting – the establishment of a more or less instantaneous bond (working relationship).

Lorenz's imprinting experiment

eggs laid by greylag goose

divided into two batches

batch 1 incubated by mother

batch 2 placed in an incubator

first object seen by goslings on hatching was mother

first object seen by goslings on hatching was Lorenz

goslings always followed mother

goslings always followed Lorenz

Imprinting underpins reproductive isolation in geese and swans. If a fertile goose's egg is added to a swan's nest and incubated with the swan's eggs, then on hatching, the goose chick imprints on the swan 'parent' birds and is brought up by them. Later, the goose may mate with a swan. If so the progeny will be a 'gwan'.

goose

swan

×

Gwan has body of a swan but the feet and 'honk' of a goose.
It is an infertile hybrid. Swans and geese have evolved apart sufficiently for their progeny to be infertile, but not sufficiently to prevent the formation of a hybrid.

Figure 5.38 Behavioural isolation following imprinting.

Natural selection and speciation

Natural selection operates on individuals, or rather on their phenotypes. Phenotypes are the product of a particular combination of alleles, interacting with the effects of the environment of the organism. Consequently, natural selection causes changes to the composition of gene pools. However, the effects of these changes vary. We can recognise different types of selection.

1 **Stabilising selection** occurs where environmental conditions are stable and largely unchanging. Stabilising selection does not lead to evolution, but rather it maintains favourable characteristics that enable a species to be successful, and the alleles responsible for them, and eliminates variants and abnormalities that are useless or harmful. Probably most populations undergo stabilising selections. The example in Figure 5.39 comes from human birth records on babies born between 1935 and 1946, in London. It shows there is an optimum birth weight for babies, and those with birth weights heavier or lighter are at a selective disadvantage.

The birth weight of humans is influenced by **environmental factors** (e.g. maternal nutrition, smoking habits, etc.) and by **inheritance** (about 50%).

When more babies than average die at very low and very high birth weights, this obviously affects the gene pool because it tends to eliminate genes for low and high birth weights.

the main graph shows the **birth weights of infants born in a London hospital 1935–1946** (histogram)

and the **death rate in relation to birth weight** (broken line)

The data are an example of continuous variation. The 'middleness' or central tendency of this type of data is expressed in three ways:

1 **mode** (modal value) – the most frequent value in a set of values

2 **median** – the middle value of a set of values where these are arranged in ascending order

3 **mean** (average) – the sum of the individual values, divided by the number of values

This is an example of **stabilising selection** in that the values (weights) at the extremes of a continuous variation are at a selective disadvantage. This means that infants of these birth weights are more likely to die in infancy.

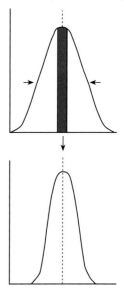

Figure 5.39 Birth weight and infant mortality, a case of stabilising selection.

2 **Directional selection** is associated with changing environmental conditions. In these situations, the majority of an existing form of an organism may no longer be best suited to the environment. Some unusual or abnormal forms of the population may have a selective advantage.

An example of directional selection is the development of resistance to an antibiotic by bacteria. Certain bacteria cause disease, and patients with bacterial infections are frequently treated with an antibiotic to help them overcome the infection. Antibiotics are very widely used. In a large population of a species of bacteria, some may carry a gene for resistance to the antibiotic in question. Sometimes such a gene arises by spontaneous mutation. Sometimes the gene is acquired in a form of sexual reproduction between bacteria of different populations.

A 'resistant' bacterium has no selective advantage in the absence of the antibiotic, and must compete for resources with non-resistant bacteria. But when the antibiotic is present, most bacteria of the population are killed off. Resistant bacteria remain and create the future population, all of which now carry the gene for resistance to the antibiotic (Figure 5.40). The gene pool has been changed abruptly.

Figure 5.40 Directional selection.

A* Extension 5.11:
Speciation – speed and types

A* Extension 5.12:
Convergent evolution versus adaptive radiation

Activity 5.26: Darwin pond

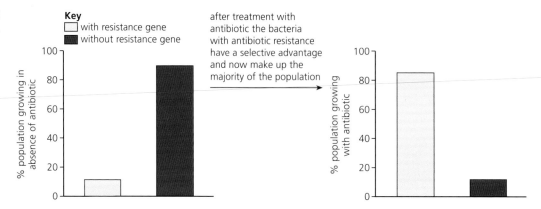

New evidence for evolution

Evidence from fossils (palaeontological evidence) was at one time a main source of information about life forms now extinct. Fossilisation is an extremely rare, chance event; scavengers and bacterial action normally dismember and decompose dead plant and animal structures before they can be fossilised. Of the organisms that have been fossilised, most are not found, recovered and interpreted. Nevertheless, numerous fossils have been uncovered. They include:

- petrified remains (organic matter of the dead organism is replaced by mineral ions)
- moulds (the organic matter decays, but the vacated space becomes a mould)
- traces (an impression of a form, such as of a leaf, or a footprint)
- preserved, intact whole organisms (trapped in amber, ice, or in anaerobic, acidic peat, for example).

21 Most fossils are preserved in sedimentary rocks. Why is this so, and how are sedimentary rocks formed?

A* Extension 5.13:
Credible opposition to the idea of organic evolution?

Additionally, it has sometimes been possible to date quite accurately the rocks surrounding fossils by exploiting the known rates of decay of certain isotopes, including carbon (^{14}C), and the ratio of potassium to argon ($^{40}K/^{40}Ar$) present in lava deposits. Using the decay rate of ^{14}C gives ages of fossils formed in the last 60 000 years. Using the ratio of $^{40}K/^{40}Ar$ gives an approximate age of sedimentary rocks (and their fossils) below and above a lava layer from geological time back to the Cambrian period (580 mya), although these are unreliable for the most recent half million years.

Exciting and illuminating fossils finds abound. Two of the most moving are, perhaps, those of the first hominid (a 'southern ape', named Lucy) at Hadar in Ethiopia in 1974, and the footsteps at Laetoli in Tanzania in 1976, found in volcanic ash, dated 3.6 mya, and our first record of bipedalism.

Today, studies in **comparative physiology and biochemistry** are a new tool in the investigation of evolutionary change (Figure 5.45, page 54). Most living things have DNA as their genetic material. The genetic code is virtually universal. The processes of 'reading' the code and protein synthesis, using RNA and ribosomes, are very similar in prokaryotes and eukaryotes, too. Processes such as respiration involve the same types of steps and similar or identical intermediates and biochemical reactions, similarly catalysed. ATP is the universal energy currency. Among the autotrophic organisms, the biochemistry of photosynthesis is virtually identical, as well.

So, early biochemical events in the evolution of life have been 'inherited' widely, as and when forms of life diversified. However, large molecules like nucleic acids and the proteins they code for are subjected to some changes with time, so knowledge of these changes may be an aid to the study of the timings of evolutionary change. It is possible to measure the relatedness of different groups of organisms by the amount of difference between specific molecules such as DNA, proteins and enzyme systems. One aspect of these investigations is **proteomics**. This is the study (qualitative and quantitative) of the proteins coded for by specific genes of the human genome.

How have these approaches been applied to evolution in practice?

Immunological studies

The immune reaction provides a mechanism of detecting differences in specific proteins, and therefore (indirectly) their relatedness. **Serum** is the liquid produced from blood when blood cells and fibrinogen have been removed. Protein molecules present in the serum act as antigens (page 82) when serum is injected into animals with an immune system that lacks these particular proteins. Typically, a rabbit is used when investigating relatedness to humans. The injected serum triggers the production of antibodies against the injected 'foreign' proteins. Then, fresh serum produced from the treated rabbit's blood (it now contains antibodies against human proteins) is tested against serum from a range of animals. The more closely related the animal is to humans, the greater the precipitation observed (Figure 5.41).

Figure 5.41 The immune reaction and evolutionary relationships.

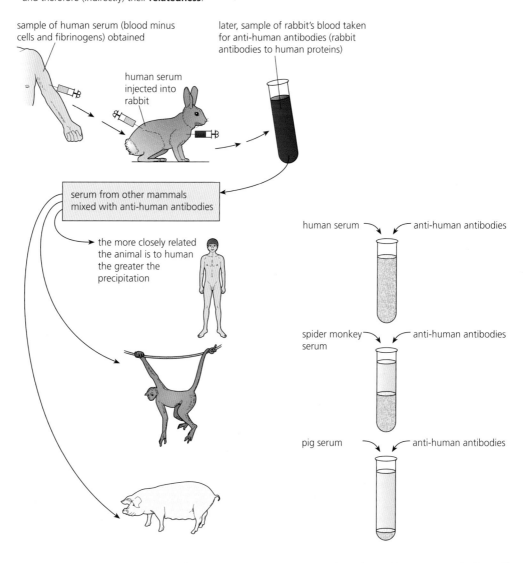

Immunological studies are a means of detecting differences in specific proteins of species, and therefore (indirectly) their **relatedness**.

sample of human serum (blood minus cells and fibrinogens) obtained

later, sample of rabbit's blood taken for anti-human antibodies (rabbit antibodies to human proteins)

human serum injected into rabbit

serum from other mammals mixed with anti-human antibodies

the more closely related the animal is to human the greater the precipitation

human serum — anti-human antibodies

spider monkey serum — anti-human antibodies

pig serum — anti-human antibodies

The precipitation produced by reaction with human serum is taken as 100%. For each species in Table 5.9, the greater the precipitation, the more recently the species shared a common ancestor with humans. This technique, called **comparative serology**, has been used by taxonomists to establish phylogenetic links in a number of cases, in both mammals and non-vertebrates.

Of course, we do not know the common ancestor to these animals and the blood of that ancestor is not available to test anyway. But if the 584 amino acids that make up blood albumin change at a constant rate, then the percentage immunological 'distance' between humans and any of these animals will be a product of the distances back to the common ancestor plus the difference 'forward' again to any one of the listed animals. Hence the differences between a listed animal and human can be halved to gauge the difference between a modern form and the common ancestor.

Since the radiation of the primates is known from geological and fossil evidence, the forward rate of change since the lemur gives the rate of the molecular clock – namely 35% in 60 million years, or 0.6% every million years. This calculation can now be applied to all the data (Table 5.9, right-hand column).

Table 5.9 Relatedness investigated via the immune reaction.

Species	Precipitation (%)	Difference from human (%)	Difference to common ancestor (half difference from human)(%)	Postulated time since common ancestor (million years)
human	100	–	–	–
chimpanzee	95	5	2.5	4
gorilla	95	5	2.5	4
orang-utan	85	15	7.5	13
gibbon	82	18	9	15
baboon	73	27	13.5	23
spider monkey	60	40	20	34
lemur	35	65	32.5	55
dog	25	75	37.5	64
kangaroo	8	92	46	79

Genetic differences in DNA

The technique of DNA hybridisation involves matching DNA from different species to test the degree of base pairing that occurs (Figure 5.42). This tells us the approximate degree of divergence between closely related groups, such as families within the primates. This data can then be correlated with data on the estimated number of years since they shared a common ancestor (Table 5.9, above).

DNA as a molecular clock

Measurement of changes in DNA from selected species has potential as a molecular clock, too. DNA in eukaryotic cells occurs in both the chromosomes of the nucleus (99%) and also in the mitochondria. Mitochondrial DNA (mtDNA) is a circular molecule, very short in comparison with nuclear DNA. Cells contain any number of mitochondria, typically between 100 and 1000.

Mitochondrial DNA has approximately 16 500 base pairs. Mutations occur at a very slow, steady rate in all DNA, but chromosomal DNA has with it enzymes that may repair the changes in some cases. These enzymes are *absent* from mtDNA.

Thus mtDNA changes 5–10 times faster than chromosomal DNA – involving about 1–2 base changes in every 100 nucleotides per million years. Consequently, the length of time since organisms (belonging to different but related species) have diverged can be estimated by extracting and comparing samples of their mtDNA.

DNA hybridisation is a technique that involves matching the DNA of different species, to discover how closely they are related.

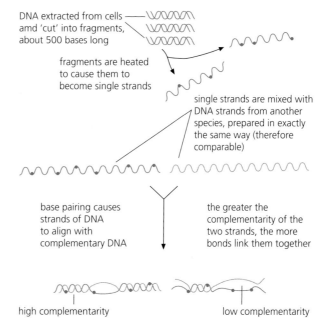

DNA extracted from cells amd 'cut' into fragments, about 500 bases long

fragments are heated to cause them to become single strands

single strands are mixed with DNA strands from another species, prepared in exactly the same way (therefore comparable)

base pairing causes strands of DNA to align with complementary DNA

the greater the complementarity of the two strands, the more bonds link them together

The closeness of the two DNAs is measured by finding the temperature at which they separate – the fewer bonds formed, the lower the temperature required.

high complementarity   low complementarity

The degree of relatedness of the DNA of **primate species** can be correlated with the estimated number of years since they shared a common ancestor.

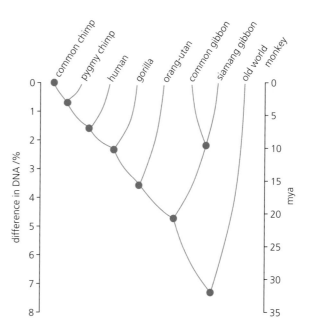

Figure 5.42 Genetic difference between DNA samples.

Furthermore, at fertilisation, the sperm contributes a nucleus only (no cytoplasm and therefore no mitochondria). So, all the mitochondria of the zygote come from the egg cell, and there is no mixing of mtDNA genes at fertilisation. All the evidence about relationships from studying differences between samples of mtDNA is easier to interpret in the search for early evidence of evolution (Figure 5.43, overleaf).

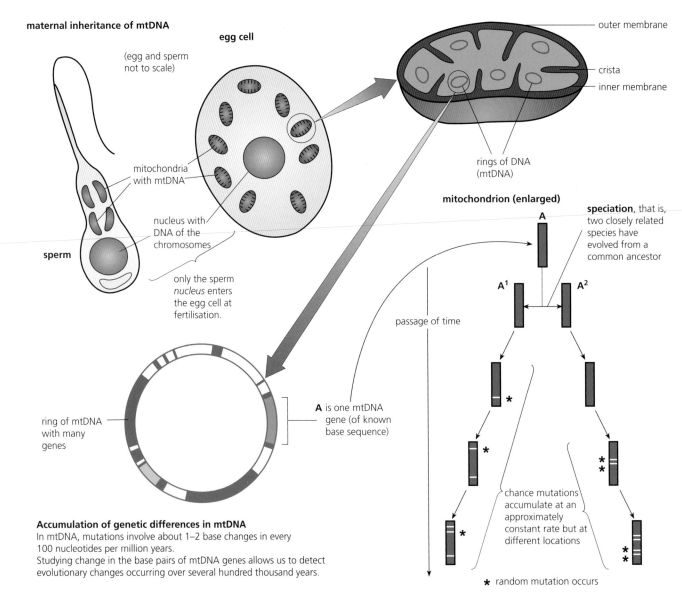

Figure 5.43 The use of mitochondrial DNA in measuring evolutionary divergence.

Ribosomal RNA studies

Of the vast numbers of micro-organisms of the biosphere, those that have been found to survive and prosper in extremely challenging environmental conditions are collectively referred to as the **extremophiles**. The different types of known extremophiles are increasing as these strange habitats become better understood, but they include micro-organisms that:

- are salt-loving (halophiles), found in salt lakes and where sea water has become concentrated and salt has crystallised
- require extremely alkaline conditions above pH 10 (alkalinophiles), found in soda lakes
- survive high temperatures (thermophiles) or extremely high temperatures (hyperthermophiles)
- withstand 250 atmospheres pressure (barophiles), as well as extremely high temperatures
- survive extremely cold habitats (psychrophiles).

These micro-organisms of extreme habitats have cells that we can identify as **prokaryotic**. That is, they are tiny cells with no true nucleus present, and their cytoplasm lacks the range of organelles typical of eukaryotic cells. However, the biochemistry of the cells of extremophiles has proved distinctly different from existing known life forms. In particular, it is the larger RNA molecules present in the ribosomes that have proved to be tell-tale molecules.

How are the ribosomal RNA molecules of extremophiles analysed?

First, **ribosomes** are isolated from the cytoplasm of cells, and then the RNA that makes up these tiny organelles (the sites of protein synthesis, you will remember) is extracted. On analysis, the sequence of nucleotides present (that is, the sequence of the bases cytosine, guanine, adenine and uracil in this RNA) is determined. Comparisons of the ribosomal RNA base sequences in these cells with those of previously known bacteria and eukaryotes have lead to the discovery of new evolutionary relationships.

The outcome has been the development of a new scheme of classification of living things. We now recognise three major forms of life, and these are called **domains**. The organisms of each domain share a distinctive, unique pattern of ribosomal RNA, which establishes their close evolutionary relationship. These domains are:

- the **Archaea** or **Archaeabacteria** (the extremophile prokaryotes)
- the **Bacteria** or **Eubacteria** (the true bacteria)
- the **Eukarya** (all eukaryotic cells – the protoctista, fungi, plants and animals).

Look carefully at the branching tree diagram showing the three domains (Figure 5.44).

You can see that the shortest branches (these are the most closely related prokaryotic groups – they are marked by an asterisk in the tree diagram) all turn out to be hyperthermophilic species. That is, they inhabit deep ocean vents where volcanic gases are discharged into water at high temperatures and pressure. This suggests the possibility that their universal ancestor was a hyperthermophilic prokaryote, too. Life on Earth may have originated in these hostile environments.

These evolutionary relationships have been established by comparing the sequence of bases (nucleotides) in the ribosomal RNA (rRNA) present in species of each group.

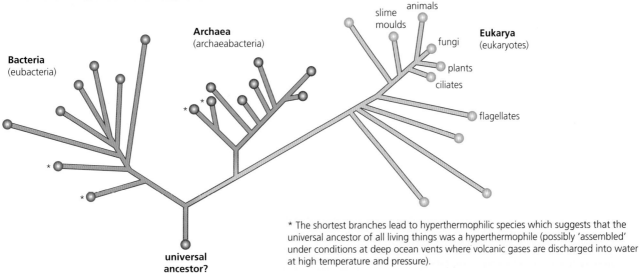

* The shortest branches lead to hyperthermophilic species which suggests that the universal ancestor of all living things was a hyperthermophile (possibly 'assembled' under conditions at deep ocean vents where volcanic gases are discharged into water at high temperature and pressure).

Figure 5.44 Ribosomal RNA and the classification of living organisms.

22 Distinguish the different forms of RNA present in cells by means of their specific roles in protein synthesis.

The role of the scientific community in validating evidence

We can illustrate the process of validation of new scientific knowledge by reference to the recent biochemical evidence for the evolution of species by natural selection, outlined above. You can experiment with aspects of this work, and discover how the pathways and timing of evolution are disclosed by biochemical studies, in the new resource 'DNA to Darwin', described in Figure 5.45 (overleaf).

Firstly, a small team of interested scientists who have acquired the techniques of ribosomal RNA analysis, for example, apply their skills to ribosomes from a range of micro-organisms, and make the initial chance discoveries of profound differences (which may be unsuspected or entirely anticipated).

Activity 5.27: Wider
reading – 'Speciation'

Once the research team is internally confident of their results, these are presented as papers for publication to learned journals of science, such as *Nature, Philosophical Transactions of the Royal Society, Biological Science, Science,* or perhaps *Annual Reviews of Biochemistry.* Papers are written with all the necessary detail for methods to be transparent, so that the work could be repeated by others.

On receipt of the paper, the editorial team of the journal sends copies to other appropriately skilled scientists for confidential critical review. The outcome of this process varies between outright rejection, minor suggestions for improvement, or perhaps immediate publication.

Publication leads to recognition of the group as significant contributors in their field of enquiry. It will likely help them secure further financial support to expand their enquires. They will be invited to contribute to future, international conferences of interested workers in the field, usually staged annually. Here they may present further notes, short reports or papers of subsequent work, and they will contribute to the critical discussions of the work of others.

A consensus on the significance of discoveries and of appropriate future lines of enquiry emerges from such meetings, and from other, more informal discussions. Sometimes there are periods when contentious, contrasting interpretations are confidently held by opposing 'camps', and we can say that for a time this frontier of new learning is 'wide open'. When discoveries and hypotheses have gained wide acceptance, new scientific knowledge has been established.

Notice that the product of these scientific processes is a convincing hypothesis, which might be *disproved by contrary observations at any time.* All explanations in science are of this type. That is, scientific knowledge is always only tentative. It is the best available explanation we can offer at that time. Any explanation may come to be seen as wrong (or, more likely, incomplete) and often is, sooner or later.

Figure 5.45 The 'DNA to
Darwin' resource

DNA to Darwin
www.dnadarwin.org

DNA to *Darwin* is an educational project funded by
The Wellcome Trust (www.wellcome.ac.uk),
and lead by Dean Madden of the NCBE, Reading University (www.ncbe.reading.ac.uk).

DNA to *Darwin* allows you to explore the molecular evidence for evolution, using your computer to analyse data from research projects in molecular genetics at:

- *The Wellcome Trust Sanger Institute*
- *The Royal Botanic Gardens, Kew*
- *Max Planck Institute for Evolutionary Anthropology*

The case studies available for analysis are from research in microbiology, plant and animal biology, and human evolution:

Microbes	**Plants**	**Animals**	**Humans**
SIV and HIV	Who's the daddy?	Mammoths	Fox P2
Malaria	Ant dispersal	Taste receptors	Lactose tolerance
MRSA	First flowers	Colour vision	Caspase

Explore this site! You will become familiar with DNA and protein
sequence data and computer-based methods of analysis.

End-of-topic test

An end-of-topic test is provided as part of the accompanying *Edexcel Biology for A2* Dynamic Learning resources, with (separate) answers.

Sample assessment material produced by Edexcel is available via the Edexcel web site: www.edexcel.org.uk.

6 Infections, immunity and forensics

STARTING POINTS
- DNA occurs in the chromosomes as a double helix, the strands held by complementary base pairing and hydrogen bonds.
- In protein synthesis, the genetic code of the chromosome is transcribed into a single strand of messenger RNA (mRNA), which passes out to ribosomes in the cytoplasm. In a ribosome, the sequence of triplets of bases in mRNA is translated into the sequence of amino acids that condense together to form proteins.
- Micro-organisms consist of a range of unicellular organisms including the bacteria, which are prokaryotes. Viruses are parasitic agents when present in a host cell, but are otherwise non-living entities.
- Infectious diseases are caused by organisms (many of them micro-organisms) or by viruses, which invade the body, passed on from other organisms. The body has natural defence mechanisms, which disease-causing organisms and viruses have to overcome.
- Death of an organism is not the cessation of biochemical activity, but rather the disorganised breakdown of structures and processes, involving hydrolytic enzymes from various sources. Forensics is the science of investigating the timing and cause of death.

6.1 DNA, the genetic code and protein synthesis

The late Francis Crick, co-discover with James Watson of the structure of DNA, described the next stage of the enquiry – the discovery of the **genetic code** – as follows:

'With the double helix clearly in view, the next problem was, what did it do – how did it influence the rest of the cell? We already knew the answer in outline. Genes determine the amino acid sequence of proteins. Because the backbone of the nucleic acid structure appeared so regular, we assumed correctly that it was the base sequence that carried this information. Since the DNA was in the nucleus of the cell and since protein synthesis seemed to take place outside the nucleus, in the cytoplasm, we imagined that a copy of each active gene had to be sent to the cytoplasm. As there was plenty of RNA there, and no apparent trace of DNA, we assumed that this messenger was RNA. It was easy enough to see how a stretch of DNA would make an RNA copy – a simple base-pairing mechanism could do the trick – but it was less easy to see how the resulting messenger RNA (as we would now call it) could direct protein synthesis, especially as very little was then known about this latter process.

Moreover, **there was an informational problem**. We knew there were about a couple of dozen different kinds of amino acids, yet there were only four different bases in DNA and RNA.'

F. Crick (1988) *What Mad Pursuits – A Personal View of Scientific Discovery*, Penguin Books

The structure of DNA and the roles of nucleic acids in protein synthesis were introduced in *Biology for AS*, pages 70–79 (Activity 6.1).

1 What did Crick have in mind when he observed that 'it was easy enough to see how a stretch of DNA would make an RNA copy'?

DL
www
Activity 6.1: DNA – a reminder and a revision exercise

Revisiting the genetic code – the case for a triplet code

So, we know that proteins are made from some 20 different types of amino acid. Also, an average protein contains at least several hundred amino acids condensed together in a specific sequence. However, DNA consists of only four different bases. Thus there are only four 'letters' to the base code 'alphabet' with which to code 20 amino acids. It was immediately clear to Crick and Watson that combinations of three bases would be the most likely to code for the amino acids (Table 6.1, overleaf). This is known as the **triplet code**.

Table 6.1 The case for a triplet code.

DNA contains four bases, which make up the 'alphabet' of the code:
Adenine
Thymine
Guanine
Cytosine

- If 1 base codes for 1 amino acid (singlet code), then 4 amino acids can be coded.
- If 2 bases code for 1 amino acid (doublet code), then 4^2 (= 16) amino acids can be coded.
- If 3 bases code for 1 amino acid (triplet code), then 4^3 (= 64) amino acids can be coded.
- If 4 bases code for 1 amino acid (quadruplet code), 4^4 (= 256) amino acids can be coded.

Conclusion:
While the doublet code has too few combinations to code for 20 amino acids, the triplet code has too many – although some codons may be punctuations (coding for 'stop, end of gene', for example), and some codons may be redundant, perhaps?

HSW 6.1: Criteria 1b, 2 and 11a – The discovery of the structure and role of nucleic acids

Deciphering the code

The details of the code was eventually discovered by the preparation of lengths of nucleic acid (mRNA, in effect) that were then fed into cell-free systems containing all the cellular components necessary for protein synthesis (ribosomes, tRNAs, amino acids, and particular enzymes, and so on) but lacking any mRNA of cellular origin. The polypeptides formed were then analysed.

Initially, the synthetic RNA was made of single nucleotides such as –UUU–UUU–UUU– (which was found to code for phenylalanine), –CCC–CCC–CCC– (which codes for praline), and –AAA–AAA–AAA– (which codes for lysine). Subsequently, synthetic mRNA with known sequences of nucleotides was produced, enabling the complete code to be deciphered (Figure 6.1).

Amino acid	Abbreviation
alanine	Ala
arginine	Arg
asparagine	Asn
aspartic acid	Asp
cysteine	Cys
glutamine	Gln
glutamic acid	Glu
glycine	Gly
histidine	His
isoleucine	Ile
leucine	Leu
lysine	Lys
methionine	Mel
phenylalanine	Phe
proline	Pro
serine	Ser
threonine	Thr
tryptophan	Trp
tyrosine	Tyr
valine	Val

The genetic code (the code is given here in terms of the mRNA codons)

	second base				
first base	**U**	**C**	**A**	**G**	third base
U	U U U } Phe U U C U U A } Leu U U G	U C U U C C } Ser U C A U C G	U A U } Tyr U A C U A A stop U A G stop	U G U } Cys U G C U G A stop U G G Trp	U C A G
C	C U U C U C } Leu C U A C U G	C C U C C C } Pro C C A C C G	C A U } His C A C C A A } Gln C A G	C G U C G C } Arg C G A C G G	U C A G
A	A U U A U C } Ile A U A A U G Met or start	A C U A C C } Thr A C A A C G	A A U } Asn A A C A A A } Lys A A G	A G U } Ser A G C A G A } Arg A G G	U C A G
G	G U U G U C } Val G U A G U G	G C U G C C } Ala G C A G C G	G A U } Asp G A C G A A } Glu G A G	G G U G G C } Gly G G A G G G	U C A G

Figure 6.1 The 20 amino acids found in proteins and the genetic code.

Look at the genetic code again – there are some important features.

1 The code is described as 'degenerate' because it contains more information than is required – there are more codons than there are amino acids to be coded. So, while methionine and tryptophan are coded by single codons (AUG and UGG respectively), most of the 20 amino acids are coded by several codons. Note that the 'degeneracy' is due mostly to the third base in the codon. Taking alanine as an example, the first two bases in the codon (GC) seem to trigger recognition that alanine is required by transfer RNAs, whereas the third base (U, C, A or G) seems relatively unimportant.

2 Some codons are 'punctuation codons', rather than coding for an amino acid. So, for example, UAA, UAG and UGC are 'stop' codons; their presence triggers termination of a polypeptide chain. Also, when AUG occurs at the start of a gene it marks the position where translation begins, although elsewhere in a gene, AUG codes for the amino acid methionine.

3 The code is non-overlapping, and each succeeding triplet codes for an amino acid that is then assembled into a polypeptide in the same sequence as the codons occur in the gene. In an overlapping code, the end of one triplet would also be the start of another – a highly complex arrangement (Table 6.2).

Table 6.2 Non-overlapping and overlapping codes.

A sequence of five codons of a strand of mRNA:	AUGUUGCCGAAGGGA
How these are 'read' (non-overlapping):	AUG UUG CCG AAG GGA

In an overlapping code, these might be 'read' as:	AUG
	  UGU
	    GUU
	      UUG
	        and so on

Or as:	AUG
	  GUU
	    UGC
	      CCG
	        and so on

DL
www
Activity 6.2: The structure of the eukaryotic cell – a revision exercise

Activity 6.3: Wider reading – 'What is Life?' (and pre-released reading assessment experience)

4 The code is more-or-less **universal** – the same codons specify the same amino acids in all genes of most organisms. One exception has been found in human mitochondrial genes.

The process of protein synthesis

The steps to the expression of a gene begin when the genetic information in DNA is transcribed into a molecule of RNA, known as **messenger RNA** (mRNA), by complementary base pairing. mRNA is an intermediary molecule, carrying information from the gene about the formation of the protein it codes for, out into the cytoplasm. Remember, mRNA is single-stranded nucleic acid in which the base uracil pairs with adenine in place of thymine found in DNA. The events of **transcription** in eukaryote chromosomes are illustrated in Figure 6.2 (overleaf).

Look at the sequence of events described there, now.

The enzyme **RNA polymerase** binds to a **promoter region**, the 'start' signal for transcription, located immediately before the gene, and the new nucleic acid strand is formed in the 5′ to 3′ direction.

■ Extension: Direction in the DNA molecule

In the DNA double helix, the phosphate groups along each strand are bridges between carbon-3 of one sugar molecule and carbon-5 of the next. One chain runs from 5′ to 3′ while the other runs from 3′ to 5′ – that is, the two chains of DNA are **antiparallel**. The existence of direction in DNA strands becomes important in replication and when the genetic code is transcribed into mRNA.

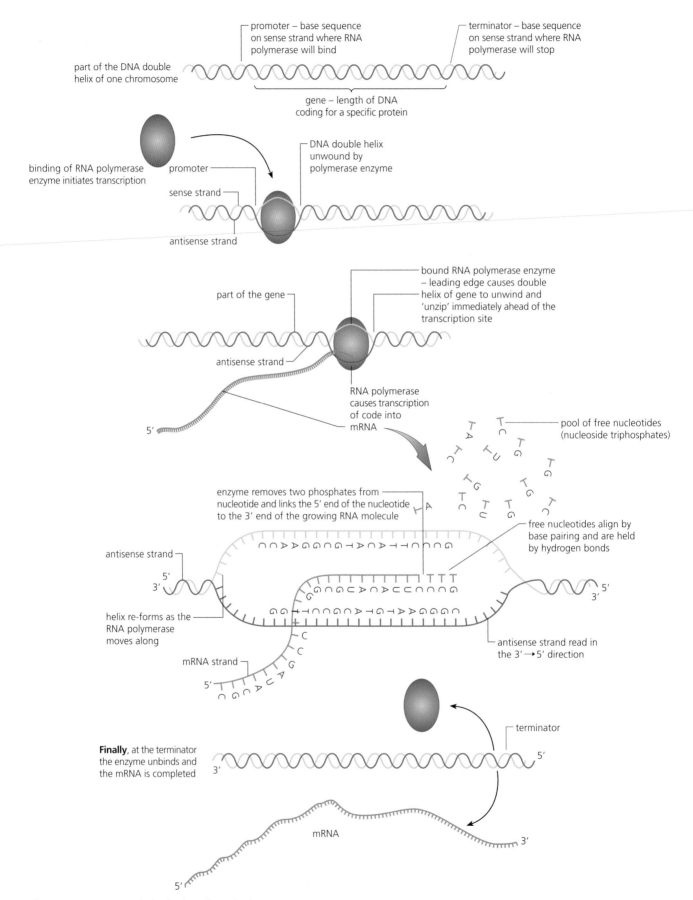

Figure 6.2 Gene transcription in the eukaryotic chromosome.

During transcription, only one strand of the DNA double helix serves as a template for synthesis of mRNA. This is called the **antisense strand**. The partner strand is called the **sense strand**. Sense and antisense strands are compared in Table 6.3 below.

Table 6.3 Sense and antisense strands of DNA.

Sense strand	Antisense strand
■ carries the promoter sequence of bases to which RNA polymerase binds and begins transcription ■ has the same base sequence as the mRNA (the mRNA has base U in place of T) ■ carries the terminator sequence of bases at the end of each gene that causes RNA polymerase to stop transcription	■ is the template sequence for transcription by complementary base pairing – the enzyme involved is RNA polymerase ■ has the same base sequence as the tRNA (the tRNA has base U in place of T) ■ is 'read' in the 3' to 5' direction, and mRNA synthesis occurs in the 5' to 3' direction (by addition of the 5' end of a nucleotide to the 3' end of the RNA molecule already synthesised)

RNA polymerase draws on the pool of free nucleotides in the nucleus, in the formation of the mRNA strand. As with DNA replication, these nucleotides are present in the form of nucleoside triphosphates (although in RNA synthesis uridine triphosphate replaces thymidine triphosphate). As the RNA is formed, it falls away from the antisense strand that has acted as template, and hydrogen bonds re-form between the two DNA strands.

The process continues until a base sequence known as the **terminator** is reached. Then, both RNA polymerase and the completed, new strand of mRNA are freed from the site of the gene.

2 Explain what is meant by 'anti-parallel strands'.

Some eukaryotic genes are discontinuous

Where the exact sequence of bases in a particular gene has been determined, it is sometimes discovered that non-coding, 'nonsense' sequences are present (Figure 6.3). In other words, some eukaryotic genes have units of non-gene DNA within their boundaries.

Figure 6.3 Post-transcriptional modification of mRNA.

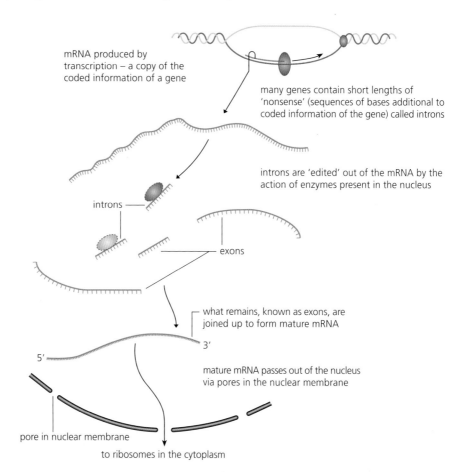

mRNA produced by transcription – a copy of the coded information of a gene

many genes contain short lengths of 'nonsense' (sequences of bases additional to coded information of the gene) called introns

introns are 'edited' out of the mRNA by the action of enzymes present in the nucleus

introns

exons

what remains, known as exons, are joined up to form mature mRNA

5'   3'

mature mRNA passes out of the nucleus via pores in the nuclear membrane

pore in nuclear membrane

to ribosomes in the cytoplasm

The sections that carry meaningful information are called **exons**, whereas the intervening lengths of DNA (they are 'interruptions', in effect) are called **introns**. Genes 'split' in this way are very common in higher plants and animals, although some genes contain no introns at all.

When a split gene is transcribed into mRNA, obviously the mRNA formed also contains the sequence of introns and exons, just as they occur in the DNA. The persistence of introns would undoubtedly present problems in the subsequent protein-synthesis steps, if they remained. In fact, the 'nonsense' sequences are now removed. In an enzyme-catalysed reaction known as **post-transcriptional modification**, the introns are detached, and the remaining exons joined together as a single strand. The introns are now disposed of. The resulting (shortened) length of mRNA is described as 'mature' (Figure 6.3). It passes out into the cytoplasm, to ribosomes, where it is involved in protein synthesis.

Translation – protein synthesis in ribosomes

The first step in protein synthesis in the cytoplasm involves the activation of amino acids by combining them with short lengths of a different sort of RNA, called **transfer RNA** (tRNA, Figure 6.4). This activation process requires ATP. It is this tRNA, once attached to its amino acid, which facilitates the translation of the three-base sequence of each codon of mRNA into a sequence of amino acids in a protein.

How is this brought about?

In the tRNAs, the shape of the molecule is a clover-leaf, but there is a different tRNA for each of the 20 amino acids involved in protein synthesis. At one end of the tRNA molecule is a site where one *specific* amino acid can be joined (and no other type). At the other end, there is a

Figure 6.4 Transfer RNA (tRNA) and amino acid activation.

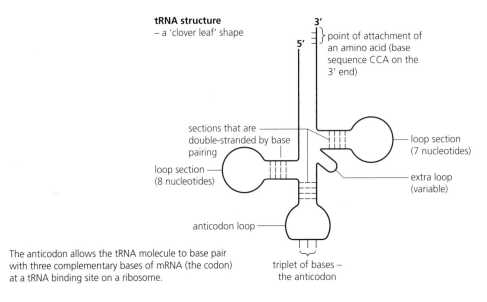

tRNA structure
– a 'clover leaf' shape

3'
5'
} point of attachment of an amino acid (base sequence CCA on the 3' end)

sections that are double-stranded by base pairing

loop section (7 nucleotides)

loop section (8 nucleotides)

extra loop (variable)

anticodon loop

triplet of bases – the anticodon

The anticodon allows the tRNA molecule to base pair with three complementary bases of mRNA (the codon) at a tRNA binding site on a ribosome.

amino acid activation reaction

Each amino acid is linked to a specific tRNA before it can be used in protein synthesis by the action of a tRNA activating enzyme (there are 20 different tRNA activating enzymes, one for each of the 20 amino acids).

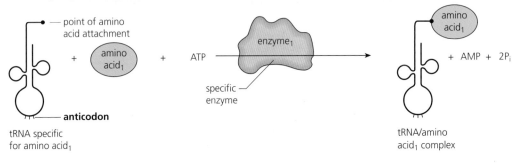

point of amino acid attachment

+ amino acid₁ + ATP → enzyme₁ specific enzyme → amino acid₁ + AMP + 2Pᵢ

anticodon

tRNA specific for amino acid₁

tRNA/amino acid₁ complex

sequence of three bases called an **anticodon**. This anticodon is complementary to the codon of mRNA that codes for that specific amino acid.

Of course, the amino acid is attached to its tRNA by enzyme action. These enzymes are also specific to the particular amino acids (and types of tRNA) to be used in protein synthesis. That is, the structure of each tRNA allows recognition by a specific tRNA-activating enzyme, which causes the attachment of a specific amino acid to the tRNA. The specificity of the enzymes is a way of ensuring the correct amino acids are used in the right sequence. Some amino acids have more than one type of tRNA specific to them.

The next step, the translation process, occurs in the ribosomes. These tiny organelles consist of a large and a small subunit, both composed of RNA (known as rRNA) and protein. During translation, the mRNAs bind with the small subunit. Here occur the three sites where the tRNAs interact (Figure 6.5).

1   At the first site (site **A**), codons of the incoming mRNA bind to specific tRNA–amino acid complexes through their anticodons (**complementary base pairing**).
2   The second site (site **P**) is where the growing polypeptide chain is held before being combined (by condensation reaction) with the new amino acid attached to its tRNA, held at site A. The condensation reaction results in the formation of a peptide bond.
3   The third site (site **E**) is where the resulting 'vacant' tRNA leaves the ribosome following transfer of its amino acid to the growing protein chain.

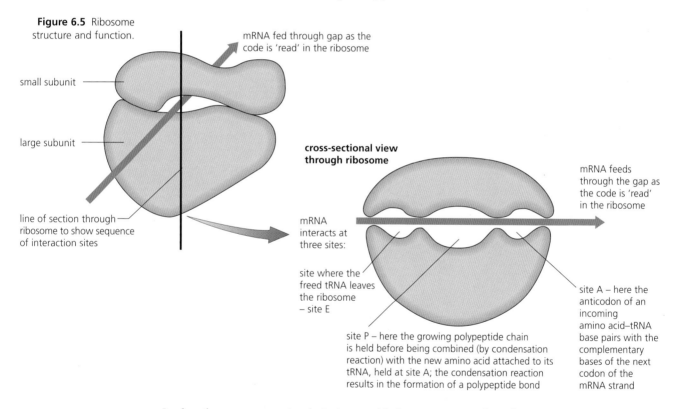

Figure 6.5 Ribosome structure and function.

mRNA fed through gap as the code is 'read' in the ribosome

small subunit

large subunit

line of section through ribosome to show sequence of interaction sites

cross-sectional view through ribosome

mRNA feeds through the gap as the code is 'read' in the ribosome

mRNA interacts at three sites:

site where the freed tRNA leaves the ribosome – site E

site P – here the growing polypeptide chain is held before being combined (by condensation reaction) with the new amino acid attached to its tRNA, held at site A; the condensation reaction results in the formation of a polypeptide bond

site A – here the anticodon of an incoming amino acid–tRNA base pairs with the complementary bases of the next codon of the mRNA strand

In the ribosome, a protein chain is assembled, one amino acid residue at a time. This occurs as the ribosome moves along the messenger RNA 'reading' the codons from the 'start' codon.

Translation occurs in the 5′ to 3′ direction, the organelle moving along the mRNA from the 'start' codon towards the 3′ end and the 'stop' codon. As the ribosome moves along, complementary anticodons of the specific **amino acid–tRNA complexes**, slot into place. They are temporarily held in position by hydrogen bonds.

While held there, the amino acids of neighbour amino acid–tRNAs are joined by **peptide linkages**. This frees the first tRNA, which moves back into the cytoplasm for re-use. Once this is done, the ribosome moves on to the next mRNA codon. The process continues until a 'stop' codon occurs (Figure 6.6, overleaf).

3 Draw and label the structure of a peptide linkage between two amino acids.

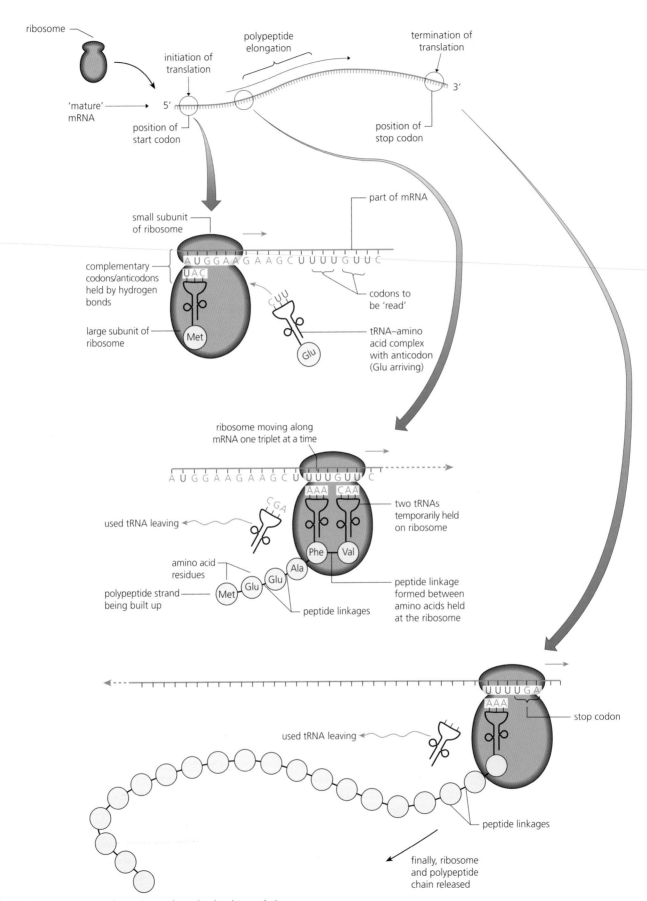

Figure 6.6 Initiation, elongation and termination in translation.

4 State the sequence of changes catalysed by RNA polymerase.

Many ribosomes occur freely in the cytoplasm, and these are the sites of synthesis of proteins that are to remain in the cell and fulfil particular roles there. It is common for several ribosomes to move along the mRNA at one time; the structure (mRNA, ribosomes and their growing protein chains) is called a **polysome** (Figure 6.7).

Other ribosomes are bound to the membranes of the endoplasmic reticulum (known as rough endoplasmic reticulum, RER), and these are the sites of synthesis of proteins that are subsequently secreted from cells or packaged in lysosomes there.

Figure 6.7 A polysome.

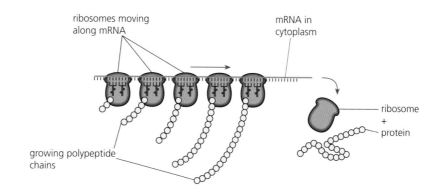

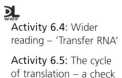
Activity 6.4: Wider reading – 'Transfer RNA'

Activity 6.5: The cycle of translation – a check on the steps

Remarkable mRNA!

We have seen that the information of genes is copied by transcription into mRNA, and that these single strands of nucleic acid pass to the ribosomes in the cytoplasm for protein synthesis. This represents a one-way flow of coded information from nucleus to cytoplasm (Figure 6.8). This principle was stated by Francis Crick as the **central dogma** of molecular biology.

Figure 6.8 The central dogma of molecular biology.

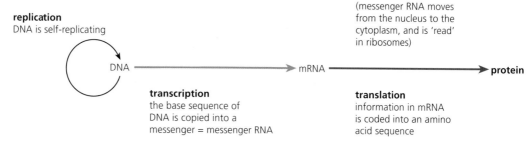

One implication of the central dogma is a strictly limited 'messenger role' for mRNA – involving *only* the transfer of information from a specific gene in the nucleus, and its realisation in the form of a particular protein in ribosomes.

We need to revisit this idea, now – it's not entirely correct!

1 The Human Genome Project (HGP), an initiative to map the entire human genome, was a much later development arising from Watson and Crick's discovery of DNA structure in 1953. By 2000, the sequencing of the human genome project had been achieved. At the same time as the HGP got underway, teams of scientists set about the sequencing of the DNA of other organisms, and more than 30 have so far been completed, too.

   Now that our genome has been 'read', it turns out to contain less than 30 000 genes. The coding sequences that represent these genes add up to only 3% of the entire genome – the remaining 97% is often (still) referred to as 'junk DNA'. This is now thought to be a highly inaccurate misnomer.

A* Extension 6.1: RNA
and the origin of life?
(HSW Criteria 1 and 7)

Some (just possibly, much) of our 'junk DNA' is transcribed into RNA at some stage in the life of the cell or organism. However, RNA of this origin may never be used for direct translation into proteins. Instead it appears that it may have roles such as:

- assisting in the transport of other molecules around the cell, to specific locations
- functioning directly as enzymes, operating in the cytoplasm alongside (traditional) protein enzymes (A* Extension 6.1)
- regulating or modulating the activity of genes – for example, in the control of gene activity in eukaryotic cells, specific lengths of RNA (coded for elsewhere along the chromosome) may be required to bind to a gene as a transcriptional factor before the enzyme RNA polymerase can transcribe the information of the gene itself, into mRNA
- interfering with gene expression, so as to 'silence' a gene – this type of RNA acts by binding to a particular gene's RNA as soon as it has been transcribed, destroying it before it can reach ribosomes in the cytoplasm.

2 It has been known for some time that one gene may give rise to more than one protein, as a result of post-transcriptional changes to mRNA. We have seen that in the production of 'mature' mRNA (Figure 6.3) selected lengths of so-called 'nonsense' DNA – introns – are edited out. Where the editing process is conducted in alternative ways, the result is different proteins being produced, and different effects on cell development or behaviour.

When the genome sequences of humans and other organisms became available for detailed comparison, it became clear how this process accounted for many of the profound differences between complex organisms with numerous similarities in their genes sets (such as humans and mice, for example). Alternative splicing mechanisms include an exon being omitted, or an intron being retained, or alternative splicing sites being recognised.

Activity 6.6: Keeping in
touch with
developments

In conclusion, the role of RNA in cell biology is a rapidly developing area of study on which we need to keep a careful eye. The days of RNA as a 'mere messenger' are surely over (Activity 6.6).

DNA profiling

DNA profiling (also called DNA 'fingerprinting') is a technique that allows us to establish the identity of individual organisms with near certainty. This is possible because the sequence of bases in the DNA of each organism produced by sexual reproduction is unique – except in the case of identical twins. As far as humans are concerned, we have already noted that the DNA of our chromosomes contains less than 30 000 genes, and that these account for only about 3% of the genome. In other words, 97% of the bases present in our DNA do not code for proteins.

The non-coding regions (they include the introns, Figure 6.3), contain sections where short sequences of bases are repeated many times. These are called short tandem repeats, but are often known as **satellite DNA**. It is these regions that are used in genetic profiling. Actually, it appears the satellite regions are of two types:

- minisatellites of about 20–50 bases, possibly repeated 50 to several hundred times
- microsatellites of 2–5 bases repeated 5–15 times.

We inherit a distinctive combination of these apparently non-functional 'repeat regions', half from our mother and half from our father. The same satellites occur at the same loci on both chromosomes of a homologous pair, but the number of times the sequence is repeated on each chromosome of a pair may differ. It is for these reasons that each of us has a unique sequence of nucleotides in our DNA (except for identical twins). It is the microsatellites that we use as the genetic markers.

5 In the DNA sequence shown, identify the microsatellite sequence present and count how many times it is repeated in the maternal and paternal chromosomes.
maternal chromosome: taccggtagactgactgactgactgactgactgactgacttaggtgccaa
paternal chromosome: cggtagccataggtgccagactgactgactgactgacttaccggtacgg

The steps involved in DNA profiling

To produce a genetic 'fingerprint', a sample of DNA is obtained free from other cell contents, and then 'cut' into short lengths. Electrophoresis is then used to separate these pieces according to their size, and the result is converted into a pattern of bands similar to a bar code. These steps are now considered in detail.

1 Extracting and cutting up DNA

DNA may be extracted from tissue samples by mechanically breaking up the cells, filtering off the debris, and breaking down cell membranes by treatment with detergents. The protein framework of the chromosomes is then removed by incubation with a protein-digesting enzyme (protease). The DNA, now existing as long threads, is isolated from this mixture of chemicals by precipitation with ethanol, and is thus 'cleaned'. The DNA strands are then re-suspended in aqueous, pH buffered medium. They are now ready for 'slicing' into fragments.

DNA is then sliced or chopped into fragments by addition of restriction endonuclease (**restriction enzyme**). These enzymes occur naturally in bacteria, where they protect against viruses that enter the bacterium, by cutting the viral DNA into small pieces, thereby inactivating it. (Viral DNA might otherwise take over the host cell – page 72.) Viruses that specifically parasitise bacteria are called bacteriophage or **phage**. Restriction enzymes were so named because they *restrict* the multiplication of phage viruses.

Many different restriction enzymes have been discovered and purified, and today they are used widely in genetic engineering experiments. A distinctive and important feature of restriction enzymes is that they cut at particular base sequences (Figure 6.9), and are of two types, forming

6 What are the products of digestion by protease enzymes?

Figure 6.9 Isolating and cutting of DNA.

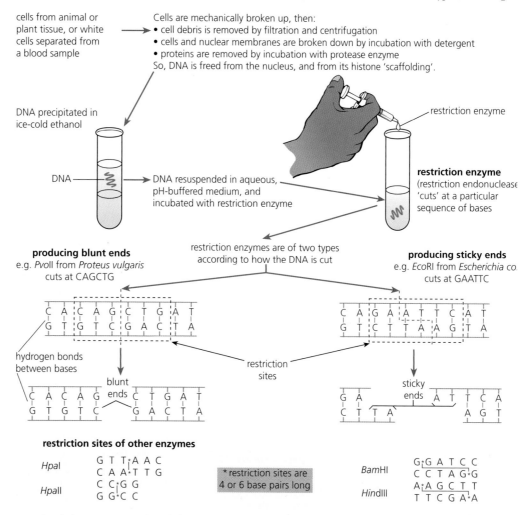

Restriction enzymes are named after the micro-organisms they are found in. Roman numbers are added

either 'blunt ends' or 'sticky ends' to the cut fragments. Sticky ends are single-stranded extensions formed in the double-stranded DNA after 'digestion' with a restriction enzyme that cuts in a staggered fashion. In DNA profiling, a selected restriction enzyme is used to cut at specific base-sequence sites adjacent to microsatellite sequences.

2 Isolating DNA fragments – electrophoresis

Electrophoresis is a process used to separate particles, including biologically important molecules such as DNA, RNA, proteins and amino acids. Electrophoresis is typically carried out on an agarose gel (a very pure form of agar) or on polyacrylamide gel (PAG). Both these substances contain tiny pores, which allow them to act like a molecular sieve. Through these gels, small particles can move quite quickly, whereas larger molecules move much more slowly.

Biological molecules separated by electrophoresis also carry an electrical charge. In the case of DNA, phosphate groups in DNA fragments give them a net negative charge. Consequently, when DNA molecules are placed in an electric field they migrate towards the positive pole.

So, in electrophoresis, separation occurs on the size and by the charge carried. This is the double principle of electrophoretic separations. Separation of DNA fragments produced by the actions of restriction enzyme is shown in Figure 6.10. Note that the bands of DNA fragments are not visible on the gel until, in this case, a DNA-binding dye visible in white light has been added. An alternative approach to identifying the separated 'restriction fragments' involving 'Southern blotting' is described next.

Figure 6.10
Electrophoretic separation of DNA fragments.

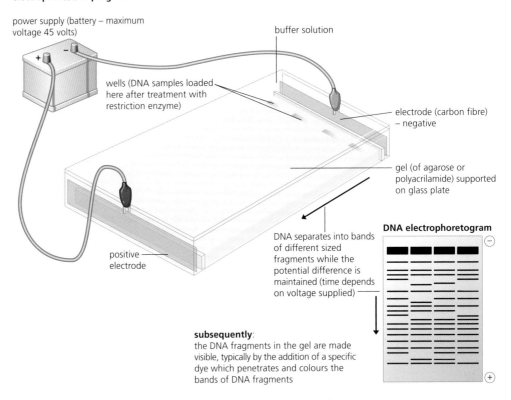

electrophoresis in progress

power supply (battery – maximum voltage 45 volts)

buffer solution

wells (DNA samples loaded here after treatment with restriction enzyme)

electrode (carbon fibre) – negative

gel (of agarose or polyacrilamide) supported on glass plate

positive electrode

DNA separates into bands of different sized fragments while the potential difference is maintained (time depends on voltage supplied)

DNA electrophoretogram

subsequently:
the DNA fragments in the gel are made visible, typically by the addition of a specific dye which penetrates and colours the bands of DNA fragments

---

■ Extension: DNA fingerprints via fluorescent materials and UV light

On completion of separation of DNA fragments by electrophoresis, once the current is switched off, a DNA-binding dye that fluoresces in UV light may be added. In this technique, the different bands can be detected and their positions recorded by photography. Alternatively, DNA probes that are fluorescent may be used.

The technique known as **Southern blotting**, along with the use of radioactively labelled DNA probes, is another approach to identifying the pattern of restriction fragments obtained by electrophoresis (Figure 6.11). In this method, the extracted DNA is cut into fragments, and the fragments are separated by electrophoresis, exactly as previously described. Then the gel is placed on a blotting paper wick fed by alkaline buffer solution. A film of nylon netting is placed onto the gel, and more blotting paper is applied above, capped by a weight. The effect is that the buffer solution is drawn up through the gel and contact between alkali and the DNA fragments breaks the hydrogen bonds between complementary bases. The DNA becomes single-stranded.

Figure 6.11 Southern blotting and labelled probes.

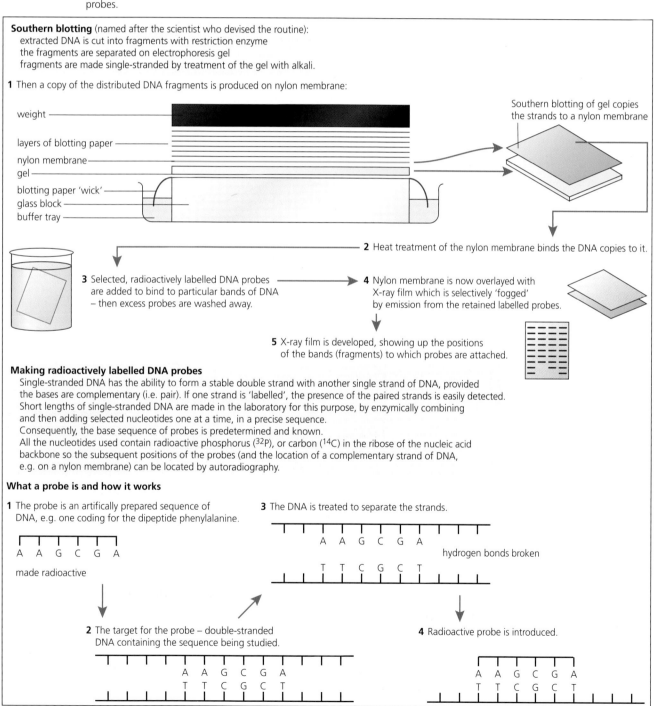

Southern blotting (named after the scientist who devised the routine):
extracted DNA is cut into fragments with restriction enzyme
the fragments are separated on electrophoresis gel
fragments are made single-stranded by treatment of the gel with alkali.

1 Then a copy of the distributed DNA fragments is produced on nylon membrane:

weight
layers of blotting paper
nylon membrane
gel
blotting paper 'wick'
glass block
buffer tray

Southern blotting of gel copies the strands to a nylon membrane

2 Heat treatment of the nylon membrane binds the DNA copies to it.

3 Selected, radioactively labelled DNA probes are added to bind to particular bands of DNA – then excess probes are washed away.

4 Nylon membrane is now overlayed with X-ray film which is selectively 'fogged' by emission from the retained labelled probes.

5 X-ray film is developed, showing up the positions of the bands (fragments) to which probes are attached.

Making radioactively labelled DNA probes
Single-stranded DNA has the ability to form a stable double strand with another single strand of DNA, provided the bases are complementary (i.e. pair). If one strand is 'labelled', the presence of the paired strands is easily detected.
Short lengths of single-stranded DNA are made in the laboratory for this purpose, by enzymically combining and then adding selected nucleotides one at a time, in a precise sequence.
Consequently, the base sequence of probes is predetermined and known.
All the nucleotides used contain radioactive phosphorus (^{32}P), or carbon (^{14}C) in the ribose of the nucleic acid backbone so the subsequent positions of the probes (and the location of a complementary strand of DNA, e.g. on a nylon membrane) can be located by autoradiography.

What a probe is and how it works

1 The probe is an artifically prepared sequence of DNA, e.g. one coding for the dipeptide phenylalanine.

A A G C G A
made radioactive

3 The DNA is treated to separate the strands.

A A G C G A
hydrogen bonds broken
T T C G C T

2 The target for the probe – double-stranded DNA containing the sequence being studied.

A A G C G A
T T C G C T

4 Radioactive probe is introduced.

A A G C G A
T T C G C T

As a result, a single copy of the (invisible) distribution of fragments brought about by electrophoresis is transferred to the nylon netting. Then the nylon film is removed, and the distribution of DNA fragments detected by the application of selected radioactive DNA probes, followed by autoradiography.

3 Polymerase chain reaction

There are various circumstances where the amount of DNA available, or which can be recovered (such as at a crime scene), is very small indeed – apparently too little for analysis, in fact. It is now possible, however, to submit minute samples to a process known as the **polymerase chain reaction (PCR)**, in which the DNA is replicated in an entirely automated process, *in vitro*, to produce a large amount of the sequence (Figure 6.12). A single molecule is sufficient as the

Figure 6.12 The polymerase chain reaction.

The **polymerase chain reaction** is an automated process, carried out by a machine (PCR thermal cycler), and having three steps:
1 strand separation (breaking of the hydrogen bonds) by heating to 93 °C
2 binding of primer to one end of each strand (the primer is synthesised to order – complementary to base sequence at 3′ end of DNA sample) at 55 °C
3 synthesis of new strands, starting from the primer molecules by heat-stable polymerase, in the presence of excess nucleotides, at 72 °C
This 'heating–cooling' cycle is repeated 25–30 times, and produces approximately 30 million copies of the original DNA strand.
(**Note**: N–N region of the DNA is the satellite repeated sequence required for DNA profiling.)

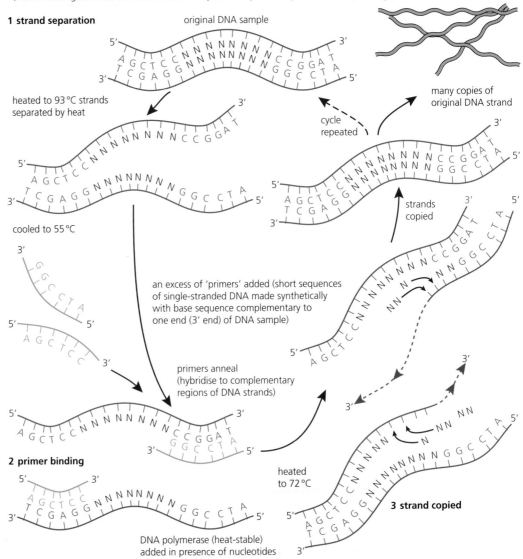

1 DNA profiles used to establish family relationships

Is the male (F) the parent of both children?

Examine the DNA profiles shown to the right.

Look at the children's bands (C).

Discount all those bands that correspond to bands in the mother's profile (M).

The remaining bands match those of the biological father.

DNA fingerprinting has been widely applied in biology. In ornithology, for example, DNA profiling of nestlings has established a degree of 'promiscuity' in breeding pairs, the male of which was assumed to be the father of the whole brood. In birds, the production of a clutch of eggs is extended over a period of days, with copulation and fertilisation preceding the laying of each egg. This provides the opportunity for different males to fertilise the female.

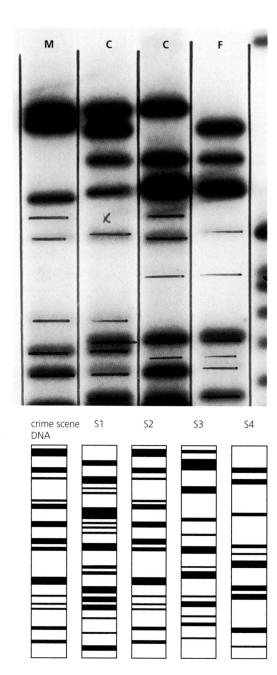

2 DNA profiling in forensic investigation

Identification of criminals

At the scene of a crime (such as a murder or burglary), hairs – with hair root cells attached – or blood may be recovered. If so, the resulting DNA profiles may be compared with those of DNA obtained from suspects.

Examine the DNA profiles shown to the right, and suggest which suspect should be interviewed further.

Identification in a rape crime involves the taking of vaginal swabs. Here, DNA will be present from the victim and also from the rapist. The result of DNA analysis is a complex profile that requires careful comparison with the DNA profiles of the victim and of any suspects. A rapist can be identified with a high degree of certainty, and the innocence of others established.

Identification of a corpse which is otherwise unidentifiable is achieved by taking DNA samples from body tissues and comparing their profile with those of close relatives or with DNA obtained from cells recovered from personal effects, where these are available.

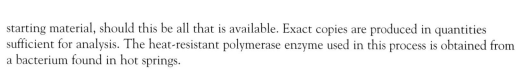

Figure 6.13 DNA profiles used to investigate relatedness.

starting material, should this be all that is available. Exact copies are produced in quantities sufficient for analysis. The heat-resistant polymerase enzyme used in this process is obtained from a bacterium found in hot springs.

DNA profiling in forensic investigations

DNA profiles using several probes from different repeated sequences, produced by the above technique, result in a unique banding pattern for every individual. Applied to biological specimens taken from the scene of a serious crime, such as a rape attack or murder, they may provide reliable evidence (Figure 6.13). For example, samples such as a few hair roots or a tiny amount of blood or semen may be sufficient to carry out DNA profiling. Specimens may also be collected from people suspected of being present at the crime. The greatest care has to be taken to ensure the authenticity of the sample – there must be no possibility of contamination if the outcome of subsequent testing is to be meaningful.

DNA profiling helps to eliminate innocent suspects, and to identify a person or people who may be responsible for the crime. It can also be used to help establish whether individuals are genetically related. It cannot prove anyone's guilt or connection with absolute certainty, however. An example is shown in Figure 6.13.

DNA fingerprinting may also help forensic scientists identify corpses otherwise too decomposed for recognition, or where only parts of the body remain, as may occur after bomb blasts or other violent incidents, including natural disasters.

DNA profiling in determining paternity

A* Extension 6.2: Studying plant genomes

Another very important application of DNA profiling is in issues of parentage. A range of samples of DNA from the people who are possibly related are analysed side by side. The banding patterns are then compared (Figure 6.13). Because a child inherits half its DNA from its mother and half from its father, the bands in a child's DNA fingerprint that do not match its mother's must come from the child's father.

DNA profiling also has wide applications in studies of wild animals, for example, concerning breeding behaviour, and in the identification of unrelated animals as mates in captive breeding programmes of animals in danger of extinction.

6.2 Introducing micro-organisms

Micro-organisms, or microbes, are organisms too small to be studied by the naked eye. They are an extraordinary and diverse group – many with a very long evolutionary history. At the same time, microbes show great powers to adapt in a changing environment, and they can achieve some incredible biochemical feats, despite their sizes. Just a relative few of the millions of different microbes are dangerous to us because they cause serious disease, but most microbes are more than just harmless – they carry out processes essential for the survival of all life.

The range of micro-organisms

Microbes occur in huge numbers – too large to contemplate for the most part. They occur on and in ourselves, and in the environment at large – more-or-less everywhere. There are many more different species of micro-organisms than there are other forms of life. All these fall into one of four groups: bacteria, viruses, fungi (though not all fungi are micro-organisms, of course) and unicellular protoctista (protozoa and algae).

We can say that the one universal characteristic of these organisms is their tiny size. However, there are large differences in size among them, from the viruses (in the range 10–400 nm), to the larger unicellular algae (from 10 to several hundred µm). You are already familiar with these units of length used in microscopy.

7 How many micrometres (µm) are there in 1.4 mm? Express 660 nm as µm.

Finally we should recognise at the outset that micro-organisms influence all aspects of life, with far-reaching effects on the environment, health, disease and decay, the food and drink industries, biotechnological industries old and new, industrial enzymology and genetic engineering. Here, we focus on bacteria and viruses, and on their roles in decomposition and recycling of nutrients, and in disease.

The structure of bacteria

A* Extension 6.3: The long history of microbiology – pure and applied

The structure of the bacterium, *Escherichia coli* is illustrated in Figure 6.14. This organism was observed and named by a nineteenth century bacteriologist, Professor T. Escherich. *E. coli* occurs in huge numbers in the lower intestine of humans and other endothermic (once known as 'warm blooded') vertebrates (such as the mammals), and it is a major component of the faeces of these animals. In fact, *E. coli* is described as a very common gut commensal. By 'commensal' we mean a partner in an association between two organisms of different species, living together and sharing food sources. In commensalisms, one species benefits (*E. coli*, in this case) and the other is normally not harmed.

Look at the drawing of the bacterial cell in Figure 6.14.

Note that the organisation is significantly different from a plant or animal cell. Bacteria are known as prokaryotes because they do not have a nucleus.

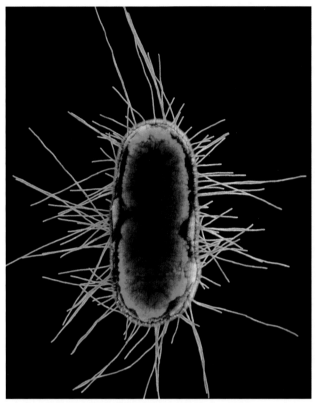

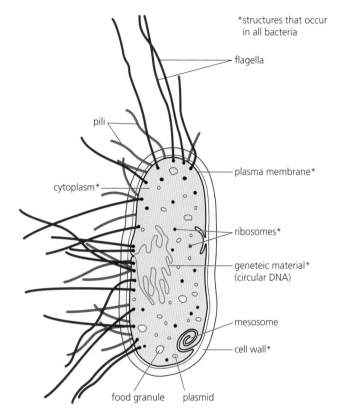

electron micrograph of *Escherichia coli* (×25 000)

Figure 6.14 The structure of *Escherichia coli*.

The components of the bacterial cell

Cell walls

Cell walls give shape to cells – and protection against rupture due to osmosis. They may also help to protect against harm by other organisms. Bacterial cells have a rigid wall containing giant molecules (polymers) consisting of amino-sugars and peptide units, known as murein or peptidoglycan. (This is a different substance from cellulose, of which plant cell walls are made.) Some bacteria have additional layers on the outer surface of their wall (Gram-negative bacteria, see A* Extension 6.4).

Cytoplasm

Cytoplasm of a bacterial cell is about 75% water in which are dissolved proteins (mainly enzymes), lipoproteins, sugars, amino acids and fatty acids, inorganic salts, and the waste products of metabolism.

Ribosomes

In the cytoplasm are numerous ribosomes. These tiny spherical organelles of protein and ribonucleic acid (RNA) are the sites of protein synthesis. Here, messenger RNA is 'read' and used to dictate the sequence of amino acids in proteins, giving the primary structure of the bacterium's proteins. Bacterial ribosomes are known as 70S ribosomes because they are smaller than those in the cytoplasm of plant and animal cells and fungi (called 80S ribosomes). The 'S' refers to the rate at which particles sediment in high-speed centrifugation.

Food stores

Food stores are common in the cytoplasm of many bacteria. They occur as small granules of lipid or glycogen, held in tiny sacs formed from lipid membrane. These are energy-rich reserves – reservoirs of cell-building materials.

Plasma membrane

The plasma membranes of bacterial cells consist of phospholipids and proteins arranged as shown in the **fluid mosaic model** (*Biology for AS*, page 45). Long carbohydrate molecules occur attached to some lipid molecules (forming **glycolipids**) or protein molecules (forming **glycoproteins**) on the outer surface of the membrane. This membrane is a barrier across which all nutrients and waste products must pass by diffusion (including osmosis) or active transport using metabolic energy.

Genetic material (circular DNA)

The genetic material of a bacterium consists of a single circular chromosome of a DNA helix, located in the cytoplasm (not contained within a nucleus), attached to the plasma membrane. The chromosome of *E. coli* has about 4×10^6 base pairs (adenine with thymine, guanine with cytosine) – about 4000 genes. These genes are copied as messenger RNA, as required.

Plasmids

Plasmids are additional hereditary material – small rings of DNA, present in the cytoplasm of some but not all bacteria. Today, plasmids are often exploited as 'vectors' in genetic engineering.

Mesosomes

Mesosomes are infoldings of the plasma membrane found in some bacterial cells. In the photosynthetic bacteria, they are where the photosynthetic pigments are housed.

Flagella and pili

Flagella are rigid protein strands that arise from basal bodies in the plasma membrane in some bacteria. They bring about movement by rotating from their base, driven by the basal body.

Pili (or fimbiae) are tiny tubular structures that arise from the cell membrane of some bacteria. They enable bacteria to attach to surfaces and to other bacteria.

Capsule

A slime layer or capsule is made up of additional materials that are laid down on the outer surface of the wall. Capsules are firmly attached, whereas slime layers may diffuse into the surrounding medium.

DL
www
Activity 6.8: Prokaryotic and eukaryotic organisation compared

A* Extension 6.4: Staining properties of the walls of bacteria

■ Extension: *E coli* 157

Although most strains of *E. coli* are totally harmless, one strain, known as 0157:H7, can cause severe diarrhoea and kidney damage. This strain is found in some healthy cattle, and contamination of meat may occur in the slaughtering process. Domestic and personal hygiene measures are important in the handling and storage of uncooked meat, and when young people visit farms or handle animals. Infected people normally recover within 5–10 days, without specific treatments. Children and the elderly are most likely to develop complications.

The structure of viruses

Viruses are disease-causing agents, rather than 'organisms'. The distinctive features of viruses are:

- they are not cellular structures, but rather consist of a core of nucleic acid surrounded by a protein coat, called a capsid
- in some viruses, there is an additional external envelope of membrane made of lipids and proteins (for example, HIV, Figure 6.22, page 79);
- they are extremely small when compared with bacteria – most viruses are in the size range 20–400 nm (0.02–0.4 µm), and are visible only by means of the electron microscope

- they can reproduce only inside specific living cells, so viruses function as endoparasites in their host organism
- they have to be transported in some way between hosts
- viruses are highly specific to particular host species, some to plant species, some to animal species and some to bacteria
- viruses are classified by the type of nucleic acid they contain, either DNA or RNA, and whether they have a single or double strand of nucleic acid (Figure 6.15).

Figure 6.15 A classification of viruses.

A* Extension 6.5: Replication of a virus

8 Distinguish between the structures of bacteria and viruses.

DNA viruses

1 single-stranded: 'M13' virus of bacterial hosts

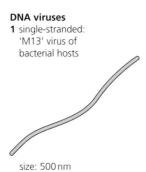

size: 500 nm

2 double-stranded: herpes simplex virus of animal hosts

size: 200 nm

RNA viruses

1 single-stranded: poliovirus of animal hosts

 size: 25 nm

human immunodeficiency virus, HIV (retrovirus)

 size: 100 nm

2 double-stranded: reovirus of animal hosts

 size: 80 nm

Are viruses 'living' at any stage?

Figure 6.16 The tobacco mosaic virus (TMV) is a potential infective agent of several species of crop plants, not only of the tobacco plant.

Viruses are an assembly of complex molecules, rather than a form of life. Isolated from their host cell they are inactive, and are often described as crystalline. Within susceptible cells, they are highly active genetic programmes that will take over the biochemical machinery of the host. Their component chemicals are synthesised, and then assembled to form new viruses. On breakdown (lysis) of the host cell, viruses are released, and may cause fresh infections (Figure 6.16). So, viruses are not living organisms, but may become active components of host cells.

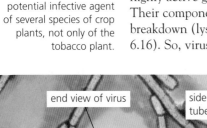

end view of virus

side view shows hollow tube construction

transmission electron micrograph of TMV (×40 000) negatively stained

enlarged drawing of part of the virus

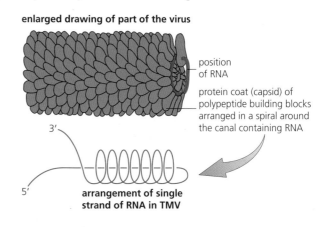

position of RNA

protein coat (capsid) of polypeptide building blocks arranged in a spiral around the canal containing RNA

3′

5′

arrangement of single strand of RNA in TMV

healthy leaves

infected leaf

Micro-organisms and the decomposition of organic matter

9 Explain how it is that animal life is dependent upon the actions of saprotrophs.

When organisms die, their bodies are broken down to simpler substances (such as CO_2, H_2O, NH_3, and various ions) by a succession of organisms (mostly micro-organisms), as illustrated in Figure 6.17. So, too, is the waste matter that organisms excrete. The scavenging actions of detritivores often begin the process, but micro-organisms play a pivotal role. It is saprotrophic bacteria and fungi that always complete the breakdown processes. As a result, nutrients of the ecosystem are not lost – rather, they are recycled and re-used.

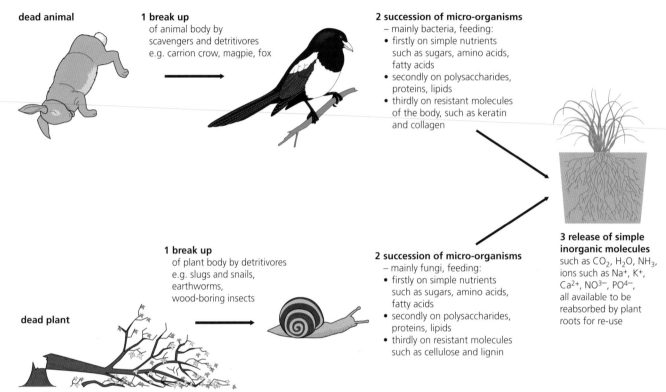

dead animal

1 break up
of animal body by scavengers and detritivores e.g. carrion crow, magpie, fox

2 succession of micro-organisms
– mainly bacteria, feeding:
- firstly on simple nutrients such as sugars, amino acids, fatty acids
- secondly on polysaccharides, proteins, lipids
- thirdly on resistant molecules of the body, such as keratin and collagen

1 break up
of plant body by detritivores e.g. slugs and snails, earthworms, wood-boring insects

dead plant

2 succession of micro-organisms
– mainly fungi, feeding:
- firstly on simple nutrients such as sugars, amino acids, fatty acids
- secondly on polysaccharides, proteins, lipids
- thirdly on resistant molecules such as cellulose and lignin

3 release of simple inorganic molecules
such as CO_2, H_2O, NH_3, ions such as Na^+, K^+, Ca^{2+}, NO_3^-, PO_4^-, all available to be reabsorbed by plant roots for re-use

Figure 6.17 The sequence of organisms involved in decay.

Nutrients provide the chemical elements that make up the biochemical molecules of cells and organisms. Recycling of nutrients is essential for the survival of living things, because the available resources of many elements are limited. We have seen that all organisms are made of carbon, hydrogen and oxygen, together with the mineral elements nitrogen, calcium, phosphorus, sulphur and potassium, and several others, in increasingly small amounts.

Plants obtain their essential nutrients as carbon dioxide and water, from which they manufacture sugar. Then, with the addition of mineral elements absorbed as ions from the soil solution, they build up the complex organic molecules they require (Figure 5.1, page 2). Animals, on the other hand, obtain nutrients from other organisms as complex organic molecules in their food, which they digest, absorb and assimilate into their own cells and tissues. Then upon death of all these organisms, nutrients are recycled and re-used.

The cycling processes by which elements are released and re-used are called **biogeochemical cycles**. This is because the cycles of change involves both living things (the biota) and the non-living (abiotic) environment, consisting of atmosphere, hydrosphere (oceans, rivers and lakes) and the lithosphere (rocks and soil). One familiar example of such a cycle is the **carbon cycle** (Figure 5.24, page 29).

Activity 6.9: Cellulose breakdown – a connection with global warming

10 Outline a pathway for carbon atoms, from the hydrosphere, into the aquatic biota, then into the lithosphere, and finally back to the atmosphere, not involving human activity.

Look at this example of a biogeochemical cycle again, now.

In this cycle, we see that decay by saprotrophic microbes contributes to atmospheric carbon dioxide (and hydrogencarbonate ions in water) upon which green plants draw for photosynthesis. However, there are also pathways by which carbon becomes a component of the lithosphere before being released and possibly re-used by the biota, eventually.

Defence against infectious disease

Infectious disease is caused when another organism or virus invades the body and lives there parasitically. The invader is known as a **pathogen** and the infected organism – a human in this case – is the **host**. So a pathogen is an organism or virus that causes a disease. The range of disease-causing organisms that may infect humans includes not only micro-organisms such as certain bacteria and fungi, but viruses, some protozoa (single-celled animals) and also certain non-vertebrate animals in the phyla of flatworms and of roundworms.

Not all bacteria or fungi are parasitic and pathogenic – indeed, only a relative few species are. On the other hand, no virus can function outside a host organism, so we can say that all viruses are parasitic. A virus, once introduced into a host cell, takes over the machinery of protein and nucleic acid synthesis, and coerces the host cell to manufacture more virus components and assemble them.

■ Extension: Communicable and non-communicable diseases

Pathogens may pass from a diseased host to healthy organisms, so these diseases are known as infectious or communicable diseases. However, diseases may also be caused by unfavourable environmental conditions, and these are described as non-infectious or non-communicable diseases – cardiovascular disease is an example.

Lines of defence against infectious disease

The first line of defence is an intact body surface. Both our external skin and the internal linings of lungs, trachea and gut are potential ports for entry to the body's tissues and organs by pathogens. Not surprisingly, protective measures have evolved at these surfaces.

DL
www
Activity 6.10: Skin structure – a revision exercise

A* Extension 6.6: *Schistosoma* – a skin-burrowing pathogen (HSW Criterion 12)

The external skin is covered by keratinised protein of dead cells of the epidermis (Activity 6.10). This is a tough and impervious layer, and an effective barrier to most organisms unless the surface is broken, cut or deeply scratched. However, folds or creases in the skin that are permanently moist can harbour micro-organisms that degrade the barrier and cause infection, as in athlete's foot – a commonly occurring fungal disease of humans. Also, the aquatic larvae of certain pathogenic non-vertebrates may burrow through (A* Extension 6.6).

The internal surfaces of our breathing apparatus (the trachea, bronchi and the bronchioles) and of the gut, lack the keratin layer of external skin, and instead are lined by moist **epithelia**. These internal barriers are potentially vulnerable to bacteria, but are protected by the secretion of copious quantities of mucus. **Cilia** are organelles that project from the surface of certain cells. They occur in large numbers on the lining (epithelium) of the air tubes serving the lungs (bronchi). The beating action of cilia continually sweeps the mucus away from the delicate air sacs of the lungs.

11 Suggest how mucus secreted by the lungs may protect lung tissue.

In the gut**,** digestive enzymes provide some protection, particularly in the stomach. Present in the wall of the stomach are millions of tiny pits called gastric glands, which secrete the components of **gastric juice**. This juice includes hydrochloric acid – sufficiently acidic to create an environment of pH 1.5–2.0, which is the optimum pH for protein digestion by the protease enzymes of the gastric juice. These proteases, of which pepsin is one, are also formed in cells of the gastric glands and are secreted in an inactive state. The hydrochloric acid then activates them. The combined effects of acid and activated protease enzyme kill many bacteria present in the incoming food.

A* Extension 6.7: An unwelcome stomach visitor – *Helicobacter pylori* (HSW Criterion 11a)

Activity 6.11: Investigating probiotic and prebiotic foods

A* Extension 6.8: Thrush

A second form of defence results from the interaction of the populations of bacteria present in huge numbers in many regions of the body. Bacteria outnumber the cells of our body by about a factor of 10, and our lower gut in particular is home to several hundred species of bacteria. More than 50% of the solid mass of our faeces consists of them. While many of these bacteria are harmless, some produce beneficial substances (such as vitamin K), and yet others release harmful by-products of their metabolism. For example, some species cause inflammation (page 80) by irritating the gut lining (mucosa), possibly leading to ulcerative colitis. Others cause damage to the DNA of cells here, leading to the possibility of tumour growth and colon cancer.

However, interactions between the bacterial populations present as they compete for space and food influence the composition of the community of bacteria present. So, for example, *Lactobacillus* (lactic acid bacteria) and *Bifidobacterium* (bifidobacteria) make lactic acid that lowers the pH of the gut and inhibits growth or even kills other bacteria. Other species produce and release proteins that kill other bacteria. We might call these species 'good bacteria' – as the advertisers of certain dietary products do!

'**Probiotic**' and '**prebiotic**' foods are designed to influence the balance between beneficial and harmful bacteria present in the colon. Probiotics do this by delivering particular naturally occurring bacterial species, resistant to gastric, bile and pancreatic juices. They are able to reach, survive and thrive in the lower gut. Prebiotic foods contain plant extracts that are not broken down by the digestive juices when taken in, but provide a specific substrate for species of beneficial bacteria, enabling them to preferentially flourish in the colon.

Symptoms of bacterial and viral infections

Tuberculosis

Tuberculosis (TB), a major, worldwide public health problem of long standing, is caused by a rod-shaped bacterium, *Mycobacterium tuberculosis* (Figure 6.18). It was first identified by Robert Koch in 1882. Viewed under the microscope after staining by the Ziehl-Neelsen technique (basic dye fuchsine and phenol), the cells show up bright red. They are known to bacteriologists as 'acid-fast bacilli' because an acid–alcohol rinse after the staining step does not remove the red colouration. This is unique to bacteria of the genus *Mycobacterium*, and is due to dye staining the quantities of wax and other lipids in the walls of cells of this genus. This is how the pathogen is identified in infected patients.

Figure 6.18
Photomicrograph of a colony of *Mycobacterium tuberculosis.*

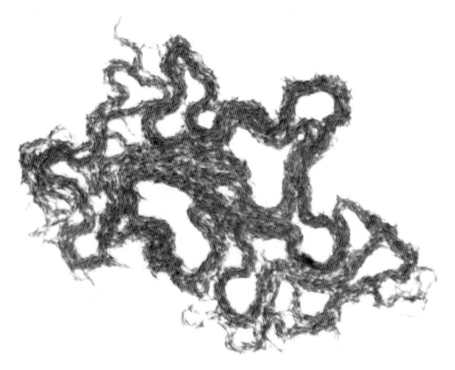

How the disease spreads

People with pulmonary TB cough persistently. The droplets they spread in the air are infected with live *Mycobacterium* (Figure 6.19). Tuberculosis is chiefly spread by droplet infection in this way. Because of their lipid-rich cell walls, the bacilli are protected from drying out, so the pathogen may survive for many months in the air and the dust of homes. This is another source of infection. Overcrowded and ill-ventilated living conditions are especially favourable for the transmission of the infection. However, it still requires quite prolonged contact with a viable source before people succumb (Figure 6.20), for the bacterium is not strongly infectious.

A bovine form of TB occurs in cattle, and the bacillus can enter the milk. Unpasteurised milk from infected cows is another potential source of infection for humans. In some rural communities especially, this type of milk is used in food, particularly for children. Today, all milk in Britain is supplied by 'tuberculin-tested' cows that are certified free of *Mycobacterium*. In the UK, TB is not now contracted by this route.

Figure 6.19 Droplet infection.

Figure 6.20 Chest X-ray showing TB in the lungs.

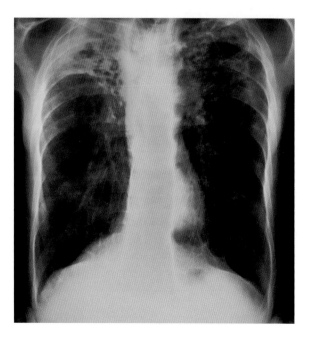

How TB develops

Once inside the lungs, the bacteria are engulfed by macrophages (page 82) in the alveoli and bronchioles. If the recipient is in good health, these white cells kill the pathogen (with the help of T-lymphocytes, which migrate in from lymph nodes). Alternatively, and with strains of *Mycobacterium* that are more virulent, the pathogens may remain alive within the macrophage, although localised and effectively controlled by the immune system. But if recipients are malnourished or in inferior health, with a weakened immune system, a chronic infection may develop, typically within the lungs. Cavities appear as bacteria destroy the lung tissues. Blood vessels are broken down and fluid collects. The patient coughs blood in the sputum. The structural damage to the lungs can be seen by X-ray examination (Figure 6.20).

The pathogen, carried in the blood stream, can lead to TB in almost any part of the body, including the meninges of the brain, or bone tissue, the lymph glands, the liver, the central nervous system, the kidneys or the genital organs. Generally, patients show loss of appetite, loss of weight, excessive sweating, and decline in physical activity.

Treatment of TB

Today, TB is treatable, but it is still a 'killer' disease if not diagnosed early in the infection. In 2005, there were 357 deaths due to TB in England and Wales.

The disease is contagious, so on confirmation of the diagnosis of a case of active tuberculosis, all contacts of the patient are traced and screened by a community public health team. Infectious patients are isolated and treated with specific anti-TB drugs until they cease to cough up viable bacilli. Then, anti-TB drugs continue to be administered to the patient, now back in the community, until it is clear the infection has been eradicated from the body.

12 How may strains of the TB-causing organism develop resistance to anti-TB drugs?

We have seen that micro-organisms develop resistance to antibiotics and other drugs used against them, with time. In the case of TB, patients are now treated with several drugs simultaneously because of the emergence of multiple-drug-resistant TB (MDR-TB). This is particularly in the case of AIDS patients. MDR-TB is especially common in the USA and South East Asia.

Changing pattern of the disease 1900–2000

There is evidence that TB was present in some of the earliest human communities, and it has persisted as a major threat to health where vulnerable people lived in crowded conditions. In Koch's time, 1 in 7 of all deaths among Europeans were due to TB.

Today, in the UK this disease is relatively rare, but about 20% of the world population are infected. The reduction in TB in the UK throughout most of the past century was due to steadily improving living conditions (housing and diet) (Figure 6.21). However, today there is evidence of a resurgence of the disease here, probably due to the globalisation of travel, as well as to the emergence of MDR-TB.

Figure 6.21 The decline in deaths from TB in England and Wales, 1900–2000.

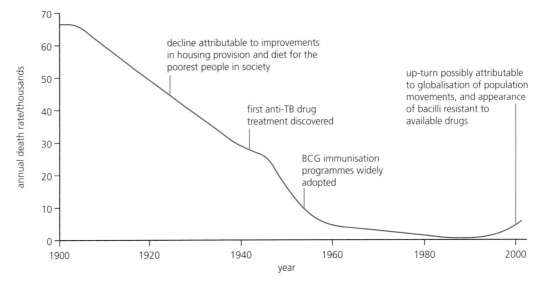

Human immunodeficiency virus

Human immunodeficiency virus (HIV) was first identified in 1983 as the cause of a disease of the human immune system known as autoimmune deficiency syndrome (AIDS). HIV is a tiny virus, about 100 nm in diameter (Figure 6.22). It consists of single strands of RNA together with enzymes, enclosed by a protein coat. It is encapsulated within a membrane derived from the human host cell it was formed in.

The virus first appeared in central Africa in the 1950s, perhaps as a mutation of a similar virus present in African green monkeys (but other theories about the origin of HIV exist). From Africa, HIV was spread to the Caribbean and later to the USA and Europe. Now, AIDS occurs worldwide. It is probably already the greatest threat to public health because it kills people in the most productive stage of their lives.

TEM of HIV viruses (×300 000)

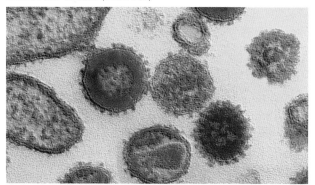

TEM of HIV viruses budding from a human lymphocyte (host cell)

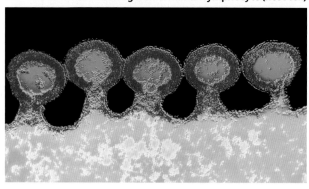

HIV virus with part of capsule and outer protein coat cut away

enzymes, including reverse transcriptase — protein coats — single-stranded RNA — capsule of lipid bilayer and glycoprotein

Figure 6.22 The human immune deficiency virus (HIV).

HIV is a retrovirus

Retroviruses reverse the normal flow of genetic information, which is from DNA of genes to messenger RNA in the cytoplasm. That information always flows in this direction in cells is known as the **central dogma** of cell biology (page 63). However, in retroviruses the information in RNA in the cytoplasm is translated into DNA of a chromosome in the host's nucleus.

How does a retrovirus work?

Taking HIV as an example, the virus binds to a host cell (lymphocyte, *Biology for AS*, Figure 1.13, page 14) membrane, and the core of the virus passes inside. In the host cell, the RNA and virus enzymes are released. One enzyme from the virus, called **reverse transcriptase**, copies the genetic code of the RNA strand into a DNA helix. This DNA then enters the host nucleus and is 'spliced' into the host's DNA of a chromosome. Here it may be replicated with the host's genes every time the host cell divides. In these cases the viral genes remain 'latent', giving no sign of their presence in the host cells.

Activity 6.12: Wider reading – 'AIDS'

The onset of AIDS

At a later stage, some event in the patient's body activates the HIV genes. The outcome is AIDS. The average interval between HIV infection and the onset of AIDS is about 8–10 years. The result is the synthesis of viral messenger RNA which passes out into the cytoplasm, there coding for viral proteins (enzymes and coat protein) at the ribosomes. Viral RNA (single stranded), enzymes and coat protein are formed into viral cores, which move against the cell membrane and 'bud-off' new viruses (Figure 6.22). These infect more lymphocytes (T-cells, page 82 – known as CD4 T cells) and the cycle is rapidly repeated. The body's reserve of lymphocytes dwindles and eventually no infection, however trivial, can be resisted (Figure 6.23).

Figure 6.23 The profile of an AIDS infection.

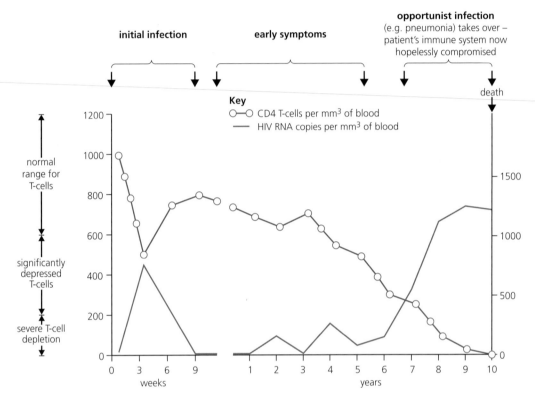

13 What feature of the HIV virus and the disease it causes create particular problems for the people and economies of less-developed countries such as Zimbabwe or Zambia?

Why AIDS is difficult to treat

AIDS, like any virus disease, cannot be controlled by antibiotics, which is one reason why it is currently difficult to treat. Another significant problem is HIV's rapid mutation rate, which effectively allows it to hide from the body's immune system and makes the development of any vaccine very difficult. (See *Avoiding development of drug-resistance in HIV*, page 89.)

6.3 Responses to infection

We have already noted that mostly, pathogens do not gain easy entry to the body. However, this does sometimes happen. Consequently it is fortunate there are internal 'lines of defence' too. The body responds to localised damage (cuts and abrasions, for example) by inflammation. If a blood vessel is ruptured, then the blood clotting mechanism is activated. In the blood and tissue fluid, the immune system is triggered.

Inflammation

Inflammation is the initial, rapid, localised response of the tissues to damage, whether due to a cut, scratch, bruising, or a deep wound. We are quickly aware the site of a cut or knock (contusion) has become swollen, warm and painful. Inflammation is triggered by the damaged cells themselves, which release 'alarm' chemicals, including histamine and prostaglandins. The initial outcome is that the volume of blood in the damaged area is increased, and white cells and plasma accumulate outside the enlarged capillaries. Ultimately, tissue repair is also initiated.

The blood circulation plays a complex part in the resistance to infection that will result if micro-organisms enter the body. For example, the increased blood flow removes toxic products released by invading micro-organisms and by damaged cells (Figure 6.24).

Meanwhile, the white cells in the blood fall into two functional groupings as regards their roles in the defence against disease. General phagocytic white cells engulf 'foreign' material.

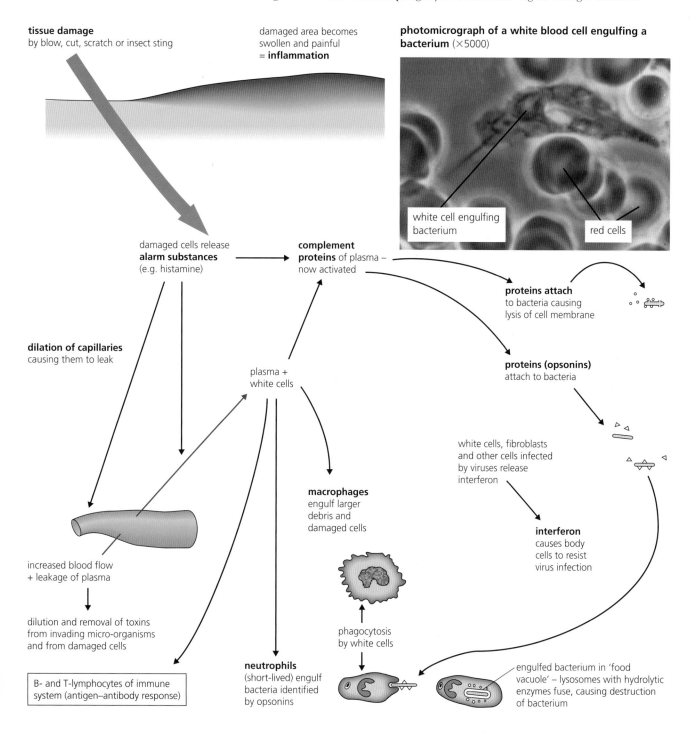

Figure 6.24 Inflammation at a damage site, the processes.

These are the neutrophils and the macrophages. Neutrophils make up 60% of all white cells in the blood, but they are short-lived. Macrophages are the principal 'rubbish-collecting cells' found throughout the body tissues. Other white cells produce the antibody reaction to infection or invasion of foreign matter (see below).

The blood also delivers special proteins (**complement proteins**), which are activated by the presence of infection. Complement proteins enhance the work of white cells in overcoming infections by contributing to the general inflammation response, and by stimulating the immune response. Some trigger the lysis of invading micro-organisms. Opsonins bind to pathogenic bacteria and so increase phagocytosis.

The increased permeability of capillaries allows the leakage of blood clotting factors, and so the cascade of reactions leading to localised **clotting** of the blood and sealing of a haemorrhage is triggered where a break in the circulation has occurred.

Cells infected with viruses produce proteins called **interferons**. These bind to neighbouring, healthy cells and trigger synthesis of antiviral proteins. Viral replication is halted.

The antimicrobial protein **lysozyme** is always present in perspiration, tears, saliva, nasal secretions and also in tissue fluids. Lysozyme is an enzyme capable of breaking down the walls of certain bacteria. Consequently, this protein, too, is part of the body's response to infection.

Non-specific responses to infection

All the above responses to infection are referred to as non-specific responses because they help to destroy *any* invading pathogen. By contrast, the immune response we discuss next is triggered by and directed towards *specific* pathogens.

The immune response

The **immune response** is our main defence once invasion of the body by harmful micro-organisms has occurred. It is particular leucocytes called **lymphocytes** that are responsible for the immune response. They make up 20% of the leucocytes circulating in the blood plasma (or found in the tissue fluid – remember, white cells also move freely through the walls of blood vessels). In fact, lymphocytes detect any matter entering from outside our bodies (including 'foreign' macromolecules as well as micro-organisms) as different from 'self' (body cells and our own proteins). We call 'non-self' substances **antigens**.

What recognition of 'self' entails

Cells are identified by specific molecules – markers, if you like – that are lodged in the outer surface of the plasma membrane. These molecules that identify a cell are highly variable glycoproteins on the cell surface. Glycoproteins occur attached to proteins in the fluid mosaic model of the plasma membrane, as introduced in *Biology for AS*, page 45.

The glycoproteins that identify cells are known as the **major histocompatability complex antigens (MHC)**. There are genes on one of our chromosomes (chromosome 6, actually) that code for MHC, so each individual's MHC is genetically determined, and is a feature we inherit. As with all inherited characteristics that are products of sexual reproduction, variation occurs. Each of us has distinctive MHC antigens present on the plasma membrane of most of our body cells. Unless you have an identical twin, your MHC antigens are unique.

Now, lymphocytes of our immune system have antigen receptors that recognise our own MHC antigens, and differentiate between these and 'foreign' antigens detected in the body.

Lymphocytes and the antigen–antibody reaction

We have two distinct types of lymphocyte, based on the ways they function:

- B-lymphocytes (**B-cells**) secrete antibodies (humoral immunity)
- T-lymphocytes (**T-cells**) assist B-cells, as we shall shortly see, and may attack infected cells (cell-mediated responses).

Both cell types originate in the red bone marrow from **stem cells**, but they undergo different development processes in preparation for their distinctive roles (Figure 6.25).

T-cells leave the bone marrow during development, and undergo differentiation in the thymus gland before circulating, and being stored in lymph nodes. It is while they are present in the thymus gland that the body apparently selects out lymphocytes that would otherwise react to the body's own cells. The role of T-cells is **cell-mediated immunity** – an immune response not directly involving antibodies – although some have a role in the activation of B-cells, as we shall see. Some T-cells are effective against pathogens located within host cells.

B-cells complete their maturation in the bone marrow, prior to circulating in the body and being stored in lymph nodes. The role of the majority of B-cells, after recognition and binding to a specific antigen, is to proliferate into cells (called **plasma cells**) that secrete antibodies into the blood system. This is known as **humoral immunity**.

Now, while both T- and B-cells have molecules on the outer surface of their plasma membrane that enable them to recognise antigens, each lymphocyte has *only one type* of surface receptor. Consequently, each lymphocyte can recognise only one type of antigen.

14 Explain the significance of the role of the thymus gland in destroying T-cells that would otherwise react to body proteins.

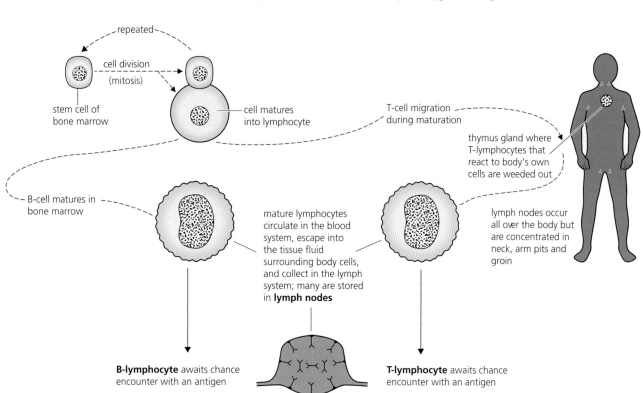

Figure 6.25 T- and B-lymphocytes.

When an infection occurs, the leucocyte population responds. Their numbers increase enormously, and many collect at the site of the invasion. A complex response to infection is begun. The special roles of T- and B-cells in this response are as follows.

1 On the arrival of a specific antigen in the body, B-cells with surface receptors (antibodies) that recognise that particular antigen, bind to it.
What exactly is an antibody?
An **antibody** is a special protein called an **immunoglobulin**, made of four polypeptide chains held together by disulphide bridges (–S–S–), forming a molecule in the shape of a Y (Figure 6.26, overleaf). The arrangement of amino acid residues in the polypeptides that form the 'fork' region in this molecule is totally unique to that antibody. It is this region that forms the highly specific binding site for the antigen. Antibodies initially occur attached to the plasma membrane of B-cells, but later are also mass produced and secreted by cells derived from the B-cell by exocytosis (Figure 6.27, page 85), but only after that B-cell has undergone an activation step (step **5**, below).

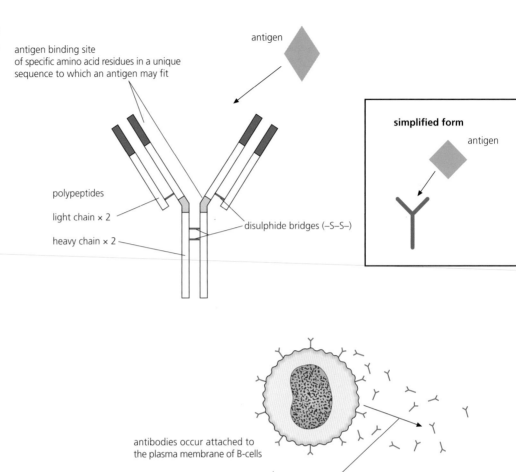

Figure 6.26 The structure of an antibody.

2 On binding to the B-cell, the antigen is taken into the cytoplasm by phagocytosis, before being expressed on the plasma membrane of the B-cell.

3 Meanwhile, T-cells can only respond to antigens when presented on the surface of other cells. Phagocytic cells of the body, including **macrophages**, engulf antigens they encounter. This occurs in the plasma and lymph. Once these antigens are taken up, the macrophage presents them externally by attaching the antigens to their surface membrane proteins – the MHC antigens. This is called **antigen presentation** by a macrophage.

4 T-cells come in contact with these macrophages and briefly bind to them. The T-cell is immediately activated. They become 'armed' or **activated helper T-cells**.

5 Activated helper T-cells now bind to B-cells with the same antigen expressed on their plasma membrane (step **2** above), and each activated T-cell sends a message to the B-cell, activating it. It is now an 'armed' or activated B-cell.

6 Activated B-cells immediately divide very rapidly by mitosis forming a clone of cells called **plasma cells**. A TEM of plasma cells shows them to be packed with endoplasmic reticulum (RER). In these organelles, the antibody is mass produced, and is then exported from the B-cell by exocytosis. The antibodies are normally produced in such numbers that the antigen is overcome.

The production of an activated B-cell, its rapid cell division to produce a clone of plasma cells, and the resulting production of antibodies that react with the antigen, is called **clonal selection**. Sometimes several different antibodies react with one antigen – this is **polyclonal selection**.

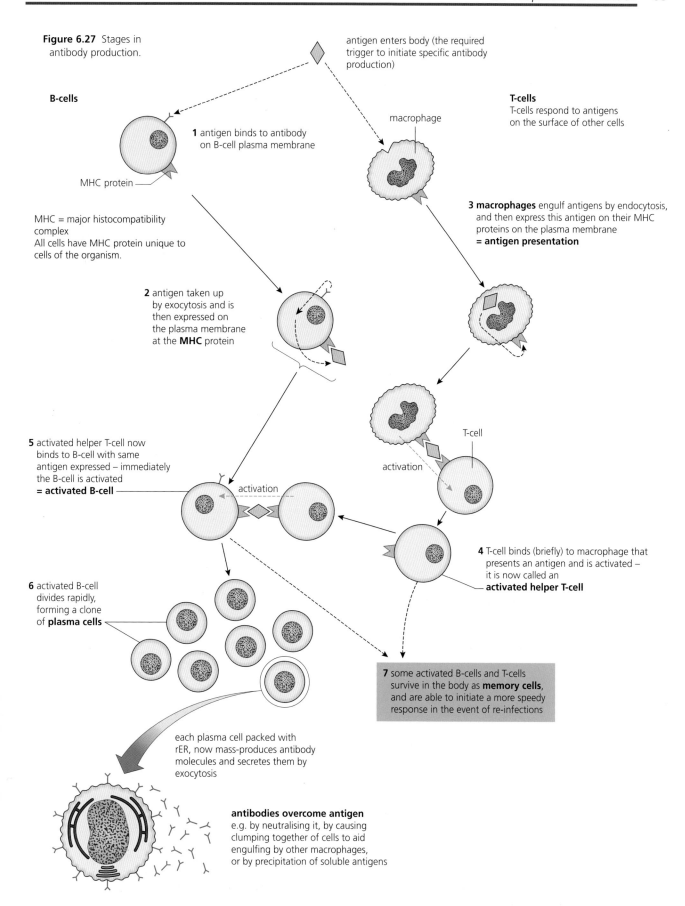

Figure 6.27 Stages in antibody production.

antigen enters body (the required trigger to initiate specific antibody production)

B-cells

1 antigen binds to antibody on B-cell plasma membrane

MHC protein

MHC = major histocompatibility complex
All cells have MHC protein unique to cells of the organism.

2 antigen taken up by exocytosis and is then expressed on the plasma membrane at the **MHC** protein

T-cells
T-cells respond to antigens on the surface of other cells

macrophage

3 macrophages engulf antigens by endocytosis, and then express this antigen on their MHC proteins on the plasma membrane
= antigen presentation

5 activated helper T-cell now binds to B-cell with same antigen expressed – immediately the B-cell is activated
= activated B-cell

activation

T-cell

activation

4 T-cell binds (briefly) to macrophage that presents an antigen and is activated – it is now called an
activated helper T-cell

6 activated B-cell divides rapidly, forming a clone of **plasma cells**

7 some activated B-cells and T-cells survive in the body as **memory cells**, and are able to initiate a more speedy response in the event of re-infections

each plasma cell packed with rER, now mass-produces antibody molecules and secretes them by exocytosis

antibodies overcome antigen
e.g. by neutralising it, by causing clumping together of cells to aid engulfing by other macrophages, or by precipitation of soluble antigens

Figure 6.28 Profile of antibody production in infection and re-infection.

Memory cells are retained in lymph nodes. They allow a quick and specific response if the same antigen reappears.

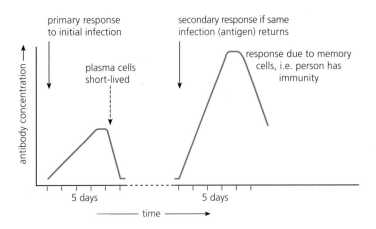

Figure 6.29 The roles of B- and T-cells in the immune system – a summary.

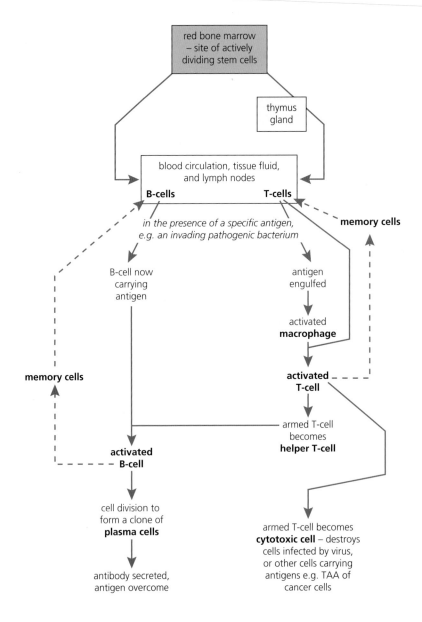

15 Identify where antigens and antibodies may be found in the body.

16 Outline in tabulated form the parts played by the blood in the protection of the body.

A* Extension 6.9: An additional role for T-cells

Activity 6.13: Wider reading – 'Fight for your life'

A* Extension 6.10: The origins of vaccination – the process of immunisation

HSW 6.2: Criterion 9 – Controversy about vaccination

17 Identify those steps involved in plasma cell formation that the existence of memory cells avoids in the event of re-infection.

18 State what we mean by immunity.

7 After these antibodies have tackled the foreign matter and the disease threat it introduced, the antibodies disappear from the blood and tissue fluid, along with the bulk of the specific B-cells and T-cells responsible for their formation. However, certain of these specifically activated B- and T-cells are retained in the body as **memory cells**. These are long-lived cells, in contrast to plasma cells and activated B-cells. Memory cells make possible an early and effective response in the event of a re-infection of the body by the same antigen (Figure 6.28). This is the basis of natural immunity (see below).

It is now helpful to summarise the complex roles of B- and T-cells in the immune system (Figure 6.29).

Vaccination

Vaccination is the deliberate administration of antigens that have been made harmless, after they are obtained from disease-causing organisms, in order to confer immunity in future. It makes very important contributions to public health, today.

Vaccines are administered either by injection or by mouth. They cause the body's immune system to briefly make antibodies against the disease (*without becoming infected*), and then to retain the appropriate memory cells. Active artificial immunity is established in this way. The profile of response in terms of antibody production caused by any later exposure to the antigen is exactly the same as if the immunity was acquired after the body overcame an earlier infection.

Vaccines are manufactured from dead or attenuated bacteria, or from inactivated viruses, purified polysaccharides from bacterial walls, toxoids, and even recombinant DNA produced by genetic engineering.

So successful has vaccination been – where vaccines are widely available and the take up is by about 85–90% of the relevant population – that some formerly common and dangerous diseases have become very uncommon occurrences, in many human communities. As a result, the public there has sometimes become casual about the threat such diseases still pose.

The recommended schedule of vaccinations for children brought up in the UK can be accessed via the website www.doh.gov.uk.

In summary – types of immunity

So, our immune system provides protection to the body from the worst effects of many of the pathogens that may invade. This immunity may be acquired passively or actively, and by natural or by artificial means. Table 6.4 explains the differences.

Table 6.4 Types of immunity that humans display.

Type of immunity	Natural	Artificial	Longevity of immunity
passive immunity – the organism acquires antibodies from elsewhere	antibodies acquired from the mother's blood circulation, while *in utero*, or received in the mother's milk supply, particularly present in the colostrum (first formed) milk	antibodies acquired from administration of a vaccine (e.g. against tetanus, which is recommended to be re-administered about every 10 years)	passive immunity fades with time because the recipient does not acquire memory cells, and so is unable to make the antibodies in future
active immunity – the organism manufactures its own antibodies after the body's defences have been exposed to specific antigens	ability to produce antibodies in future after infection and then recovery from a disease (e.g. chicken pox), due to retention of B and T memory cells, which respond in the case of re-infection	antibodies acquired from administration of a vaccine (e.g. against meningitis C), which provides protection, and also induces the production and retention of B and T memory cells	active immunity persists for a prolonged period and possibly throughout life, after it has been acquired

An 'evolutionary race' between pathogen and host?

Many important diseases have menaced human life since the establishment of our earliest settlements (by 5000 years ago). In these early communities, cattle herds and other domesticated animals were often the source of lethal pathogens that successfully adapted to the human body, including smallpox, diphtheria, influenza, chicken pox and mumps. These diseases, unlike malaria, needed no carrier (the vector of malaria is the female mosquito), and they spread particularly readily.

One result of continuing exposure to diseases is that the human body has, over time, acquired varying degrees of resistance, particularly after exposure to less virulent strains. Also, protection for the host may arise as a by-product of other developments. (For example, sickle-cell trait is the result of a mutation involving the haemoglobin of our red cells, but confers some protection against malaria.) However, these diseases do not die out. Indeed, from time to time their virulence increases, as illustrated by the various strains of influenza that arise and threaten a new pandemic.

How do new, virulent strains arise?

Just as humans may evolve resistance in response to virulence, so pathogens may evolve greater virulence in response to our 'defences'. We can illustrate this by reference to two diseases – TB and AIDS.

Multiple-drug-resistant TB

We have seen that TB is a disease caused by the bacterium *Mycobacterium tuberculosis*. Like all bacterial diseases, TB can be successfully treated with specific antibiotics. Streptomycin was the antibiotic of choice to cure TB patients. However, resistance may develop with time – sooner or later some strains of *Mycobacterium tuberculosis* in a population develop genes for resistance to that particular antibiotic. Consequently, these bacteria survive exposure to the drug, and once competition with other (non-resistant) bacteria is removed by the antibiotic, the resistant pathogenic bacteria flourish. As a succession of antibiotics is used, and resistance develops to each with time, so multiple-drug-resistant TB (MDR-TB) has appeared in human populations.

Resistant genes develop either by mutations, or as a result of gene transfer between bacteria by conjugation (Figure 6.30), or both. In the longer term, the pharmaceutical industry faces the challenge of producing new antibiotics faster than bacteria develop resistance to them. In the mean time, it is essential that antibiotics, once prescribed, are used correctly.

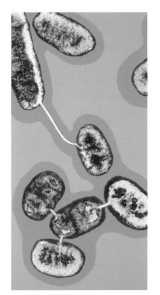

TEM of conjugation tube – once formed, this shortens, drawing the bacteria together

conjugation by (i) transfer of a plasmid

plasmid — conjugation tube formed

chromosome —

copy of plasmid DNA (coding strand)

remainder of DNA of new plasmid formed and plasmid assembled

conjugation tube connection closed

(ii) transfer of a copy of part of the chromosome

copy of part of DNA of chromosome (coding strand)

double-stranded DNA assembled and inserted into circular chromosome

Figure 6.30 How genes may pass between individual bacteria.

In particular:

- they should not be prescribed to prevent infection in healthy people
- patients must complete the course of treatment in its entirety – stopping taking a prescribed antibiotic once the patient feels the condition is improving aids the development of resistance in the pathogen
- the general health and vitality of the patient should also be sustained, all contacts identified and their health kept under surveillance.

Avoiding development of drug-resistance in HIV

AIDS is a virus disease and so cannot be treated using antibiotics. AIDS patients are offered drugs that slow down the progress of the infection – a combination of drugs reduces the number of HIV-infected cells in a patient, at least temporarily. The three most popular drugs (AZT and two protease inhibitors) interrupt the steps to nucleic acid reverse transcription. A combination of drugs is used to prevent HIV from rapidly developing resistance to any one drug, and to avoid dangerous or unpleasant side-effects that some patients experience.

Ideally, a vaccine against HIV would be the best solution – one designed to wipe out infected T4 cells together with any free virus particles in the patient's blood stream. The work of several laboratories is dedicated to this solution. Here the problem is that infected T4 cells in the latent state frequently change the membrane marker proteins they carry, due to the constantly changing HIV genome within. Remember, the genetic material of HIV is RNA, which is copied by RNA polymerase. Unlike DNA polymerase, RNA polymerase enzyme lacks a powerful 'spell-checker' function – it's a sort of dyslexic enzyme! Replicated RNA strands commonly show small differences in their nucleotide sequence. These are akin to mutations; we can say the HIV mutates at a high rate. As a result, HIV can hide from the body's immune response by frequently changing its 'identity'.

19 Explain the difference between an epidemic and a pandemic disease.

Antibiotics

Antibiotics are naturally occurring chemical substances obtained mainly from certain fungi and bacteria commonly found in the soil. When antibiotics are present in low concentrations they inhibit the growth of other micro-organisms, or cause their outright death, as demonstrated in Figure 6.31 and Activity 6.17.

Figure 6.31 Investigating sensitivity to antibiotics. (The mast ring shown here is available from suppliers.)

To the bacterial lawn of a known species was added a mast ring with each 'arm' impregnated with a different antibiotic (colour coded). Then the plate was closed and incubated. From the result (opposite) there is evidence that growth of this bacterium is more sensitive to certain antibiotics (e.g. CM, A) than to others (e.g. S, I).

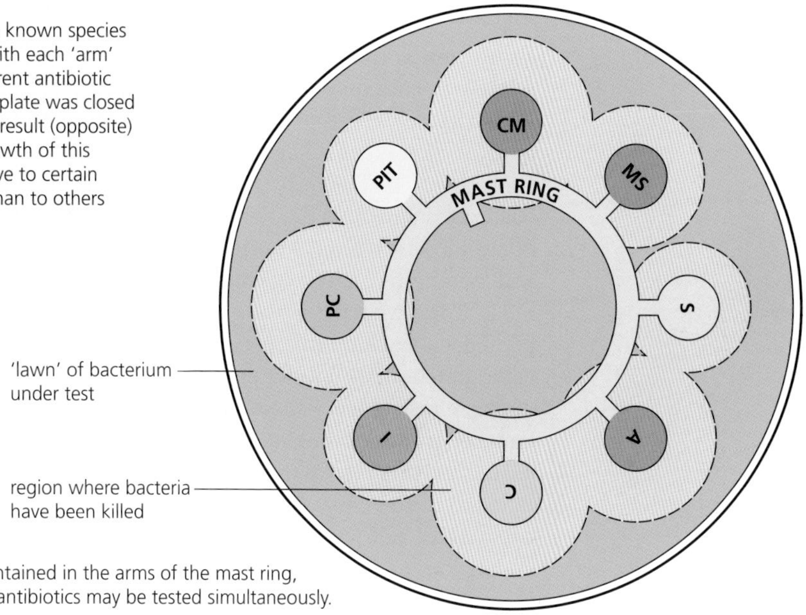

'lawn' of bacterium under test

region where bacteria have been killed

Different antibiotics are contained in the arms of the mast ring, so that sensitivity to many antibiotics may be tested simultaneously.

Activity 6.14: Wider reading – 'Penicillin man' (HSW Criteria 9a and 12)

Activity 6.15: Investigating the effect of different antibiotics on bacteria (HSW Criteria 2, 3, 4, 5 and 8)

A* Extension 6.11: Antibiotic production – from 'screening' to manufacture (HSW Criterion 2)

The first antibiotic to be discovered, isolated and developed (not an easy task; it took from 1929–1944, see Activity 6.16) was penicillin. Over 400 different antibiotics have since been isolated, but of these only about 50 have proved non-toxic to patients, and so have achieved wide usage. Antibiotics effective against a wide range of pathogenic bacteria are called **broad-spectrum antibiotics**, and these include chloramphenicol and tetracyclines. Others, including penicillin and streptomycin, are effective over a limited range of bacteria.

Antibiotics – mechanisms of action

The biochemistry of antibiotic action – the ways in which antibiotic molecules interact within bacterial cells – have been investigated. The various mechanisms of antibiotic action are summarised in Table 6.5. Note that the extent to which the particular bacterial components, metabolites or enzymes targeted by the antibiotic are also components of the host cells (eukaryotic cells) influences just how toxic the drug is to the mammalian host tissues.

The outcomes of antibiotic actions vary too. Their effects are either to destroy the bacteria against which they are effective (**bactericidal** antibiotics), or they may merely interfere with the bacterium's mechanism of multiplication (**bacteriostatic** antibiotics). In these latter cases, it is the host's immune system that finally overcomes the pathogen.

Table 6.5 The biochemical mechanisms of antibiotic action.

Mechanism targeted	Effects
cell wall synthesis	The antibiotic interferes with the synthesis of bacterial cell walls. Once the cell wall is destroyed, the delicate plasma membrane of the bacterium is exposed to the destructive force generated by excess uptake of water by osmosis. Several antibiotics, including penicillin, ampicillin, and bacitracin, bind to and inactivate specific wall-building enzymes – the bacterium's walls fall apart. (This is the most effective mechanism.)
protein synthesis	The antibiotic inhibits protein synthesis by binding with ribosomal RNA. The ribosomes of prokaryotes (known as 70S) are made of particular RNA subunits. The ribosomes of eukaryotic cells are larger (80S), and are built with different types of RNA. Antibiotics like streptomycin, chloramphenicol, tetracyclines, and erythromycin all bind to prokaryotic ribosomal RNA subunits unique to bacteria and terminate their protein synthesis.
nucleic acid synthesis	A few antibiotics interfere with DNA replication or transcription, or they block mRNA synthesis. These antibiotics – e.g. the quinolones – are not as selectively toxic as other antibiotics, because the processes of replication and transcription do not differ so greatly between prokaryotes and eukaryotes as wall synthesis and protein synthesis do.

Antibiotics – 'wonder drugs' or mixed blessing?

Before antibiotics became available to treat bacterial infections, the typical hospital ward was filled with patients with pneumonia, typhoid fever, tuberculosis, meningitis, syphilis and rheumatic fever. These diseases, all caused by bacteria, claimed many lives, sometimes very quickly. Patients of all ages were affected. Today, these infections are not the 'killers' they were (*Biology for AS*, Figure 1.27, page 26). For example, in the 1930s about 40% of patients with bacterial pneumonia died of the disease, whereas today about 5–10% may die. It is the discovery of antibiotics that has brought about these changes. (Of course, the viral forms of pneumonia and meningitis are not overcome by antibiotics, which cannot be used against viruses.)

However, we have already noted that problems arise with time. Sooner or later some pathogenic bacteria in a population develop genes for resistance to antibiotic actions. Then, when different antibiotics are used in response, the pathogenic bacteria concerned slowly acquire **multiple resistance**. For example, a strain of *Staphylococcus aureus* has acquired resistance to a range of antibiotics including methicillin. Now, so-called methicillin-resistant *Staphylococcus aureus* (**MRSA**) is referred to as a 'hospital superbug' because of the harm its presence has inflicted in these places (Figure 6.32). (Actually, 'superbugs' are found everywhere in the community, not just in hospitals.) MRSA poses the greatest threat to patients who have undergone surgery. With cases of MRSA to treat, the intravenous antibiotic called vanomycin is prescribed, but recently there have been cases of partial resistance to this drug, too.

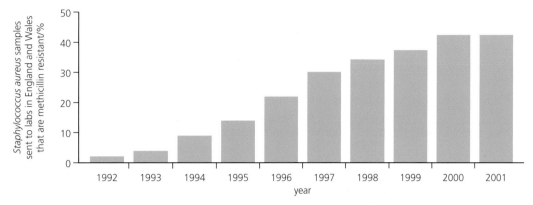

Figure 6.32 The increasing incidence of MRSA.

Similarly, a strain of the bacterium *Clostridium difficile* is now resistant to all but two antibiotics (Figure 6.33). This bacterium is a natural component of our gut 'microflora'. It is only when *C. difficile's* activities are no longer suppressed by the surrounding, huge, beneficial ('friendly') gut flora that it may multiply to life-threatening numbers and then may trigger toxic damage to the colon. Suppression of beneficial gut bacteria is a typical consequence of heavy doses of broad-spectrum antibiotics, administered to overcome infections by other superbugs. 'Superbug' infections acquired in hospitals are a major issue for the UK Health Service (Figure 6.33).

One result is that the pharmaceutical industry faces the challenge of producing new antibiotics faster than bacteria develop resistance to them. However, this is proving increasingly difficult – the number of new antibiotics being developed each year has fallen dramatically (Table 6.6).

Figure 6.33 Rates of 'superbug' infection cause deep concern (extract from an article by Lois Rogers, in *The Sunday Times*, 23 March 2008).

20 Antibiotics are widely used as 'prophylactics' in animal husbandry. What does this mean, why does this happen, and what possible dangers arise from this use of antibiotics?

Superbug deaths at 10,000 a year

THE number of patients in British hospitals dying from superbug infections has reached more than 10,000 every year, according to an expert, *writes Lois Rogers*.

The new figure is about 20% higher than the official toll of 8,000 a year.

Mark Enright, professor of molecular epidemiology at Imperial College London, said that the real number of those succumbing to methicillin-resistant *Staphylococcus aureus* (MRSA) and *Clostridium difficile* (*C. difficile*) in the UK is higher than the government's records show.

"I think it is at least 10,000 a year," he said. "A lot of people are never tested for these infections and their deaths are put down to something else."

"Antibiotic-resistant bacteria are now so well established here, we will never get rid of them," said Hugh Pennington, emeritus professor of bacteriology at Aberdeen University and a world expert.

Latest European figures show that Britain's hospitals are still teeming with treatment-resistant bacteria.

While strict hygiene measures have ensured low infection rates in other countries, microbiologists here are privately admitting that

Britain's problem is so out of control, it will be impossible to prevent the high level of deaths from continuing.

The government's pledge to reduce rates of MRSA to half the 2004 level is unattainable, they say.

According to figures from Eurosurveillance, at least 42% of MRSA bacteria in British hospitals are "superstrains", compared with rates of 20% or lower elsewhere.

In the 31-nation European anti-superbug league table, Britain lies close to the bottom, with an infection-control performance better than those of only Malta, Greece, Portugal and Romania.

Table 6.6 The pace of new antibiotic development.

	1983–87	1988–92	1993–97	1998–2002
Number of new antibiotics approved (USA) / 5-year period	16	14	8	7

The response to hospital-acquired infections

Of course, many hospitalised patients are predisposed to infection, because they are typically already in poor health. Most likely, too, they are attending for invasive treatments such as surgery, catheterisation, or injections, and their treatment programme itself sometimes impairs their natural immunity.

Micro-organisms may unfortunately be transmitted in hospitals by direct skin contact, by instrument and equipment contacts, and by airborne or droplet transmission. The same micro-organism may be transmitted by more than one of these routes.

The steps taken to control and prevent hospital-acquired infections are listed in Table 6.7. Study these measures first, and then respond to SAQ 21.

Table 6.7 Measures to control and prevent hospital-acquired infections.

1 Isolation of patients	designed to reduce transmission between sources and vulnerable patients
2 Hand washing by staff and visitors	perhaps the most effective measure in reducing risk of transmission
3 Gloves and aprons worn	disposable gloves and aprons, used during patient handling and treatment, provide a protective barrier for staff and patients – as long as they are disposable and restricted in use
4 Screening of patients for 'superbug' infections on arrival	this costly and time-consuming measure will be of increasing importance where it is known that 'pools' of resistant strains of micro-organisms exist in the community the patients come from
5 Longer term measures	■ family doctors not prescribing antibiotics as a precaution, but only in cases of established need ■ patients for whom a course of antibiotics has been prescribed must complete the full course and not abandon it as soon as they start to feel better ■ maintenance of research and development programmes designed to provide a new and developing 'arsenal' of effective antibiotics
6 Parallel development	about a half of all antibiotics sold annually are used in low doses added to feed of intensively reared farm animals, to prevent infections and to stimulate faster growth – the phasing out of this practice is necessary

Activity 6.16: Wider reading – 'Superbugs'

21 Explain how each of the measures to help control and prevent hospital-acquired infections, listed in Table 6.7, is based on our understanding of how these infections may be caused.

6.4 Forensic science

Forensic science is the application of biochemical and other scientific techniques to the investigation of crime. In the case of crime that involves the death of a person, three issues are uppermost, initially:

1 who is the dead person?
2 when did the death occur?
3 what was the cause of death?

Here we are concerned merely with the issue of 'time of death', but if forensic science is a career possibility for you, then Activity 6.17 will be of interest.

Incidentally, crime as a whole receives much attention in the media; the incidence of crime in our society may be lower than some newspaper headlines suggest. Since 'fear' and 'anxiety' are powerful forces in gaining the attention of the public, is it inevitable that details of tragic events of a criminal nature are featured so prominently? Actual crime rates are recorded by the British Crime Survey at www.crimestatistics.org.uk.

Activity 6.17: Introducing the Forensic Science Service

Determining the time of death

A sequence of changes to the body follows upon death. Most obviously, body temperature is no longer maintained, skeletal muscle flexibility changes, and decomposition of the tissues gets underway. Observation and measurement of these changes, in the context of the surrounding environmental conditions, assist in the estimation of time of death – a critical issue that a forensic scientist may be asked to resolve.

Body temperature

In life, a mammal maintains a high and relatively constant body temperature, using the heat energy generated by metabolism within the body (or by generating additional heat in the muscles when cold) and carefully controlling the loss of heat through the skin. For example, humans hold their inner body temperature (**core temperature**) just below 37 °C. In fact, human inner body temperature only varies between about 35.5 and 37.0 °C within a 24-hour period (Figure 6.34), when we are in good health. However, in a person with a fever at the time of death, the core body temperature would be significantly higher; in anyone suffering from severe hypothermia, it would be much lower.

Figure 6.34 Body temperature of a living human.

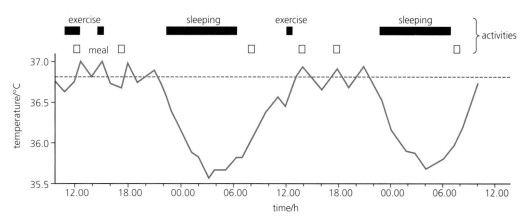

body temperature over a 48-hour period

The body temperatures shown were taken with the thermometer under the tongue. Although this is a region close to the body 'core', temperatures here may be altered by eating/drinking, and by the breathing in through the mouth of cold air, for example. More accurate values are obtained by taking the rectal temperature.

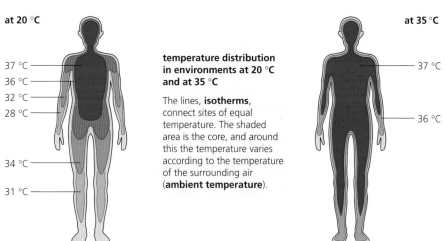

temperature distribution in environments at 20 °C and at 35 °C

The lines, **isotherms**, connect sites of equal temperature. The shaded area is the core, and around this the temperature varies according to the temperature of the surrounding air (**ambient temperature**).

On death, heat production slows quickly, but heat loss from the body to the environment by convection, radiation and conduction, and due to evaporation of water, may continue. Loss of heat is influenced by the factors listed in Table 6.8 (overleaf). Obviously, details of the external conditions and the condition of the cadaver itself are taken into consideration when estimating time of death from body temperature. A long, sensitive thermometer is required for it is the temperature of the body core that must be measured. The first 24-hours are the period during which amount of heat loss may inform on time of death.

Size of body	Heat loss from a large, compact form is much slower than from a small, thin one. It is the ratio of surface area to volume that determines rate of heat lost.
Ambient temperature	The gradient between internal and external temperatures will influence heat loss. Heat loss to air is slower than heat loss to water at the same temperature, as water is a better conductor of heat.
Body position	How compactly positioned a cadaver is will influence the effective surface area for heat loss.
Clothing	Clothing provides insulation by retaining still air around the body.
Humidity and air movements	Humidity influences heat loss by evaporation, and air currents (or water currents) influence heat loss by conduction and convection.

Rigor mortis

The stiffening of the body that occurs after death is called 'rigor mortis'. In this state, the joints become fixed and the limbs cannot be moved. The actual sequence of changes in the musculature that occur as the body cools is shown in Table 6.9, together with approximate timings. Note that rigor mortis develops slowly, and persists for only a limited period.

Time since death (approximate)	Body temperature (approximate)	Stiffness of the body
up to 3 hours	warm	not stiff
3–8 hours	warm	stiff – rigor mortis
8–36 hours	cold	decreasing stiffness
more than 36–48 hours	cold	not stiff

In people who have been vigorously physically active immediately before death, rigor mortis sets in more quickly and lasts for less time, e.g. it may have elapsed after 6–9 hours.

How is rigor mortis brought about?

The way living muscle contracts and relaxes to bring about movement is discussed in the next chapter. The protein filaments of which each muscle fibre consists are able to slide past each other. Shortening of a muscle occurs in a series of steps describes as a 'ratchet mechanism' (Figure 7.8, page 106). A great deal of ATP is used in the contraction process.

In death, supplies of oxygen to body tissues are terminated, so ATP production by aerobic respiration stops, ADP accumulates, and conditions in the tissues rapidly become anaerobic. Now, anaerobic respiration occurs in tissues until the lowered pH (due to accumulation of lactic acid) effectively inhibits enzyme action. Additionally, in the muscle tissue, the regulated movement of calcium ions is terminated, and the presence of an excess of these ions around binding sites (together with the absence of ATP) contributes to the 'locking' of the ratchet mechanism. The skeletal muscle becomes rigid.

With time, the breakdown of cell ultrastructure results in the release of hydrolytic enzymes from ruptured lysosomes. Self-digestion (**autolysis**) sets in. This process, among other things, reverses the muscle rigidity of rigor mortis and the musculature becomes limp again.

The extent of decomposition

Steps in the biochemical and microbiological breakdown of the body following death are listed in Table 6.10. Obviously, ambient temperature largely determines the speed of the processes, and so the precise timing of the observed stages is influenced by this, together with other environmental and individual factors. Very high temperatures will slow decomposition because of their effect on enzyme denaturation. Of course, extremely low temperatures are even more inhibiting of decay – which is the basis of refrigerated storage of cadavers prior to autopsy, practised in hospital mortuaries.

Table 6.10 Major steps to putrefaction – the processes of decay.	**1 Skin discolouration, first in the lower abdomen**	A greenish colour develops, spreads to the remainder of the body, and progressively darkens to reddish–green and finally purple–black. Typically, this occurs 36–72 hours after death.
	2 Skin blister formation, and bloating of the body	Gas-filled (and liquid-filled) blisters develop under the skin. Gases (chiefly H_2S, CO_2, CH_4, NH_3 and H_2) are the products of bacteriological decay of the tissues under anaerobic conditions. Gases also form and collect within the still-intact intestines, causing the bloating of the whole body. Typically, this occurs 7 days after death.
	3 Gas release and deflation of the body	Continuing breakdown of the tissues of the body then leads to liquefied matter draining away and to the escape of the trapped gases. The remainder of the body shrinks and it dries. The remaining decay processes slow down.

Forensic entomology

When any new 'habitat' is exposed, it is rapidly colonised. Initial conditions enable certain organisms to quickly dominate – but only for a limited period. The activities of these 'pioneers' trigger changes in the habitat, and so the resulting biota changes progressively, too. We met the phenomenon of succession in the previous chapter, particularly in situations where new soil appears (primary succession, page 26). In fact, the same phenomenon is repeated when any fresh, non-living organic matter is deposited – but with a sequence of organisms that is largely dictated by the new 'resource'. You can observe a fascinating demonstration of this in the decay of herbivorous dung (Activity 6.18).

DL
www
Activity 6.18: A succession of coprophilous fungi

On the other hand, the succession of insect life that may colonise an exposed corpse represents an unpleasant and possibly repulsive feature of death and decay. This occurs because blowflies in particular ('bluebottles', 'greenbottles' and 'fleshflies') can detect the odours created by bacteriological decay, generally produced within very few hours of death. Having detected a corpse, these insects immediately lay their eggs on the dead flesh. The eggs develop into larvae (maggots) and feed there. Consequently, the sequence of colonising insects, and the stages of development they exhibit, have often provided surprisingly reliable indications of time of death in the case of a body that has lain undiscovered for days and weeks. The forensic entomologist, called to examine a decaying corpse and to provide an estimate of how much time has elapsed since death, first makes and records a detailed examination of the body and of its immediate environment, as well as collecting samples for further analysis. Typical data and its potential significance are listed in Table 6.11.

Table 6.11 Data from a corpse where the presence of insects is detected.	**Precise location of the body and its accessibility to blowflies**	Burial of a corpse immediately after death isolates it from access by adult blowflies – so their eggs cannot be laid. In an exposed, uninjured corpse, maggots are found around the natural openings of the body (superficially). Maggots found deep within tissues imply that traumatic wounding has occurred.
	What insects are found around and on the corpse?	Specimens need to be preserved for later confirmation of identities. In the case of juvenile forms (e.g. maggots of fly species), live specimens may be required for rearing to adult form before their identification can be completed.
	What precise stages in insect life cycles are exhibited?	Data (including photographic evidence) and preserved specimens are required so that the exact ages and stages of development can be determined. (In blowfly larvae, size is generally a function of age.)
	Measurements of temperatures in and around the corpse	The rate of the development of an insect from egg, through the larval stages to pupation (Figure 6.35, overleaf) is largely determined by ambient air and ground temperatures.

From many studies of the insects found on decaying human bodies, a picture of a typical succession has been built up (Table 6.12, overleaf). One feature of this succession that sets it apart from other ecological successions is that as the numbers of organisms present build up, the earliest colonisers ('pioneers') are not replaced, but rather remain.

Table 6.12 Insect species succession typical of a human corpse.

State of the body	'Pioneer' organisms – and subsequent additions	Typical numbers of species present
fresh	bluebottles: *Calliphora vicina* and *Calliphora vomitoria* greenbottles: *Lucilia sericata* house fly: *Musca domestica* cow fly: *Musca autumnnalis*	17
bloated	flesh flies: *Sarcophaga* spp.	48
active decay	beetle larvae: *Dermestes* tabby moth (maggot): *Aglossa*	255
advanced decay	cheese skippers: *Piophila* spp. lesser house fly: *Fannia canicularis*	426
dry	none	211

The appearances, identification and biology of these species can be researched in:
Michael Chinnery (1976) *A Field Guide to the Insects of Britain and Northern Europe*, second edition, Collins

The blowfly and the estimation of time of death

A forensic entomologist, using larvae (or eggs) of a common blowfly collected from a human corpse about which little is initially known, is often able to make estimations of time of death. The common blowfly, *Calliphora vicina* is one such insect. The life cycle of this blowfly (a 'bluebottle') is illustrated in Figure 6.35.

Examine this life cycle diagram, now.

Figure 6.35 The life cycle of *Calliphora vicina*.

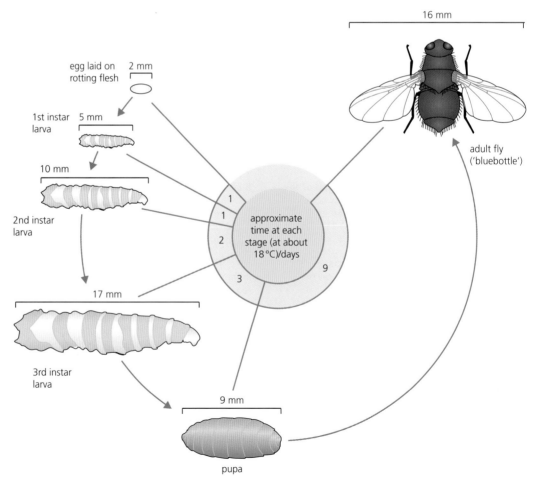

The insects are members of the phylum Arthropoda. All arthropods have a hard external skeleton, made of chitin which, while providing some protection to the body, also interferes with their growth. As a result, the larval stages in the life cycle (known as instars), which occur between an egg and the adult, must 'moult' periodically during growth. At each moult, the larva throws off its old cuticle and grows a new, enlarged one. In *Calliphora* there are three larval stages (maggots). Note also that at the end of the larval stage, this insect pupates and then undergoes complete and fairly lengthy metamorphosis (an abrupt transition in body form) to produce the adult fly.

■ Extension: Insect life cycles

Butterflies are also insects that show a life cycle with complete metamorphosis. Here the larva, a caterpillar, lives in a different environment and, incidentally, also has a different diet from the adult. However, not all insects have an abrupt metamorphosis in their life cycle, as illustrated by butterflies and blowflies. In some species, there is a gradual transition from the earliest larval stage (in the form of a miniature adult) through several instars, to the adult. The locust is an example of this.

We can now show how studies in growth of eggs and larvae of *Calliphora vicina* may be used by the forensic entomologist to make estimates of time of death.

1 Temperature, egg development and time of death

In the life cycle diagram (Figure 6.35), the egg of *Calliphora* is shown completing development into the first instar in one day, at an ambient temperature of about 18 °C. In fact, this stage of growth is highly temperature sensitive, as shown in Figure 6.36.

Look at this graph now. How might this data be used in a forensic investigation?

Figure 6.36 The effect of temperature on egg development in *Calliphora vicina*.

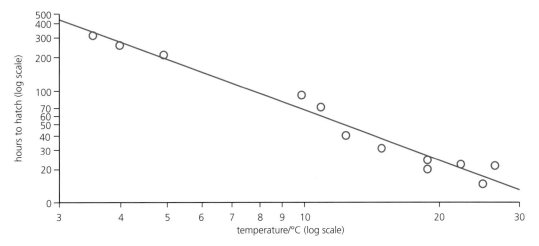

Suppose several eggs of *Calliphora vicina* are obtained from a corpse in the earliest stage of decomposition, and that the temperature of the corpse was found to be at an ambient temperature of 10 °C. The forensic entomologist would then culture this sample of eggs under laboratory conditions, but *at the same temperature*, in order to:

■ confirm that they are eggs of this species of *Calliphora*
■ determine how many further hours elapse before they hatch into the first instar larvae.

If, for example, the eggs hatched after 20 hours further incubation at 10 °C, then the entomologist would conclude (from the graph in Figure 6.36) they were laid by flies approximately 65 minus 20 hours (that is, 45 hours) before the time the sample was harvested. This time can be expected to be close to the point of death of the victim.

22 A sample of eggs of *Calliphora vicina*, collected from a corpse at 5 °C and then cultured at that temperature, hatched in 100 hours. How many hours earlier is it likely they were laid?

2 Temperature, larval and pupal development and time of death

It is also possible to estimate time of death as a result of length measurements of larvae or pupae taken from a corpse that has remained under *fairly constant temperature conditions*. This is possible as a result of an extensive laboratory investigation of maggots of *Calliphora vicina* of a range of lengths, when grown at different temperatures. The results of this study are recorded in Figure 6.37. Note that after the dotted line labelled P, the data relates to lengths of pupae.

Look at this graph now. How might this data be used in a forensic investigation?

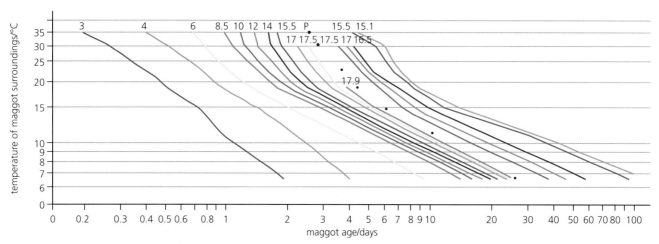

Figure 6.37 The effect of temperature on larval and pupal development in *Calliphora vicina*.

Activity 6.19:
Resources for forensic entomology

Suppose larvae of *Calliphora vicina* of length 6 mm were obtained from a corpse, and that the temperature of the corpse was found to be 20 °C (and believed to have been fairly constant). Looking at the graph in Figure 6.37 (where you find 'temperature' on the y-axis), then for a larva of length 6 mm incubated at 20 °C, we can see from the x-axis that it was approximately 1 day and 6 hours ago that they hatched from eggs.

23 Samples of pupae of *Calliphora vicina* of length 17.5 mm were collected from a corpse at 15 °C. Approximately how many days had elapsed since the larvae from which these pupae were formed hatched from eggs?

End-of-topic test

An end-of-topic test is provided as part of the accompanying *Edexcel Biology for A2* Dynamic Learning resources, with (separate) answers.

Sample assessment material produced by Edexcel is available via the Edexcel web site: www.edexcel.org.uk.

STARTING POINTS

- Movement is a characteristic of living things. It occurs within cells (for example, cytoplasmic streaming), within organisms (for example, the pumping action of the heart), and as the movements of whole organisms, known as locomotion. The issue of muscular locomotion in humans is examined here.
- Energy is transferred in cells by cell respiration. ATP, the universal energy currency, is a reactant in energy-requiring reactions and processes.
- Living things face changing environments, which may determine where they occur, but some animals are able to keep their internal conditions largely unchanged despite conditions around them. These organisms are 'regulators' – they maintain their internal environment in a steady state by a process called homeostasis.
- In the contexts of training and fitness, developments in medical technologies underpin improvement in sporting performance and the maintenance of the body in healthy exercise.

7.1 Support, movement and locomotion

Living things maintain their characteristic shape, and support their bodies in positions favourable for all the essential processes of life. For example, in green plants, leaves are held aloft in the light, whereas in most animals, support systems are adapted to allow locomotion. Locomotion is a characteristic of animals – for many, survival may depend on their ability to move, and move speedily, too, at times.

While organisms maintain themselves, mechanical forces act on them, generating stress (Figure 7.1). In particular, **stress** comes from:

- supporting the weight of the body – this is much greater on land than in water, which, by comparison, is a very supportive medium
- resisting environmental forces, such as the wind, or the waves and currents in water
- forces generated by movements of the body.

Figure 7.1 Mechanical stress the body needs to resist.

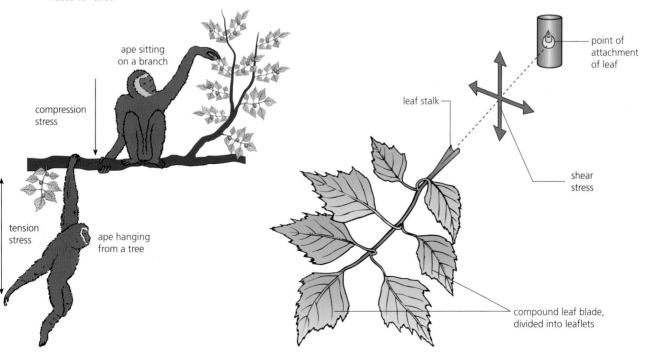

Stress forces take three forms:

- **compression** – when parts are pushed together
- **tension** – when parts are pulled apart
- **shear** – when parts tend to slide past each other.

The bodies of living things have to resist these stresses, using strengthening materials in ways that will not interfere with the body's activities. As animals and plants increase in size, their need for support increases.

Skeletons and movement

The support systems of animals are skeletons. The skeletons of many animals (but not all) are quite rigid structures. For example, mammals and other vertebrates have an internal skeleton (an **endoskeleton**) of many component parts, mostly made of bone. The arrangement of bones of the human skeleton is shown in Figure 7.2.

Figure 7.2 Muscles operate in antagonistic pairs.

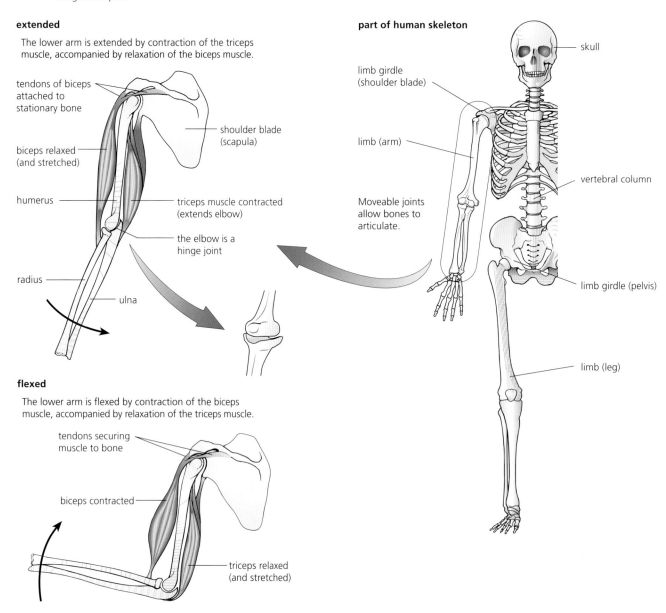

extended

The lower arm is extended by contraction of the triceps muscle, accompanied by relaxation of the biceps muscle.

tendons of biceps attached to stationary bone

biceps relaxed (and stretched)

shoulder blade (scapula)

humerus

triceps muscle contracted (extends elbow)

the elbow is a hinge joint

radius

ulna

flexed

The lower arm is flexed by contraction of the biceps muscle, accompanied by relaxation of the triceps muscle.

tendons securing muscle to bone

biceps contracted

triceps relaxed (and stretched)

part of human skeleton

skull

limb girdle (shoulder blade)

limb (arm)

Moveable joints allow bones to articulate.

vertebral column

limb girdle (pelvis)

limb (leg)

Attached to bones are muscles, and between the bones are joints. Muscles, bones and movable joints combine as a system of levers. This system allows an animal to push parts of the body against external surfaces (the ground, water or the air). These act as a resistance force to propel the animal's body forward and bring about locomotion.

Within the body itself, locomotion is the result of the interactions of the nervous, muscular and skeletal systems. The component parts and their roles in locomotion are as follows.

- **Bones** support and partially protect the body parts. Also, they articulate with other bones at joints, and they provide anchorage for the muscles. The human skeleton consists of the axial skeleton (skull and vertebral column) and the appendicular skeleton (limb girdles and limbs). In the study of locomotion, we are more concerned with the latter.
- **Ligaments** hold bones together, and form protective capsules around the movable joints. Ligaments are made of fibres of strong but very slightly elastic connective tissue.
- **Muscles** cause movements by contraction. Skeletal muscle is one of three types of muscle in the mammal's body. Skeletal muscles occur in pairs, anchored to bones across joints. They are arranged so that when one contracts, the other is stretched – a system known as **antagonistic pairs**. Contractions of skeletal muscle either merely maintain the posture and position of the body, or they go on to bring about movement at joints.
- **Tendons** attach muscles to bones at their points of anchorage. They are made of cords of dense connective tissue.

A* Extension 7.1:
Types of skeleton

An additional vital component is the **nerves**. These are bundles of many nerve fibres of individual nerve cells. They connect the central nervous system (brain and spinal cord) with other parts of the body, including the skeletal muscle. The structure and functioning of the nervous system is introduced and discussed in Chapter 8 (page 139). Here we shall review how the skeleton and muscles interact to enable movement at joints.

■ Extension: Types of movement

For the majority of animals that are on the move, there are just three basic mechanisms of locomotion available to them in the living world:
- amoeboid movement is seen in some unicellular organisms such as *Amoeba* and in white cells
- movement by cilia and flagella – whip-like organelles that project from the surface of certain cells
- muscular locomotion, such as that of vertebrates (for example, humans), which is examined in this chapter.

Movement at joints

Movable joints in the body are of different types, but they all permit controlled movements, and are all examples of **synovial joints** because a thick viscous fluid, the synovial fluid, is secreted and retained in the joint, to help lubricate it.

Look at the hip and knee joints (Figure 7.3, overleaf) and the movement they permit.

You will have already noticed that we have contrasting degrees of movement possible at our knees and hips (and at shoulder and elbow). This is because of a fundamental difference in the types of joint involved.

Ball-and-socket joint

At the hip, is a ball-and-socket joint. In this type of joint, the ball-like surface of one bone (here it is the femur of the upper leg) fits into a cup-like depression on another bone (here it is a socket called the acetabulum on the pelvic girdle, which we call the 'hip bone'). A ball-and-socket joint permits movements in all three planes, a type of movement described as **circumduction**.

Figure 7.3 Movement at hip and knee joints.

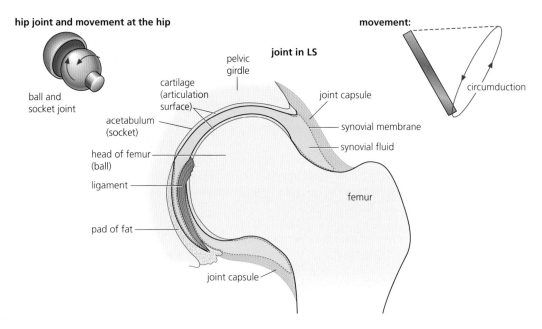

hip joint and movement at the hip

ball and socket joint

joint in LS

pelvic girdle

cartilage (articulation surface)

acetabulum (socket)

head of femur (ball)

ligament

pad of fat

joint capsule

joint capsule

synovial membrane

synovial fluid

femur

movement:

circumduction

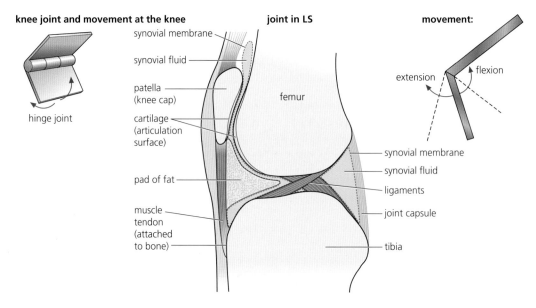

knee joint and movement at the knee

hinge joint

joint in LS

synovial membrane

synovial fluid

patella (knee cap)

cartilage (articulation surface)

pad of fat

muscle tendon (attached to bone)

femur

synovial membrane

synovial fluid

ligaments

joint capsule

tibia

movement:

extension

flexion

Activity 7.1: Joints and the muscles that move them – a check on understanding

A* Extension 7.2: Other movable joints

1 What functions does the skeleton of a mammal have?

Hinge joint

At the knee is a hinge joint. Here, movement is restricted to one plane. This is because of the shape of the articulating surfaces and due to the ligaments that hold the bones together. Movements at the knee are described as flexions and extensions.

Skeletal muscle structure

We have seen that muscles that cause locomotion are attached to the movable parts of skeletons, and so they are known as **skeletal muscles**. Skeletal muscles are attached by **tendons** and work in antagonistic pairs, as illustrated in Figure 7.2.

Skeletal muscle consists of bundles of muscle fibres (Figure 7.4). A **muscle fibre** is a long, multinucleate cell. The remarkable feature of a muscle fibre is its ability to shorten to half or even a third of the relaxed or 'resting' length. Fibres appear striped under the light microscope, and so skeletal muscle is also known as striped or striated muscle. Actually, each fibre is itself composed of a mass of myofibrils, but we need the electron microscope to see this.

skeletal muscle cut to show bundles of fibres

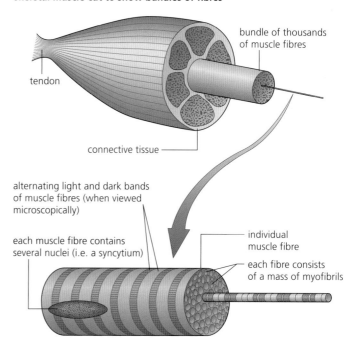

bundle of thousands
of muscle fibres

tendon

connective tissue

photomicrograph of LS skeletal muscle fibres, HP (×1500)

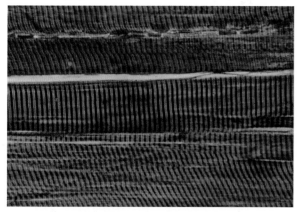

alternating light and dark bands
of muscle fibres (when viewed
microscopically)

each muscle fibre contains
several nuclei (i.e. a syncytium)

individual
muscle fibre

each fibre consists
of a mass of myofibrils

Figure 7.4 The structure of skeletal muscle.

The ultrastructure of muscle fibres

By use of the electron microscope, we can see that each muscle fibre consists of very many, parallel **myofibrils** within a plasma membrane known as the **sarcolemma**, together with cytoplasm. The cytoplasm contains mitochondria packed between the myofibrils, and the sarcolemma infolds to form a system of transverse tubular endoplasmic reticulum, known as **sarcoplasmic reticulum**, This is arranged as a network around individual myofibrils. The arrangements of myofibrils, sarcolemma and mitochondria, surrounded by the sarcoplasmic membrane, are shown in Figure 7.5.

Figure 7.5 The ultrastructure of a muscle fibre.

stereogram of part of a single muscle fibre

electron micrograph of TS through part of a skeletal muscle fibre, HP (×36 000)

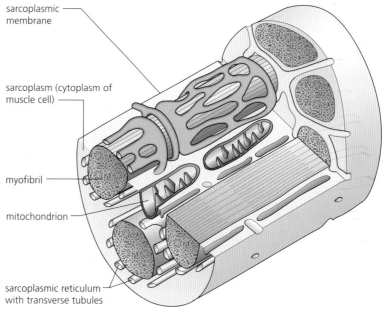

sarcoplasmic
membrane

sarcoplasm (cytoplasm of
muscle cell)

myofibril

mitochondrion

sarcoplasmic reticulum
with transverse tubules

The 'striped' appearance of skeletal muscle is due to an interlocking arrangement of two types of protein filament, known respectively as 'thick' and 'thin' filaments, that make up the myofibrils. These protein filaments are aligned, giving the appearance of stripes. This is shown in the more highly magnified electron micrograph and interpretive drawing in Figure 7.6.

The **thick filaments** are made of the particular protein called **myosin**. They are about 15 nm in diameter, and short in length by comparison with the thin filaments. The longer **thin filaments** are made of another protein, **actin**. Thin filaments are about 7 nm in diameter, and are held together by transverse bands. Each repeating unit of the myofibril is, for convenience of description, referred to as a **sarcomere**. So we can think of a myofibril as consisting of a series of sarcomeres attached end to end.

2 Explain the relationship to a muscle of:
   a a muscle fibre
   b a myofibril
   c a myosin filament.

Figure 7.6 The ultrastructure of a myofibril.

electron micrograph of LS through part of a skeletal muscle fibre, HP (×36 000)

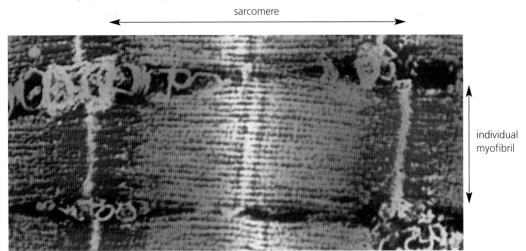

interpretive drawing of the thick filaments (myosin) and thin filaments (actin)

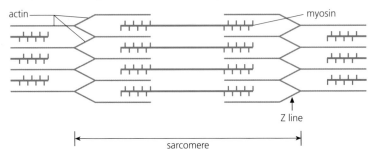

Skeletal muscle contracts by sliding of the filaments

Thick filaments lie in the central part of each sarcomere, sandwiched between thin filaments. When skeletal muscle contracts, the actin and myosin filaments slide past each other, in response to nervous stimulation, causing shortening of the sarcomeres. This occurs in a series of steps, sometimes described as a 'ratchet mechanism'. A great deal of ATP is used in the contraction process.

Shortening is possible because the thick filaments are composed of many myosin molecules, each with a bulbous 'head'. These heads protrude from the length of the myosin filament. Along the actin filament are a complementary series of binding sites to which the bulbous heads fit. However, in muscle fibres at rest, the binding sites carry blocking molecules (a protein called **tropomyosin**), so binding and contraction are not possible. The contraction of a sarcomere is best described in the following four steps.

First, the myofibril is stimulated to contract by the arrival of an **action potential**. This triggers release of calcium ions from the sarcoplasmic reticulum, around the actin molecules. Calcium ions now react with an additional protein present (**troponin**) which, when so activated, triggers the removal of the blocking molecule, tropomyosin. The binding sites are now exposed.

1 Each bulbous head to which ADP and P_i are attached (called a 'charged' bulbous head) reacts with a binding site on the actin molecule beside it and sheds the phosphate group (P_i).

2 Then the ADP molecule is released from the bulbous head, and this is the trigger for the 'rowing' movement of the head, which tilts by an angle of about 45°, pushing the actin filament along. At this step, called the **power stroke**, the myofibril has been shortened (contraction has occurred).

3 A fresh molecule of ATP binds to the bulbous head. The protein of the bulbous head includes the enzyme ATPase, which catalyses the hydrolysis of ATP. When this reaction occurs, the ADP and inorganic phosphate (P_i) formed remain attached, and the bulbous head is now 'charged' again. The charged head detaches from the binding site and straightens.

4 The cycle is repeated at binding sites further along the actin molecule, as calcium ions released from the sarcoplasmic reticulum cause troponin to remove the blocking molecule, tropomyosin.

Activity 7.2: Muscle contraction simulation

A* Extension 7.3: Other muscle fibres

Contracted and relaxed sarcomeres are shown in Figure 7.7. The cycle of movements is shown is Figure 7.8, overleaf, and is repeated many times per second, with thousands of bulbous heads working along each myofibril. ATP is rapidly used up, and the muscle may shorten by about 50% of its relaxed length.

change in a single sarcomere in relaxed and contracted myofibril

Muscles contract as the actin and myosin filaments slide between each other, shortening each sarcomere.

relaxed

thin filament = actin   thick filament = myosin

contracted

electron micrographs of muscle fibres, relaxed (left) and contracted (right)

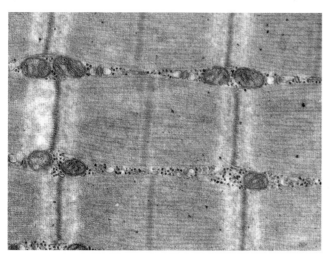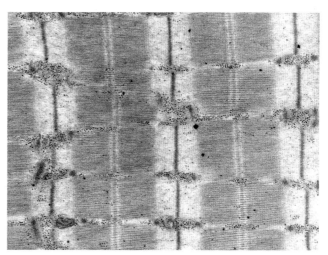

Figure 7.7 Muscle contraction of a single sarcomere.

Speed, stamina and muscle fibre composition

The basic structures of skeletal muscle and of the fibres that compose the muscle blocks that occur, surrounded by connective tissue, are illustrated in Figures 7.4 and 7.5. However, although all skeletal muscle fibres may appear the same on initial examination, in fact two distinct types exist in humans. These go by the rather intriguing names of 'fast-twitch' and 'slow-twitch' fibres. Their differences lie in their physiological properties, and these we will discuss next.

Fast-twitch muscle fibres are able to generate high force for a short time. The fibres contract rapidly, which is made possible by the high concentration of ATPase enzyme (observed by staining – Figure 7.9, page 107) among the cross-bridges of the myosin filaments.

Arrival of action potential at myofibril releases Ca^{2+} ions from sarcoplasmic reticulum.

Ca^{2+} ions react with a protein (troponin), activating it. Activated troponin reacts with tropomyosin at the binding sites on the actin molecules, thereby exposing the binding sites.

Each myosin molecule has a 'head' that reacts with ATP → P_i which remain bound.

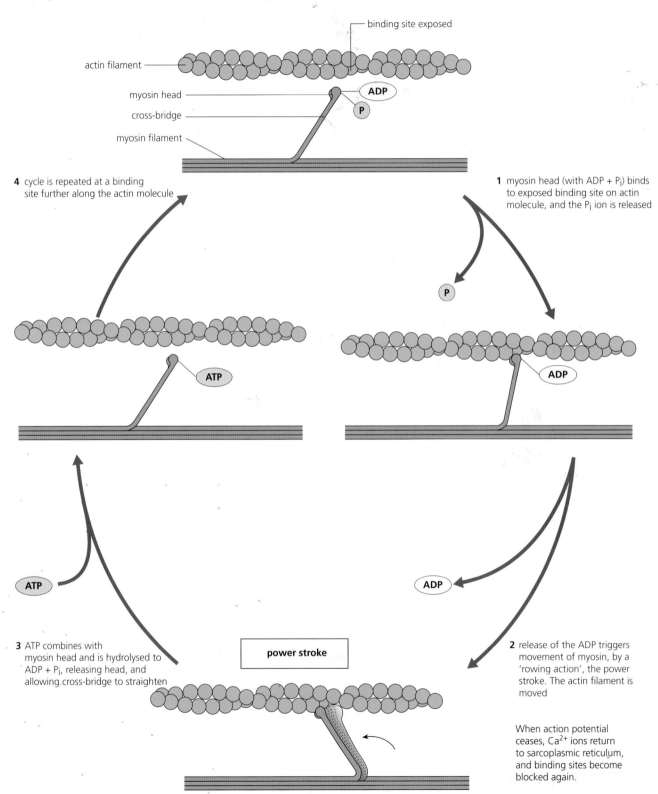

binding site exposed

actin filament

myosin head

ADP

cross-bridge

P

myosin filament

4 cycle is repeated at a binding site further along the actin molecule

1 myosin head (with ADP + P_i) binds to exposed binding site on actin molecule, and the P_i ion is released

P

ATP

ADP

ATP

ADP

3 ATP combines with myosin head and is hydrolysed to ADP + P_i, releasing head, and allowing cross-bridge to straighten

power stroke

2 release of the ADP triggers movement of myosin, by a 'rowing action', the power stroke. The actin filament is moved

When action potential ceases, Ca^{2+} ions return to sarcoplasmic reticulum, and binding sites become blocked again.

Figure 7.8 The sliding-filament hypothesis of muscle contraction.

Figure 7.9 Muscle fibres in cross-section, stained for the presence of ATPase activity.

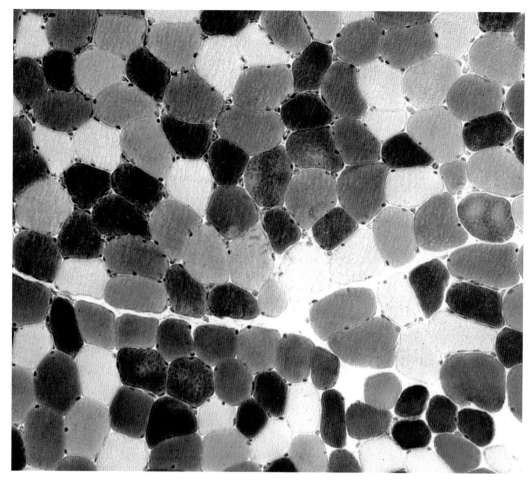

This photomicrograph shows **muscle tissue from a marathon runner.** Here there is a predominance of slow-twitch fibres (stained lightly). On the other hand, **muscle tissue from a sprint runner**, for example, would have a marked predominance of fast-twitch fibres (stained darkly).

Fast-twitch fibres rely on the glycolysis/lactate energy system, which we describe as the anaerobic energy source (page 115). This is a short-term supply route for ATP, but it is easily exhausted. Fast-twitch fibres are served by relatively few capillaries, they contain relatively few mitochondria, and very little myoglobin as well (so they are pale in appearance). However, the fibres have sarcoplasmic reticulum that is adapted for both rapid release and uptake of calcium ions, and this, too, contributes to their being able to contract rapidly (Figure 7.10).

On the other hand, **slow-twitch muscle fibres** achieve less force but sustain contraction for a longer time. The fibres have a relatively low concentration of ATPase enzyme among their myosin filaments.

Slow-twitch fibres have a high concentration of **myoglobin** (the oxygen reserve pigment found in muscles, which gives these fibres a dark red colour), plus many mitochondria, and a high concentration of the mitochondrial enzymes needed to sustain aerobic respiration. They rely little on the glycolysis/lactate pathway. Their sarcoplasmic reticulum has slow calcium-ion-shunting qualities when compared to that in fast-twitch fibres, and this, too, contributes to their slow shortening characteristics (Figure 7.10). Slow-twitch fibres are richly served by blood capillaries.

Finally, we should also note that skeletal muscles of the human limbs typically consist of about 45–55% of slow-twitch muscle fibres. However, the precise proportions of fast- and slow-twitch muscle fibres an individual has in the muscles of their arms and legs is apparently genetically determined. People have different proportions of the two. We might say that some of us are born for the marathon, some for a sprint, and some for activities requiring a balance of both (Table 7.1, overleaf).

Figure 7.10 Muscle fibres response profiles.

fast-twitch muscle fibre

slow-twitch muscle fibre

force

time

Table 7.1 Characteristics of the contrasting muscle-fibre types – a summary.

Fast-twitch fibres	Quality	Slow-twitch fibres
contract quickly, with fast release and removal of Ca^{2+} ions by sarcoplasmic reticulum	**speed of contraction**	contract slowly, with slow release and removal of Ca^{2+} ions by sarcoplasmic reticulum
glycolysis/lactate pathway predominates	**energy source**	aerobic respiration pathway, sited in the many mitochondria
little dependence on oxygen for fast contraction – little myoglobin present (light in colour)	**dependence on oxygen supply**	highly dependent on oxygen – well endowed with myoglobin oxygen store (so red in colour)
can contract with great force, but power quickly exhausted	**power and duration of contraction**	can contract repeatedly but with limited power
sprint runners typically have 80% of these fibres in some skeletal muscles	**occurrence**	marathon runners typically have 80% of these fibres in some skeletal muscles

Both fibre types occur in equal quantities in able middle-distance runners, swimmers and footballers, for example. These activities combine demands for both muscle responses and so depend on both aerobic and anaerobic energy transfer during performance.

3 The domesticated hen walks about, scratching the ground with its feet in search of food, all day. If 'alarmed' it may fly up to a safe roost, but it cannot sustain flight. What type of muscle fibres do you think make up:
  a the hen's leg muscles ('drumsticks')
  b the flight muscles ('chicken breast meat')?

Activity 7.3: Analysing states of contraction in skeletal muscle fibres

Activity 7.4: Walking simulation

Activity 7.5: Test yourself on muscle fibres – structure and physiology

Muscles, controlled movements, and posture

Muscles are involved in maintaining body posture and in subtle, delicate movements, as well as in vigorous or even violent actions, sometimes. Consequently, nervous control of muscle contraction may cause relaxed muscle to contract slightly, moderately or fully, on occasions. Activity 7.4 is concerned with the appearance of skeletal muscle fibres in all of these conditions. (Incidentally, the way a nerve cell makes 'contact' with a muscle fibre is shown in A* Extension 8.2, page 147.)

7.2 Energy transfer

The next issue to consider is how energy is made available for activities such as muscle contraction. Organisms require energy to maintain all living cells and to carry out their activities and functions. Respiration is the process by which that energy is transferred in usable form. Cellular respiration that involves oxygen is described as aerobic respiration. Most animals and plants and very many micro-organisms respire aerobically, most, if not all, the time.

Aerobic respiration

In **aerobic respiration**, sugar is oxidised to carbon dioxide and water and much energy is made available. The steps involved in aerobic respiration can be summarised by a single equation. Note that this equation is equivalent to a balance sheet of inputs (the raw materials) and outputs (the products), but it tells us nothing about the steps.

glucose + oxygen → carbon dioxide + water + energy

$$C_6H_{12}O_6 + 6O_2 →   6CO_2   + 6H_2O + energy$$

Sometimes aerobic respiration is compared to combustion – for example, people may talk about 'burning up food' in respiration. In fact this comparison is unhelpful. In combustion, the energy in fuel is released in a one-step reaction, as heat. Such a violent change would be disastrous for body tissues. In cellular respiration, a very large number of small steps occur, each catalysed by a specific enzyme (Figure 7.11). Because energy in respiration is transferred in small quantities, much of the energy is made available, and may be trapped in the energy currency molecule, ATP. However, some energy is still lost as heat in each step.

Figure 7.11 Combustion and respiration compared. (For more about respiration as a series of 'redox' reactions, see *Background Chemistry for Biologists,* in the Dynamic Learning resources.)

glucose burning in air

athlete clearing a hurdle

energy change in burning

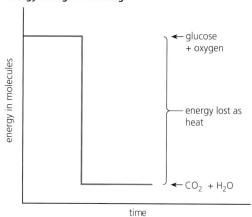

←glucose + oxygen

energy lost as heat

←CO_2 + H_2O

energy in molecules

time

energy change in cellular respiration

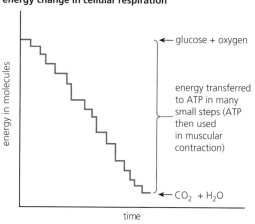

←glucose + oxygen

energy transferred to ATP in many small steps (ATP then used in muscular contraction)

←CO_2 + H_2O

energy in molecules

time

ATP – the universal energy currency

Energy made available within the cytoplasm (which comprises both the fluid part – the cytosol – and the organelles) is transferred to a molecule called adenosine triphosphate (ATP). This molecule is referred to as 'energy currency', because like money it is constantly recycled (Figure 7.12). ATP as the universal energy currency was discussed in Chapter 5 (page 6). *Refresh your memory of the structure, roles and importance of this nucleotide now.* You can check your understanding in Activity 7.6.

Activity 7.6: Understanding ATP, structure and importance

Figure 7.12 The ADP → ADP + P_i cycle.

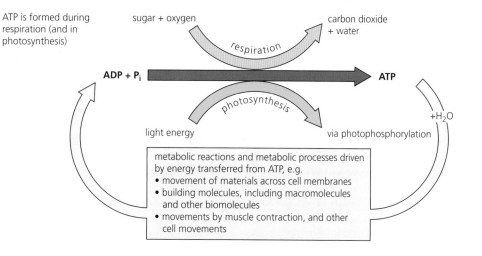

ATP is formed during respiration (and in photosynthesis)

sugar + oxygen

carbon dioxide + water

respiration

ADP + P_i

ATP

photosynthesis

light energy

via photophosphorylation

+H_2O

metabolic reactions and metabolic processes driven by energy transferred from ATP, e.g.
• movement of materials across cell membranes
• building molecules, including macromolecules and other biomolecules
• movements by muscle contraction, and other cell movements

The steps involved in aerobic cell respiration

The overall outcome of aerobic respiration is that the respiratory substrate, glucose, is broken down to release carbon dioxide, and the hydrogen of glucose is combined with atmospheric oxygen, with the transfer of a large amount of energy. Much of the energy transferred is lost in the form of heat energy, but cells are able to retain significant amounts of chemical energy in ATP.

How is energy transferred from respiratory substrates like glucose?

During aerobic cellular respiration, glucose undergoes a series of enzyme-catalysed oxidation reactions. These reactions are grouped into three major phases (Figure 7.13):

1   **glycolysis**, in which glucose is converted to pyruvate
2   the **Krebs cycle**, in which pyruvate is converted to carbon dioxide
3   the **electron-transport system**, in which hydrogen removed in the oxidation reactions of glycolysis and the Krebs cycle, is converted to water, and the bulk of the ATP is synthesised.

Figure 7.13 The three phases of aerobic cell respiration.

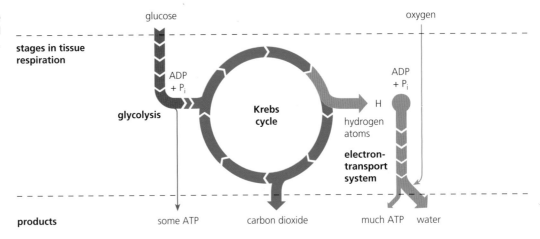

1 Glycolysis

Glycolysis is a linear series of reactions in which six-carbon sugar is broken down to two molecules of the three-carbon pyruvate ion. The enzymes of glycolysis are located in the cytosol (that is, the cytoplasm outside the organelles) – rather than in the mitochondria. Glycolysis occurs in four stages.

■   **Phosphorylation** by reactions with ATP is the way glucose is first activated, eventually forming a six-carbon sugar with two phosphate groups attached (called fructose bisphosphate). Two molecules of ATP are *consumed* per molecule of glucose respired, at this stage of glycolysis.

■   **Lysis** (splitting) of the fructose bisphosphate now takes place, forming two molecules of three-carbon sugar (called triose phosphate).

■   **Oxidation** of the three-carbon sugar molecules occurs by removal of hydrogen. The enzyme for this reaction (a dehydrogenase) works with a coenzyme, nicotinamide adenine dinucleotide (NAD^+). NAD^+ is a molecule that can accept hydrogen ions (H^+) and electrons (e^-). In this reaction, the NAD is reduced to NADH and H^+ (reduced NAD):

$$NAD^+ + 2H^+ + 2e^- \rightarrow NADH + H^+ \text{ (sometimes represented as } NADH_2)$$

(Reduced NAD can pass hydrogen ions and electrons on to other acceptor molecules – as described below – and when it does, it becomes oxidised back to NAD.)

■   **ATP formation** occurs twice in the reactions by which each triose phosphate molecule is converted to pyruvate. This form of ATP synthesis is referred to as being 'at substrate level' in order to differentiate it from the bulk of ATP synthesis that occurs later in cell respiration, during operation of the electron transport chain (see below). As two molecules of triose phosphate are converted to pyruvate, four molecules of ATP are *synthesised* at this stage of glycolysis. So in total, there is a *net gain* of two ATPs in glycolysis (Figure 7.14).

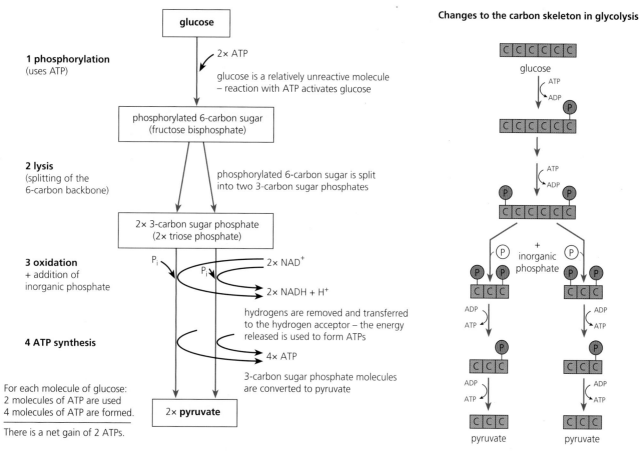

Changes to the carbon skeleton in glycolysis

Figure 7.14 Glycolysis: a summary.

4 Which of the following are produced during glycolysis?
  a CO_2
  d glycogen
  g pyruvate
  b lactate
  e ATP
  h glucose
  c NADH
  f NAD^+

2 The link reaction and the Krebs cycle

The subsequent steps in aerobic respiration occur in the organelles known as mitochondria.
Remind yourself of the structure of the mitochondrion now (Biology for AS, page 101).

In the **link reaction**, pyruvate diffuses into the matrix of the mitochondrion as it forms, and is metabolised there. First, the three-carbon pyruvate is decarboxylated by removal of carbon dioxide and, at the same time, oxidised by removal of hydrogen. Reduced NAD is formed. The product of this oxidative decarboxylation reaction is an acetyl group – a two-carbon fragment. This acetyl group is then combined with a coenzyme called **coenzyme A**, forming acetyl coenzyme A.

The production of acetyl coenzyme A from pyruvate is known as the link reaction because it connects glycolysis to reactions of the Krebs cycle, details of which now follow.

$$\text{pyruvate} \xrightarrow[\text{coenzyme A (CoA)}]{\text{NAD}^+ \quad \text{NADH} + \text{H}^+ \quad CO_2} \text{acetyl CoA}$$

In the **Krebs cycle**, acetyl coenzyme A reacts with a four-carbon organic acid (oxaloacetate, OAA). The products of this reaction are a six-carbon acid (citrate) and, of course, coenzyme A. This latter, on release, is re-used in the link reaction.

The Krebs cycle is named after Hans Krebs who discovered it, but it is also sometimes referred to as the **citric acid cycle**, after the first intermediate acid formed.

5 Outline the types of
reaction catalysed by:
a dehydrogenases
b decarboxylases.

DL
www
A* Extension 7.4: The
mitochondrion and the
steps of the Krebs cycle

HSW 7.1: Criteria 1 and
7 – Hans Krebs: science,
an international
phenomenon

Then the citrate is converted back to the four-carbon acid (an acceptor molecule, in effect) by the reactions of the Krebs cycle. These involve the following changes:

- two molecules of carbon dioxide are given off, in separate decarboxylation reactions
- a molecule of ATP is formed, as part 1 of the reactions of the cycle – as with glycolysis, this ATP synthesis is 'at substrate level' too
- three molecules of reduced NAD are formed
- one molecule of another hydrogen acceptor – FAD (flavin adenine dinucleotide) is reduced (NAD is the chief hydrogen-carrying coenzyme of respiration but FAD is another coenzyme with this role in the Krebs cycle).

Because glucose is converted to two molecules of pyruvate in glycolysis, the whole Krebs cycle sequence of reactions 'turns' twice for every molecule of glucose that is metabolised by aerobic cellular respiration (Figure 7.15).

Figure 7.15 The Krebs
cycle in summary.

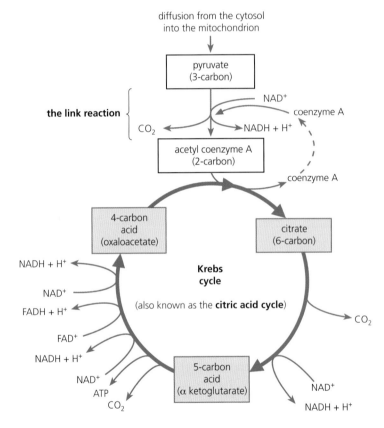

There are several other organic acid intermediates in the cycle not shown here.

Now we are in a position to summarise the changes to each molecule of glucose that occurr in the reactions of glycolysis and the Krebs cycle. A 'budget' of the products of glycolysis and two turns of the Krebs cycle is shown in Table 7.2.

Table 7.2 Net products
of aerobic respiration of
glucose at the end of the
Krebs cycle.

Step	Product			
	CO_2	ATP	reduced NAD	reduced FAD
glycolysis	0	2	2	0
link reaction (pyruvate → acetyl CoA)	2	0	2	0
Krebs cycle	4	2	6	2
Totals	**6**	**4**	**10**	**2**

■ Extension: Fats can be respired too

In addition to glucose, fats (lipids) are also commonly used as respiratory substrates – first being broken down to fatty acids (and glycerol). Fatty acid is 'cut up' into two-carbon fragments and fed into the Krebs cycle via coenzyme A. Vertebrate muscle is well adapted to the respiration of fatty acids in this way (as is our heart muscle), and they are just as likely as glucose to be the respiratory substrate.

3 Terminal oxidation and oxidative phosphorylation

The removal of pairs of hydrogen atoms from various intermediates of the respiratory pathway is a feature of several of the steps in glycolysis and the Krebs cycle. On most occasions, oxidised NAD is converted to reduced NAD, but in the Krebs cycle it is an alternative hydrogen-acceptor coenzyme known as FAD that is reduced.

Now, in this final stage of aerobic respiration, the hydrogen atoms (or their electrons) are transported along a series of carriers, from the reduced NAD (or FAD), to be combined with oxygen to form water.

As electrons are passed between the carriers in the series, energy is transferred. Transfer of energy in this manner is controlled and can be used by the cell. The energy is transferred to ADP and P_i, forming ATP. Normally, for every molecule of reduced NAD that is oxidised (that is, for every pair of hydrogens) approximately three molecules of ATP are produced.

The process is summarised in Figure 7.16. The total yield from aerobic respiration is about 38 ATPs per molecule of glucose respired.

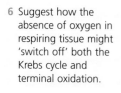

6 Suggest how the absence of oxygen in respiring tissue might 'switch off' both the Krebs cycle and terminal oxidation.

Figure 7.16 Terminal oxidation and the formation of ATPs.

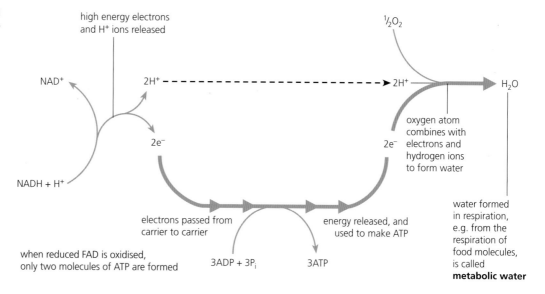

Phosphorylation by chemiosmosis?

You may remember that the 'chemiosmotic theory' grew out of studies of bacterial metabolism carried out by biochemist Peter Mitchell, over 50 years ago. For this discovery, he was eventually awarded a Nobel Prize. Specific HSW issues are raised by the story of this discovery, and these were introduced in HSW 5.1, page 7, together with important questions for discussion. Here we need to remind ourselves of the key features of this mechanism of ATP synthesis.

Chemiosmosis is a process by which the synthesis of ATP is coupled to electron transport via the movement of protons (Figure 7.17). Electron-carrier proteins are arranged in the inner mitochondrial membrane in a highly ordered way. These carrier proteins oxidise the reduced coenzymes, and energy from this process is used to pump hydrogen ions (protons) from the matrix of the mitochondrion into the space between inner and outer mitochondrial membranes.

Figure 7.17 Mitchell's chemiosmotic theory.

stereogram of a mitochondrion, cut open to show the inner membrane and cristae

Activity 7.7:
Mitochondrial structure in relation to functions – an enquiry

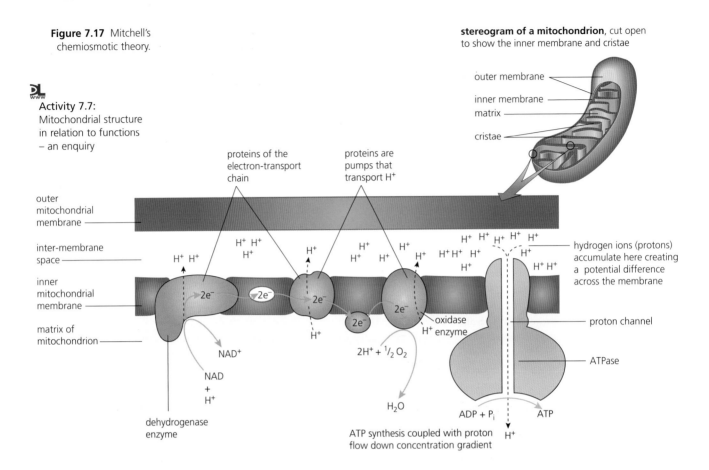

7 When ATP is synthesised in mitochondria, explain where the electrochemical gradient is set up, and in which direction protons move.

Here the H^+ ions accumulate – incidentally, causing the pH to drop. Because the inner membrane is largely impermeable to ions, a significant gradient in hydrogen ion concentration builds up, generating a potential difference across the inner membrane – a store of potential energy.

Eventually, the protons do flow back into the matrix, via channels in ATP synthetase enzymes, also found in the inner mitochondrial membrane. As the protons flow down their concentration gradient through the enzyme, the energy is transferred and ATP synthesis occurs.

■ Extension: Respiration as a source of intermediates

We have seen that the main role of respiration is to provide a pool of ATP, and that this is used to drive the endergonic reactions of synthesis. But the compounds of the glycolysis pathway and the Krebs cycle (respiratory intermediates) may also serve as the starting points of synthesis of other metabolites needed in the cells and tissues of the organism. These include polysaccharides like starch and cellulose, glycerol and fatty acids, amino acids, and many others.

8 Distinguish between the following pairs:
  a substrate and intermediate
  b glycolysis and the Krebs cycle
  c oxidation and reduction.

Investigating respiration

The rate of respiration of an organism is an indication of its demand for energy. Respiration rate, the uptake of oxygen per unit time, is measured by means of a respirometer. A respirometer is a form of manometer, because it detects change in pressure or volume of a gas. Respiration rates are investigated by manometry.

A simple respirometer is shown in Figure 7.18. Respiration by an organism trapped in the chamber alters the composition of the gas there, once the screw clip has been closed. Soda lime, enclosed in the chamber, removes carbon dioxide gas as it is released by the respiring organism. Consequently, only oxygen uptake causes a change in volume. The bubble of coloured liquid in the attached capillary tube, will move in response. The change in the volume of the apparatus, due to oxygen uptake, can be estimated from measurements of the moment of the manometric fluid during the experiment.

Figure 7.18 A simple respirometer.

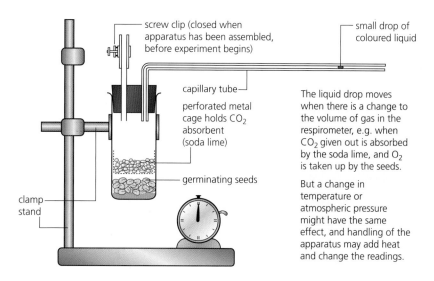

screw clip (closed when apparatus has been assembled, before experiment begins)

small drop of coloured liquid

capillary tube

perforated metal cage holds CO_2 absorbent (soda lime)

The liquid drop moves when there is a change to the volume of gas in the respirometer, e.g. when CO_2 given out is absorbed by the soda lime, and O_2 is taken up by the seeds.

germinating seeds

clamp stand

But a change in temperature or atmospheric pressure might have the same effect, and handling of the apparatus may add heat and change the readings.

9 What are the potential sources of error in using a simple respirometer?

Activity 7.8: Investigating the rate of respiration practically

Think carefully about using the simple respirometer (Figure 7.18) in a laboratory investigation of the rate of respiration – say, in a sample of woodlice or some germinating peas.

What are the potential sources of error in using this apparatus? This issue is posed in SAQ 9 – so an answer is available to you, once you have identified likely issues yourself. Then, Activity 7.8 introduces alternative apparatus, which you may be able to use in your own practical investigation.

Anaerobic respiration, or fermentation

In the absence of oxygen many organisms (and sometimes certain tissues in organisms when deprived of sufficient oxygen) will continue to respire by a process known as fermentation or **anaerobic respiration**, at least for a short time.

If deprived of oxygen, tissues of flowering plants may respire by **alcoholic fermentation** – for example, the cells of roots in waterlogged soil.

$$glucose \quad \rightarrow \quad ethanol \quad + \quad carbon\ dioxide \quad + \quad energy$$

$$C_6H_{12}O_6 \quad \rightarrow \quad 2CH_3CH_2OH \quad + \quad 2CO_2 \quad + \quad energy$$

Vertebrate muscle tissue can respire anaerobically, too, but in this case it involves the formation of lactic acid rather than ethanol. **Lactic acid fermentation** occurs in muscle fibres, but only when the demand for energy for contractions is very great, and cannot be fully met by aerobic respiration. In lactic acid fermentation, the sole waste product is lactic acid.

$$glucose \quad \rightarrow \quad lactic\ acid \quad + \quad energy$$

$$C_6H_{12}O_6 \quad \rightarrow \quad 2CH_3CHOHCOOH \quad + \quad energy$$

A* Extension 7.5: Obligate anaerobes

The pathways of fermentation

The respiratory pathways of alcoholic and lactic acid fermentation are shown in Figure 7.19 (overleaf). When oxygen is not available, glycolysis continues and pyruvate accumulates, at least initially. However, terminal oxidation and the Krebs cycle cannot take place because the aerobic oxidation of reduced NAD is now blocked. In a tissue in which reserves of oxidised NAD run out, glycolysis will also cease.

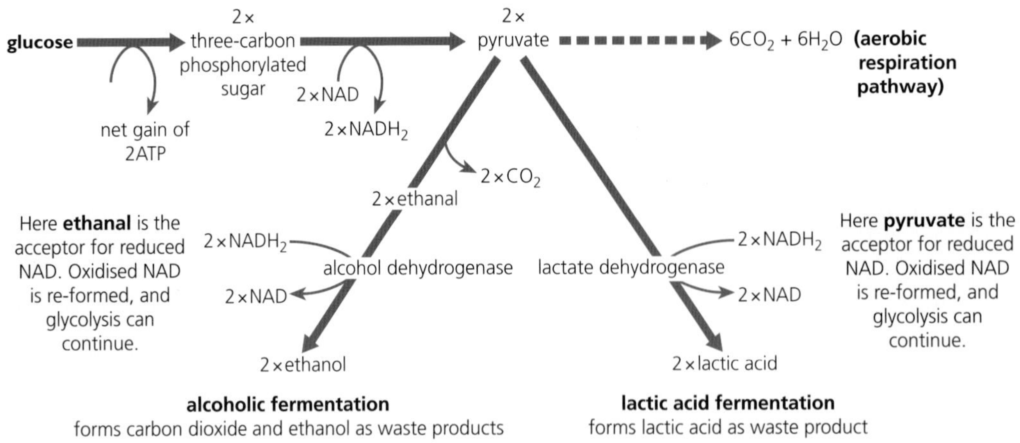

Figure 7.19 The respiratory pathways of anaerobic respiration.

A* Extension 7.6: Energy systems and skeletal muscle performance

A* Extension 7.7: The fate of lactate in muscle under anaerobic conditions

Figure 7.19 The respiratory pathways of anaerobic respiration.

alcoholic fermentation
forms carbon dioxide and ethanol as waste products

lactic acid fermentation
forms lactic acid as waste product

10 Name two products of anaerobic respiration in muscle.

In fact, in both of the alternative fermentation pathways, reduced NAD is oxidised in other reactions. In effect, oxygen is replaced as the hydrogen acceptor. In alcoholic fermentation, ethanal is the hydrogen acceptor, and in lactic acid fermentation, pyruvate is the hydrogen acceptor. Glycolysis is able to continue.

The total energy yield in both alcoholic and lactic acid fermentation is limited to the net two molecules of ATP generated in glycolysis per molecule of glucose respired.

■ Extension: Anaerobic respiration is less efficient

Anaerobic respiration is wasteful of respiratory substrate. The useful product is a tiny quantity of ATP only, when compared with the yield of ATP from aerobic respiration of the same quantity of respiratory substrate. Also, the waste products ethanol or lactic acid contain much unused chemical energy. For example, ethanol is a very good fuel, in its own right.

Lactic acid and ethanol may also be harmful to organisms if they accumulate. However, organisms may be able to tap the energy locked up in the waste products of fermentation by converting them back to sugar, which can then be respired. For example, in the vertebrate body, lactic acid is eventually converted back to glucose in the liver. Yeast, on the other hand, cannot metabolise ethanol, which makes it a useful organism in the industrial production of ethanol.

7.3 Maintenance of the body – at rest, and in activity

Environmental change is a fact of life. Conditions around organisms change all the time – some do so slowly, others dramatically. For example, temperature changes quickly on land exposed to direct sunlight, but the temperature of water exposed to sunlight changes very slowly.

How do organisms respond to environmental changes?

Some animals are able to maintain their internal environment more-or-less constant, enabling them to continue normal activities over a wide range of external conditions. These are known as 'regulators'. For example, mammals and birds maintain a high and almost constant body temperature over a very wide range of external temperatures. Their bodies are at, or close to, the optimum temperature for the majority of the enzymes that drive their metabolism. As a result, muscles contract efficiently, and the nervous system co-ordinates responses precisely, even when external conditions are unfavourable. They are often able to avoid danger, and perhaps they may also benefit from the vulnerability of prey organisms that happen to be 'non-regulators'. So regulators may have greater freedom in choosing where to live. They can exploit more habitats with more variable conditions than non-regulators.

Homeostasis

Homeostasis is the name we give to this ability to maintain a constant internal environment. Homeostasis simply means 'staying the same'. The internal environment is the blood circulating in the body, and the fluid circulating among cells (tissue fluid, which forms from the blood), delivering nutrients and removing waste products while bathing the cells. Mammals are excellent examples of animals that hold a range of internal parameters remarkably constant (Figure 7.20). They successfully regulate and maintain their blood pH, the oxygen and carbon dioxide concentrations in the blood, the pressure of blood in the arteries, heart rate, blood glucose, body temperature and water balance at constant levels or within surprisingly narrow limits.

How is homeostasis achieved?

11 In the body of a mammal, why is it essential that pH is held at a nearly constant value, and blood pressure is regulated?

polar bear on an ice floe

otter in fresh water

camels in the desert

Mammals are a comparatively recent group in terms of their evolutionary history, yet they have successfully settled in significant numbers in virtually every type of habitat on Earth. This success is directly linked to their ability to control their internal environment by homeostatis.

Whale in the sea

bat in the air

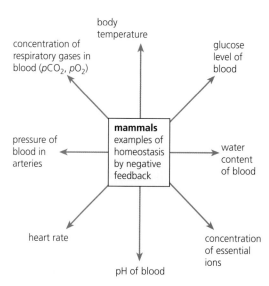

Figure 7.20 Homeostasis in mammals.

Diagram centred on **mammals** — examples of homeostasis by negative feedback, with arrows pointing to:
- body temperature
- concentration of respiratory gases in blood (pCO_2, pO_2)
- glucose level of blood
- pressure of blood in arteries
- water content of blood
- heart rate
- pH of blood
- concentration of essential ions

Negative feedback, the mechanism of homeostasis

Negative feedback is a type of control in which the conditions being regulated are brought back to a set value as soon as it is detected that they have deviated from it. We see this type of mechanism at work in a laboratory water bath (Figure 7.21, overleaf). Analysis of this familiar example will show us the components of a negative feedback system.

A negative feedback system requires a detector device that measures the value of the variable (water temperature in a water bath, for example) and transmits this information to a control unit. The control unit compares data from the detector with a pre-set value (the desired water temperature of the water bath). When the measured value is below the required value, the control unit activates an effector device (a water heater in the water bath) so that the temperature starts to be raised. Once the water reaches the set temperature, data from the detector to this effect is registered in the control box, which then switches off the response (water heater). How precisely the variable is maintained depends on the sensitivity of the detector, but negative feedback control typically involves some degree of 'overshoot'.

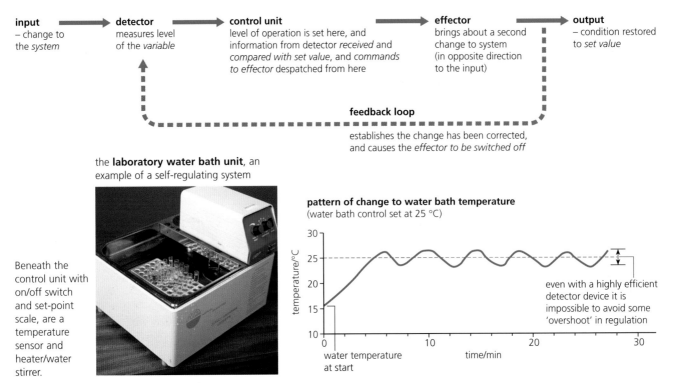

input
– change to
the *system*

detector
measures level
of the *variable*

control unit
level of operation is set here, and
information from detector *received* and
compared with set value, and *commands
to effector* despatched from here

effector
brings about a second
change to system
(in opposite direction
to the input)

output
– condition restored
to *set value*

feedback loop
establishes the change has been corrected,
and causes the *effector to be switched off*

the **laboratory water bath unit**, an
example of a self-regulating system

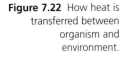

Beneath the
control unit with
on/off switch
and set-point
scale, are a
temperature
sensor and
heater/water
stirrer.

pattern of change to water bath temperature
(water bath control set at 25 °C)

even with a highly efficient
detector device it is
impossible to avoid some
'overshoot' in regulation

water temperature
at start

time/min

Figure 7.21 Negative feedback, the mechanism.

In mammals, regulation of body temperature, blood sugar level, and the amounts of water and ions in blood and tissue fluid (**osmoregulation**) are regulated by negative feedback. The detectors are specialised cells either in the brain or in other organs, such as the pancreas. The effectors are organs such as the skin, liver and kidneys. Information passes between detectors and effectors via the nerves of the **nervous system**, or via hormones (the **endocrine system**), or both. The outcome is an incredibly precisely regulated internal environment.

Homeostasis in action – control of body temperature

Heat may be transferred between an animal and the environment by **convection**, **radiation** and **conduction**, and the body loses heat in **evaporation** (Figure 7.22).

Figure 7.22 How heat is
transferred between
organism and
environment.

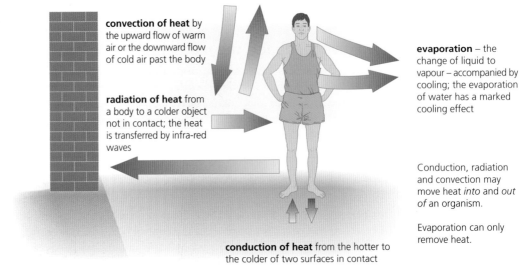

convection of heat by
the upward flow of warm
air or the downward flow
of cold air past the body

radiation of heat from
a body to a colder object
not in contact; the heat
is transferred by infra-red
waves

evaporation – the
change of liquid to
vapour – accompanied by
cooling; the evaporation
of water has a marked
cooling effect

Conduction, radiation
and convection may
move heat *into* and *out
of* an organism.

Evaporation can only
remove heat.

conduction of heat from the hotter to
the colder of two surfaces in contact

12 Deduce the times and conditions under which body temperature typically varies from the normal, in a 24-hour period (Figure 6.34).

13 What does it mean to say that most reactions in liver cells are endergonic?

14 Explain why it may become extremely difficult to lower body temperature if the core temperature rises too high during intense physical activity.

The regulation of body temperature, known as **thermoregulation**, involves controlling the amount of heat lost and heat gained across the body surface. Mammals maintain a high and relatively constant body temperature, using the heat energy generated by metabolism within their bodies (or by generating additional heat in the muscles when cold) and carefully controlling the loss of heat through the skin. An animal with this form of thermoregulation is called an **endotherm**, meaning 'inside heat'. Birds as well as mammals have perfected this mechanism. Humans hold their inner body temperature ('core temperature') just below 37 °C. In fact, human core temperature only varies between about 35.5 and 37.0 °C within a 24-hour period, when we are in good health. Under low external temperature, however, only the temperature of the inner trunk is held constant; there is a progressive fall in temperature down the limbs. This point is illustrated in Figure 6.34, page 93.

Remind yourself about this data on human body temperature variation now.

Heat production in the human body

The major sources of heat are the biochemical reactions of metabolism that generate heat as a waste product. Heat is then distributed – or transferred – by the blood circulation. The organs of the body vary greatly in the amount of heat they yield. For example, the liver is extremely active metabolically, but most of its metabolic reactions require an input of energy (they are **endergonic reactions**) and little energy is lost as heat. Mostly, the liver is thermally neutral.

When at rest, the bulk of our body heat (over 70%) comes from other internal organs, mainly from the heart and kidneys, but also from the lungs and brain (which, like a computer central processing unit, needs to be kept cool) (Figure 7.23). Under resting conditions, the skeleton, muscles and skin, which make up over 90% of the body mass, produce less than 30% of the body heat. Of course, in times of intense physical activity, the skeletal muscles generate a great deal of heat as a waste product of respiration and contraction. For example, in marathon races run under conditions of relatively high external temperature – as sometimes happens in the Olympic Games – the additional heat generated by the contracting muscles can raise athletes' core body temperatures to dangerously high levels. Occasionally, the resulting heat stroke experienced has lead to fatalities.

Figure 7.23 Heat production in the body at rest.

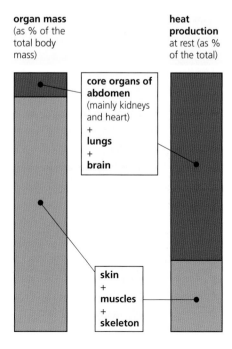

organ mass (as % of the total body mass)

heat production at rest (as % of the total)

core organs of abdomen (mainly kidneys and heart) + lungs + brain

skin + muscles + skeleton

The roles of the skin in thermoregulation

Heat exchange occurs largely at the surface of the body. Here in the skin, the following structures and mechanisms are combined in the regulation of heat loss, as detailed in Figure 7.24:

- the arterioles supplying capillary networks are dilated (**vasodilation**) when the body needs to lose heat, but constricted (**vasoconstriction**) when the body needs to retain heat
- hair erector muscles contract when heat must be retained but relax when heat must be lost
- sweat glands produce sweat when the body needs to lose heat, but do not when the body needs to retain heat.

Figure 7.24 The skin and temperature regulation.

structure of the skn

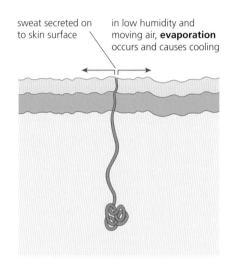

role of the sweat glands in regulating heat loss through the skin

sweat secreted on to skin surface

in low humidity and moving air, **evaporation** occurs and causes cooling

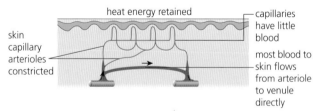

role of capillaries in regulating heat loss through the skin

In skin that is especially exposed (e.g. outer ear, nose, extremities of the limbs) the capillary network is extensive, and the arterioles supplying it can be dilated or constricted.

warm conditions

heat energy lost

capillaries filled with blood

by-pass arteriole constricted

cold conditions

heat energy retained

capillaries have little blood

skin capillary arterioles constricted

most blood to skin flows from arteriole to venule directly

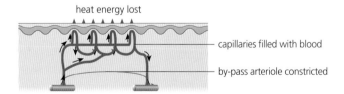

role of the hair in regulating heat loss through the skin

warm conditions

little still air retained against skin

The hair erector muscles may be contracted or relaxed.

hair erector muscles relaxed

Still air is a poor conductor of heat.

cold conditions

much still air retained against skin

hair erector muscles contracted

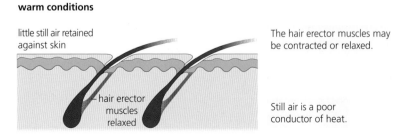

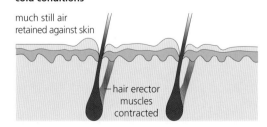

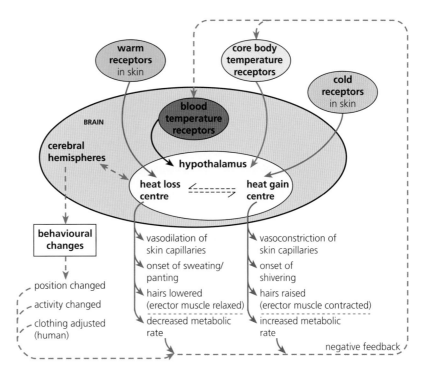

Figure 7.25 Temperature regulation of the body by the hypothalamus.

Other mechanisms in thermoregulation

If the body experiences persistent cold, heat production in increased. Under chilly conditions, heat output from muscles is raised by non-co-ordinated contraction of skeletal muscles, known as 'shivering'. This raises muscle heat production about five times above basal rate.

The hypothalamus as the control centre

The 'control box' for temperature regulation in mammals is a region of the forebrain called the **hypothalamus** (page 157). It is called the thermoregulation centre, and it consists of a 'heat loss centre' and a 'heat gain centre' (Figure 7.25). Here, temperature-sensitive nerve cells (neurones) are situated, and detect changes in the temperature of the blood flowing through the brain. The thermoregulation centre of the hypothalamus also receives information via sensory nerves from temperature-sensitive receptors located in the skin and in many internal organs.

The hypothalamus communicates with the rest of the body via the **autonomic nervous system** (see Extension, below). For example, when the body temperature is lower than normal, the heat gain centre inhibits activity of the heat loss centre, and sends impulses to the skin, hair erector muscles, sweat glands and elsewhere, that decrease heat loss (such as by causing vasoconstriction of skin capillaries) and increase heat production (by causing shivering, and enhanced 'brown fat' respiration, for example). When body temperature is higher than normal, the heat loss centre inhibits the heat gain centre activity, and sends out impulses that increase heat loss (such as by stimulating vasodilation of skin capillaries), and decrease heat production.

■ Extension: The autonomic nervous system (ANS)

The ANS controls activities and structures inside the body that are mostly under unconscious (involuntary) control. In effect, the ANS regulates the working of the interior of our body more-or-less without our knowledge. ANS nerve fibres emerge from the brain and spinal cord and pass to the muscles of the internal organs, and to various glands. The ANS as part of the nervous system is introduced in Chapter 8, page 150.

Homeostasis in action – regulation of cardiac output and ventilation rate

The needs of respiring cells for a constant supply of oxygen and for the concomitant removal of carbon dioxide are enormously variable between periods of rest and of intense physical activity. The supply of oxygen for aerobic respiration in all living cells of the body and the removal of the waste product carbon dioxide are combined achievements of our cardiovascular and ventilation systems. Our breathing rate and cardiac function is varied in order to maintain an appropriate environment in respiring tissues. This, too, is an expression of homeostasis.

At this point you may need to remind yourself of the structure the heart and the mechanism of the blood circulation (Biology for AS, page 18), and of the structure of the lungs and the process of gas exchange (Biology for AS, page 58). Then, respond to Activity 7.9 to check on your understanding of key points.

DL
www
Activity 7.9: Lungs and heart – structure and function

Cardiac output and ventilation rate in the body at rest

Our bodies have a **basal metabolic rate (BMR)** – a background rate of metabolism required to maintain a constant internal environment under conditions of minimum heart beat and breathing rate, and of essential nerve function, body temperature, posture, and so forth. Our metabolism in sleep approximately equals this BMR, which is typically $250 \, \text{kJ} \, \text{h}^{-1}$ for a woman, and $315 \, \text{kJ} \, \text{h}^{-1}$ for a man. The background rate of respiration required to sustain this BMR requires a minimal intake of oxygen by the body of about $0.2–0.3 \, \text{dm}^3$ per minute. Our cardiovascular and ventilation systems are automatically (unconsciously) regulated to deliver this quantity of oxygen (and equally importantly, to remove the carbon dioxide the cells produce as they respire at this rate).

■ Extension: VO_2 and VO_2max

Molecular oxygen combines with haemoglobin of red cells in the alveoli of the lungs, and oxygen is transported to the respiring tissues as oxyhaemoglobin. Arterial blood is relatively rich in oxygen. In the respiring tissues, oxyhaemoglobin dissociates into oxygen and haemoglobin because here the oxygen tension is much lower than in the lungs where the 'loading' of haemoglobin occurred. So the blood returning to the heart and lungs contains much less oxygen.

In fact, the difference in oxygen content between arterial and venous blood at any time is a measure of the demand and uptake of oxygen in the respiring tissues. This difference is known as VO_2.

VO_2 = the amount of oxygen being used in the body $(\text{cm}^3 \, \text{kg}^{-1} \, \text{min}^{-1})$

When the body ceases to be resting and commences physical exercise, then conditions in the respiring muscles themselves will begin to change. For one thing, their oxygen consumption – VO_2 – will increase. With increasingly vigorous exercise, VO_2 continues to increase. However, the situation will be reached where further increase is impossible, even if the maximum physical effort is maintained. This point is VO_2max.

VO_2max = the maximal oxygen uptake by the body $(\text{cm}^3 \, \text{kg}^{-1} \, \text{min}^{-1})$

The onset of vigorous physical activity

When we commence physical exercise, conditions in the respiring muscles begin to change. Their oxygen consumption increases, and as a consequence breathing rate increases, and the amount of blood circulating to the muscles changes too. Obviously the amount of oxygen in transport and being taken in by muscles (VO_2) increases, and with increasingly vigorous exercise, it will continue to increase.

How are these variations in ventilation and cardiac output controlled?

Figure 7.26 The control of ventilation rate.

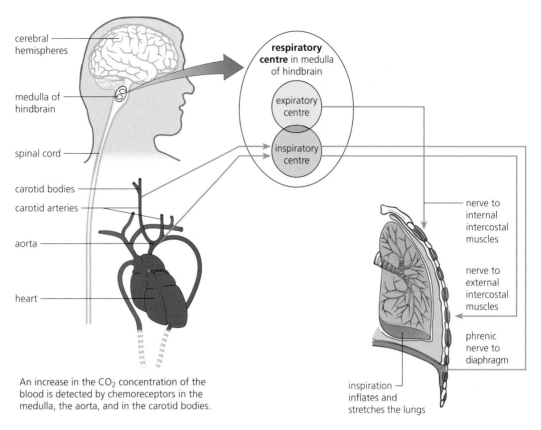

An increase in the CO_2 concentration of the blood is detected by chemoreceptors in the medulla, the aorta, and in the carotid bodies.

inspiration inflates and stretches the lungs

Control of ventilation

The **respiratory centre**, situated in the medulla of the hindbrain, controls the rate at which we breathe. Here two adjacent and interacting groups of nerve cells (neurones), known as the inspiratory centre and the expiratory centre respectively, bring about ventilation movements by reflex action. Breathing occurs automatically (involuntarily).

- The respiratory centre sends impulses to increase rate and depth of breathing.
- The expiratory centre sends impulses to inhibit the inspiratory centre and stimulate expiration.
- Alternating impulses from these two centres cause rhythmic breathing.

The breathing rate is continually adjusted. On average, our normal rate of breathing is about 15 breaths per minute. Since the tidal volume is typically 400 cm³, the volume of air taken into the lungs in one minute (ventilation rate) equals about 6 litres. We can consciously override this breathing rate with messages sent from the cerebral hemispheres (as when we prepare to shout, or sing or play woodwind or brass instruments, for example).

Breathing rates may be adjusted without conscious thought, too. This occurs during increased physical activity, when voluntary muscles use much more oxygen and more carbon dioxide is produced and transported in the blood. The main stimulus that controls breathing is the concentration of carbon dioxide in the blood. Blood carbon dioxide level is detected by chemoreceptors present in the carotid arteries and aorta (Figure 7.26).

When carbon dioxide levels increase, as during strenuous physical activity, the chemoreceptors, which are hydrogen ion detectors (CO_2 is an acid gas, in solution), send impulses to the inspiratory centre. In response, this centre sends additional impulses to the intercostal muscles and diaphragm, causing an increase in their contraction rates. (To a lesser extent, lowered oxygen concentration is also detected.)

After strenuous exercise, the concentration of CO_2 in the blood falls (and the concentration of oxygen rises). These changes are detected and the ventilation rate is regulated accordingly.

Activity 7.10: Wider reading – 'Lungs and the control of breathing'

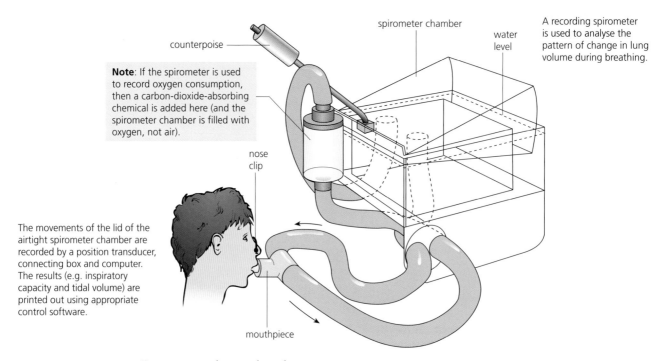

counterpoise

spirometer chamber

water level

A recording spirometer is used to analyse the pattern of change in lung volume during breathing.

Note: If the spirometer is used to record oxygen consumption, then a carbon-dioxide-absorbing chemical is added here (and the spirometer chamber is filled with oxygen, not air).

nose clip

The movements of the lid of the airtight spirometer chamber are recorded by a position transducer, connecting box and computer. The results (e.g. inspiratory capacity and tidal volume) are printed out using appropriate control software.

mouthpiece

Figure 7.27 Investigating breathing with a spirometer.

Investigating human breathing

The changes in lung volume during breathing are investigated using an apparatus called a **spirometer** (Figure 7.27). This consists of a Perspex lid enclosing the spirometer chamber, hinged over a tank of water. This chamber is connected to the person taking part in the experiment via an interchangeable mouthpiece and flexible tubing. As breathing proceeds, the lid rises and falls as the chamber volume changes. With the spirometer chamber filled with air, the capacity of the lungs when breathing at different rates can be investigated. Incidentally, if the spirometer chamber is filled with oxygen, and a carbon dioxide-absorbing chemical such as soda lime is added to a compartment on the air return circuit, this apparatus can be used to measure oxygen consumption by the body, too.

From 'traces' such as that shown in Figure 7.28, printed out from investigations of human breathing under different conditions, we have a picture of how extensively breathing may vary under various conditions.

Examine the spirometer trace now. Notice that the volume of air breathed in and out during normal, relaxed, rhythmical breathing – the **tidal volume** – is typically 400–500 cm³. The tidal volume is the volume of air taken in and out with each inhalation or exhalation. However, we have the potential for extra large intake (maximum inspiratory capacity) and extra large expirations of air (expiratory reserve volume), when required. These, together make up the **vital capacity** of our lungs. The vital capacity is the volume of air that can be exhaled after a maximum inhalation – about 4.5 dm³.

Figure 7.28 Lung volumes shown by a spirometer trace.

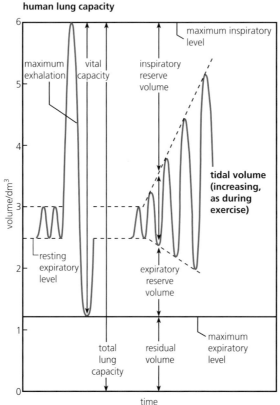

human lung capacity

maximum inspiratory level

maximum exhalation

vital capacity

inspiratory reserve volume

tidal volume (increasing, as during exercise)

resting expiratory level

expiratory reserve volume

volume/dm³

total lung capacity

residual volume

maximum expiratory level

time

■ Extension: What happens to breathing during physical exercise?

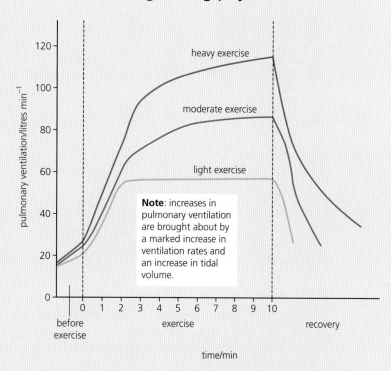

Figure 7.29 Respiratory response to exercise.

Physical activity affects oxygen consumption and carbon dioxide production more than any other physiological stress the body experiences.

During exercise, the demand for oxygen by the working muscles increases (and carbon dioxide output rises), and as a result, both the tidal volume and the ventilation rate increase and so maintain an adequate gas concentration in the lungs for rapid gaseous exchange. However, the pattern of change is quite complex, and it varies with the level of exercise, too (Figure 7.29).

To start with, planned physical exercise is preceded by a slight increase in ventilation. This is an anticipatory rise, no doubt due to the effect of the hormone adrenaline on the respiratory centre that controls breathing. It happens because we are planning the activity, and are preparing for it.

When exercise commences, there is a rapid rise in ventilation under nervous control. However, in physical activity that is less than the maximum the body can achieve (sub-maximal exercise), the sudden increase in ventilation begins to slow and normally reaches a plateau or steady state. Now the oxygen reaching the muscles is sufficient to support a level of respiration that transfers sufficient energy to the contracting muscle fibres.

During maximal exercise, on the other hand, the steady state does not occur, and ventilation continues to increase until exercise is complete.

The respiratory centre in the brain is sensitive to the concentration of carbon dioxide in the blood and responds to rising levels by increasing ventilation. Also, when the necessary energy cannot be obtained by aerobic respiration alone during continuing maximal exercise, anaerobic respiration in muscles produces lactic acid. The respiratory centre is stimulated by the level of blood lactate, too.

Activity 7.11:
Investigating the effects of exercise using a spirometer or stethoscope (HSW Criteria 2, 3, 4, 5 and 8)

A* Extension 7.8: The effects of training on the pulmonary system

When the residual volume is added to the vital capacity, we arrive at the total capacity of our lungs, typically about $6\,dm^3$. The total lung capacity is the volume of air in the lungs after a maximum inhalation.

The stethoscope may also be used to investigate aspects of breathing. For example, the ventilation rate (the number of inhalations or exhalations per minute) obtained from subjects at rest and after exercise may be compared using this apparatus (Activity 7.11).

15 Examine the spirometer trace shown here. Using the data between points A and B, measure, calculate and record:
a tidal volume and rate of breathing
b rate of oxygen consumption.

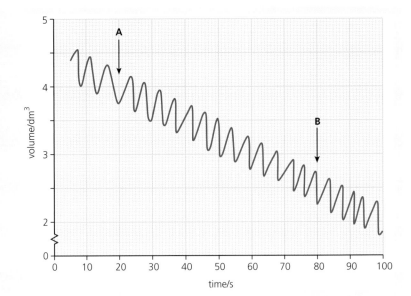

Control of cardiac output

The heart beats rhythmically throughout life, without rest, apart from the momentary relaxation between beats. Even more remarkably, the origin of each beat is within the heart itself – we say that heart beat is **myogenic** in origin.

The heart beat originates in a structure in the muscle of the wall of the right atrium, called the **sino-atrial node (SAN)**, also known as the natural **pacemaker**. Muscle fibres radiating out from the SAN conduct impulses to the muscles of both atria, triggering atrial systole (contraction).

Then a second node, the **atrio-ventricular node**, situated at the base of the right atrium picks up the excitation and passes it to the ventricles through modified muscle fibres, called the **Purkinje fibres** (Figure 7.30). Ventricular systole is then triggered.

Figure 7.30 Control of heart rate.

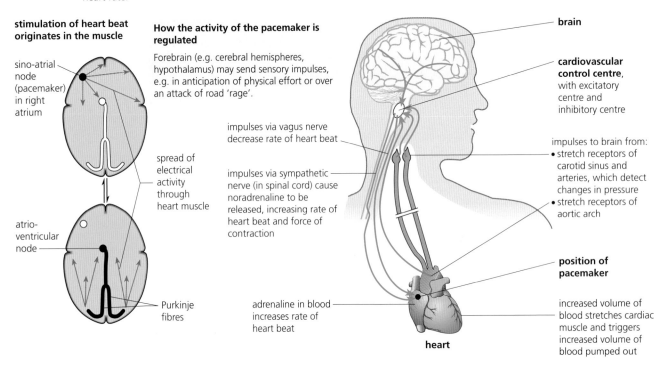

stimulation of heart beat originates in the muscle

sino-atrial node (pacemaker) in right atrium

spread of electrical activity through heart muscle

atrio-ventricular node

Purkinje fibres

How the activity of the pacemaker is regulated

Forebrain (e.g. cerebral hemispheres, hypothalamus) may send sensory impulses, e.g. in anticipation of physical effort or over an attack of road 'rage'.

impulses via vagus nerve decrease rate of heart beat

impulses via sympathetic nerve (in spinal cord) cause noradrenaline to be released, increasing rate of heart beat and force of contraction

adrenaline in blood increases rate of heart beat

brain

cardiovascular control centre, with excitatory centre and inhibitory centre

impulses to brain from:
• stretch receptors of carotid sinus and arteries, which detect changes in pressure
• stretch receptors of aortic arch

position of pacemaker

increased volume of blood stretches cardiac muscle and triggers increased volume of blood pumped out

heart

After every contraction, cardiac muscle has a period of insensitivity to stimulation, known as a **refractory period** (in effect, a period of enforced non-contraction which we may call a 'rest'), when the heart refills with blood. This period is a relatively long one in heart muscle, and doubtless an important feature, enabling the heart to beat throughout life.

The heart's own rhythm, set by the SAN, is about 50 beats per minute, but conditions in the body can override this basic rate and increase heart performance, even when the body is resting. Of course, the action of the pacemaker is further modified during physical activity, from the 75 beat per minute of the 'at rest' heart, up to 200 beats a minute in very strenuous exercise.

How is the pacemaker regulated? Look at Figure 7.30 now.

Nervous control of the heart is by reflex action (page 141). The heart receives impulses from the cardiovascular centre in the medulla of the hindbrain, via two nerves:

- a sympathetic nerve, part of the sympathetic nervous system, which speeds up the heart
- a branch of the vagus nerve, part of the parasympathetic nervous system, which slows down the heart.

Since the sympathetic nerve and the vagus nerve have opposite effects in this matter of regulation of heart beat, we say they are **antagonistic**.

The cardiovascular centre has nerves supplying it, too. For example, it receives impulses from **stretch receptors** located in the walls of the aorta, in the carotid arteries, and in the wall of the right atrium, when changes in blood pressure occur at these positions.

When blood pressure is high in the arteries, the rate of heart beat is lowered by impulses from the cardiovascular centre, via the vagus nerve. When blood pressure is low, the rate of heart beat is increased.

The rate of heart beat is also influenced by impulses from the higher centres of the brain. For example, emotion, stress and anticipation of events can all cause impulses from the sympathetic nerve to speed up heart rate.

In addition, the hormone **adrenaline**, which is secreted by the adrenal glands (page 179) and carried in the blood, causes the pacemaker to increase the heart rate.

Electrocardiography

The impulses (action potentials) that originate in the SAN (pacemaker) of the heart during the cardiac cycle produce electrical currents that are also conducted through the fluids of the body as a whole and can be detected at the body surface by electrocardiography. Here, electrodes are attached to the patient's chest, and the electrical activity detected is displayed as an electrocardiogram (ECG) by means of a chart recorder (Figure 7.31, overleaf).

Electrocardiography has clinical applications; it is an aid in the diagnosis of cardiovascular disease (CVD – *Biology for AS*, page 24). Some heart conditions detected via ECG analysis are listed in Table 7.3.

16 Suggest conditions or situations in which the body is likely to secrete adrenaline.

17 During vigorous activity, the heart beats more quickly. Outline the sequence of events that causes this raised heart rate.

Table 7.3 Heart conditions detected by abnormal ECG traces.

Arrhythmia	Arrhythmia is a condition of irregularity in heart rhythm due to a defect in the conduction system of the heart. It may be due to: ■ drugs, such as nicotine or alcohol ■ anxiety ■ hypothyroidism ■ potassium deficiency.
Ventricular fibrillation	Asynchronous contraction of the ventricle muscle fibres results in a failure of the heart to pump sufficient blood because some muscle fibres are contracting while others are relaxing.
Heart block	The most common site of blockage is at the atrio-ventricular node.
Tachycardia	A normal adult heart beats between 60 and 100 times per minute at rest – a heart rate over 100 beats a minute is called tachycardia. Tachycardia may be relatively harmless and need no treatment, but other forms can be life-threatening.

normal electrocardiogram (ECG), analysed

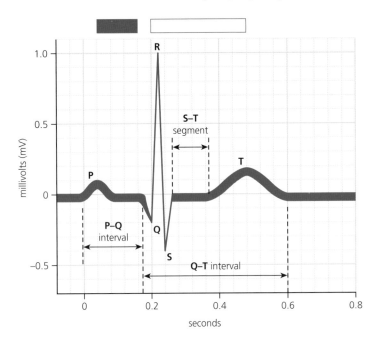

Key

■	atrial contraction (atrial systole)
□	ventricular contraction (systole)
P wave	atrial depolarisation – leads to atrial contraction
P–R interval	time for impulse to be conducted from SAN to ventricles, via AVN
QRS complex	onset of ventricular depolarisation – leads to ventricular contraction
T wave	ventricular repolarisation – relaxation phase

abnormal traces showing

1 tachycardia
heart rate is over 100 beats/minute

2 ventricular fibrillation
uncontrolled contraction of the ventricles – little blood is pumped

3 heart block
ventricles not always stimulated

electrical activity detected through electrodes attached to the patient's chest is displayed on the chart recorder as an electrocardiogram

Figure 7.31
Electrocardiography – an electrocardiogram is taken to detect abnormalities that may confirm a suspected heart attack, for example.

www
Activity 7.12:
Transcription and translation – the steps

Another aspect of body regulation – gene expression

We now appreciate that our genes are also part of the day-by-day regulation processes by which body activities are controlled and maintained. In the human genome, which contains less than 30 000 genes, only about 10% of the genes code for the proteins and enzymes required for 'construction' of the body. Of course, these are especially 'active' (we say they are being expressed) during growth and development from fertilised egg to adult. The remainder of our genes are selectively involved in the everyday activities of cells, tissues and organs. While some of these genes code for proteins that are continuously required, others – the majority, in fact – are expressed only when commanded in various ways so to do. We need to examine the 'gene switch' mechanisms by which gene expression is selectively initiated, next. *But first, remind yourself about the process of gene transcription into mRNA and the translation process in ribosomes by which protein synthesis occurs (Activity 7.12).*

Gene switches – the mechanism

Adjacent to each gene is a region called the **promoter region**. When transcription of the gene occurs, the RNA polymerase enzyme attaches to this relatively short length of DNA of the coding strand, prior to transcribing the genetic code of the gene into mRNA. However, in order for the transcription process to be initiated, one or more **transcription factors** are also required to be present and to bind with the enzyme – effectively activating it and so permitting transcription of the gene by the enzyme.

Transcription factors are proteins that are coded for by other parts of the chromosomes. Remember, only about 3% of our genome consists of genes. Some of the remainder of our DNA is involved in gene regulation by coding for transcription factors. Some of these factors are always present in the cell, but production of most is restricted to particular cells or produced only at certain stages in the life of the cell or organism (Figure 7.32). The expression of genes is regulated in this way – cells do not waste energy and materials making mRNA and proteins not specifically required at a particular time.

Note also that many transcription factors require to be activated by **signal proteins**. These are typically hormones. Hormones are produced in ductless glands and are circulated indiscriminately in the blood stream. However, they are effective only in cells and tissues with specific receptor molecules on the plasma membrane. We refer to such cells as 'target cells'. In this subtle way, gene expression may be precisely co-ordinated with particular conditions or requirements of the organism.

DL
www

A* Extension 7.9:
Gene switching in the
prokaryotes

Figure 7.32 Introducing
the gene switch
mechanism.

Gene switches – the components

RNA polymerase – the enzyme
that synthesises an RNA copy
of a DNA template

transcription factor – protein(s)
required for initiation of
transcription of a eukaryotic gene

gene – segment of DNA that codes for an
RNA molecule and a polypeptide, together
with an adjacent binding site

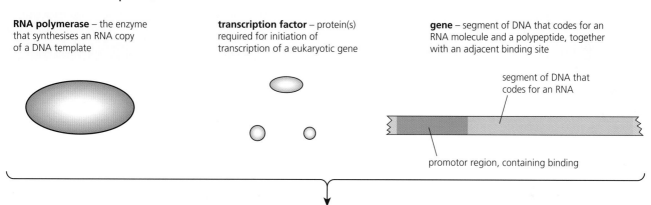

segment of DNA that
codes for an RNA

promotor region, containing binding

How the gene switch components are assembled, leading to transcription

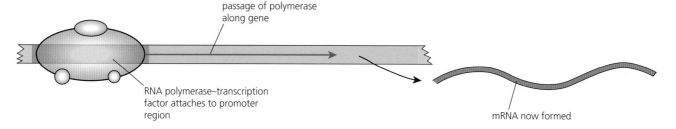

passage of polymerase
along gene

RNA polymerase–transcription
factor attaches to promoter
region

mRNA now formed

More about:
transcription factors

- some are always present in the cell

- most are synthesised only in
  particular cells, or at certain stages
  in a cell's life

- some exist in inactive form and only
  become activated by signal protein

signal proteins

- typically a hormone (or growth factor, or other molecule)

- formed in the Golgi apparatus, packaged in secretory
  vesicles and discharged by exocytosis – they trigger
  effects in other cells

- some work directly by crossing the plasma membranes of
  target cells, then entering the nucleus to reach and activate
  transcription factor(s)

- most attach to a receptor molecule on the plasma membrane
  of target cells, where they trigger release of a messenger
  molecule (protein, lipid or nucleotide) which then enters the
  nucleus and activates transcription factor(s)

repressor molecules

- prevent RNA transcription – part of
  some switch mechanisms

- work by attaching to the DNA of the
  promoter region of a gene, or
  directly to the transcription factor(s)

7.4 Exercise – its effects on body performance

There is evidence that regular, moderate exercise improves human health. By moderate exercise, we mean the daily investment of at least 30 minutes on sport or on activities such as brisk walking, cycling or gardening. The main advantages associated with this level of activity are listed in Table 7.4. On the other hand, a completely sedentary lifestyle is associated with a heightened risk of coronary heart disease (CHD) and strokes, cancer, obesity (with increased risk of type II diabetes), and osteoporosis.

Table 7.4 Health benefits correlated with regular, moderate activity.

Parameter	Possible connection with good health
favourable body mass index (BMI) and waist : hip ratio (*Biology for AS*, page 29)	regular activity may assist maintenance of correct body weight, and so reduce likelihood of becoming overweight or obese
balance between low-density and high-density lipoproteins (LDLs and HDLs) in plasma (*Biology for AS*, page 28)	regular activity favours raised levels of blood HDLs (as cholesterol is carried to liver and metabolised) at the expense of high levels of blood LDLs, thereby reducing the risk of atherosclerosis
improved sensitivity of muscle fibres to blood insulin levels	effective regulation of blood glucose levels, thereby reducing the risk of type II diabetes developing
prolonged periods of arterial vasodilation	lowered blood pressure results, which carries with it a reduced risk of coronary heart disease and strokes
maintenance (and improvements) in bone density	prevention or delay in onset of the bone-wasting disease, osteoporosis, in which bones become brittle and lack sufficient calcium (Activity 7.15)
risk of contracting certain cancers ('cancer' is not one, but several different diseases)	with regular activity, there is a significantly reduced risk of contracting colorectal and breast cancers
psychological well-being and sound mental health	exercise promotes these

Activity 7.13: Finding out about osteoporosis

How can we be sure the associations between physical activity and health, listed in Table 7.4, are not purely coincidental? Correlations like these provide circumstantial evidence of the roles of particular factors, but the connection is *suggested* rather than *proved*.

Other studies are required to establish how particular circumstances might operate on the functioning body to *cause* a healthy or a diseased state, if in fact they do. Typically, causal relationships may be established between particular activity levels and states of health by means of:

- clinical trials, which investigate, among other things, the biochemical or structural changes that are induced in subjects
- intervention studies, which work with vulnerable groups of patients, changing habits and lifestyles, and establishing the extent to which the incidence of disease (CHD, for example) is reduced when compared with rates in other patients – these others act as a control group.

Physical activity and health

Athletes and other sports people undertake planned physical activity programmes of aerobic training, and these levels of training certainly improve healthy and effective operation of body systems. For example:

1 Studies on the operation of the pulmonary systems of both adolescents and adults involved with sub-maximal exercise training for sport activity show that their tidal volume increases and ventilation rate decreases during their training exercise regime. (See **Extension: What happens to breathing during physical exercise?**, page 125.) Consequently, air remains in their lungs longer between breaths. The result is that the exhaled air from trained people during exercise contains only 14–15% oxygen, whereas for the untrained under identical conditions, exhaled air contains an average of 18% oxygen. Untrained people must ventilate

more frequently to achieve the same oxygen uptake, in effect. Clearly, a trained pulmonary system contributes to physical performance, and improves conditions for the cardiovascular system.

2 Similarly, there is an effect of regular exercise and training on the cardiovascular system. Training involves sessions of vigorous activity that raise the heart rate to a high level. As a consequence, because cardiac muscles are slightly elastic, the walls of the chambers of the heart (particularly the ventricle walls) are stretched and the cardiac muscle walls are progressively thickened. So, athletes develop larger ventricle cavities and thicker ventricle walls, and the heart of an athlete is larger than that of a non-athlete. This phenomenon is called **cardiac hypertrophy**. Also, cardiac hypertrophy is accompanied by a decreased resting heart rate. Table 7.5 illustrates these points. Examine the data, and then answer SAQ 18.

Table 7.5 Effects of training exercise on the cardiovascular system (data from male subjects).

	Heart rate/min^{-1}	Stroke volume/cm^3	Cardiac output/cm^3 min^{-1}
At rest			
before training	72	70	5040
after training	50	100	5000
During strenuous activity			
before training	200	110	22 000
after training	190	180	35 000

18 Copy and complete the table below to summarise the effects of training on the heart at rest and during exercise.

	Heart rate	Stroke volume	Cardiac output
athlete at rest			
athlete during exercise			

The marked improvements in body functions as a result of training, illustrated above, are the results of planned, vigorous exercise undertaken as part of a training programme. While these improvements cannot be expected as a result of regular moderate exercise, it is the case that regular, more moderate exercise may well improve a person's sense of well-being and their physical health. It does apparently reduce susceptibility to infectious diseases, too (see below).

Excessive exercise and vulnerability to disease?

It has also become apparent that athletes of all ages who engage in prolonged and unusually strenuous training programmes, and who leave them fatigued and exhausted, are vulnerable to health problems not experienced as a result of more moderate exercise. This discovery emerged from earlier observations of the health records of vulnerable groups, including:

■ the number of school boys who contracted pneumonia after periods of intense sports training, compared with other students who merely participated moderately
■ the incidence of upper respiratory tract infections (URTIs) in athletes following participation in gruelling marathon races, when compared with control groups who had maintained moderate training but had not competed.

A* Extension 7.10: The common cold versus flu

By URTIs, we refer to infections such as the common cold and sore throats, for example – but, incidentally, not to influenza (A* Extension 7.10).

Figure 7.33 The intensity of physical activity and susceptibility to URTIs.

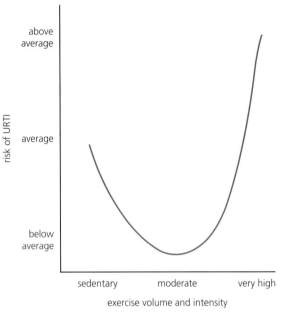

The fact that athletes engaged in excessively heavy training programmes become prone to infections is one conclusion we can draw from the graph in Figure 7.33. Here, various observations of the relationship between the incidence of URTIs and the levels of training exercise undertaken are illustrated. For example, this graph also suggests that moderate exercise offers some protection against URTIs. The question is, are these suggested relationships merely coincidences, or is there also a causal relationship (HSW Criterion 5)?

What credible explanations can be offered?
It is possible that:

■ when athletes travel to competitive sporting venues and make close contact with others, some of those contacts may unwittingly expose them to unfamiliar pathogens
■ the intense stresses of excessive physical activity may temporarily suppress the immune system.

The first of these explanations is a likely, but a completely unpredictable possibility. However, when it does occur – leading to exposure to pathogenic microbes – it makes the second explanation of the greatest significance. And the condition of our immune system is something that can be measured.

At this point it will help your understanding if you revise issues concerned with the body's response to infection (page 75), particularly the summary of the immune system at work, Figure 6.29 (page 86) (Activity 7.14).

Activity 7.14: Revising the immune system

Table 7.6 Effects of exercise on the immune system.

Moderate exercise	Component of immune system	Sustained, vigorous exercise
increased numbers of phagocytic white cells provide non-specific immunity boost against microbes and other antigens that invade the body or which are present on the surfaces of the upper respiratory tract	**general phagocytic white cells (part of non-specific immune system)**	general suppression of the immune system in the body under stress and possible inflammatory response in muscle tissues (where fibres have been mechanically damaged by heavy exercise), leading to reduced non-specific immune response elsewhere
normal functioning	**B-cells and T-cells (helper T-cells) interacting to form plasma cells, thereby forming specific antibodies**	reduction in helper T-cell activity, leading to reduced antibody production
normal functioning	**activated T-cells acting as cytotoxic cells (destroying cells carrying specific antigens)**	cytotoxic cell activity reduced

Studies on stressed athletes have shown that both aspects of our immune system – the *non-specific* and the *specific* immune system, targeted on particular antigens – are affected by both moderate and excessive physical activity. The effects are summarised in Table 7.6. However, the *mechanism* by which the immune system is impaired in those who have undergone sustained, vigorous exercise is not clear. Is it a direct effect, or is the psychological stress of competition at extremes of physical endurance the factor that temporarily reduces the activity of the immune system? Whatever the cause, there is an increased risk of URTIs in these athletes for 1–2 weeks subsequent to their competitive events.

Exercise and the musculo-skeletal system

So, exercise is good for us! Couch potatoes are certainly out of fashion these days! However, sometimes we can injure ourselves when training for or playing sports or in taking particularly vigorous exercise. There are two general types of injury:

■ traumatic injuries are those usually involving a blow from a single application of force – they typically arise in contact sports
■ over-use injuries happen over a period of time – they typically arise from repetitive training, or from the persistent high forces the professional sports person's bones, joints and muscles experience.

Injury causes damage to cells, and dead or damaged cells release chemicals that trigger an inflammatory response (page 80) – the first phase of healing and recovery.

Damage to joints – the roles of medical technologies

Joints are especially vulnerable to injury, both traumatic and from over-use. Repeated force on joints readily leads to wear and tear. Similarly, over-use results in damage to the joints, often very similar to the effects of ageing. We can illustrate how vulnerable a joint is by reference to the structure and components of the knee joint (Figure 7.34).

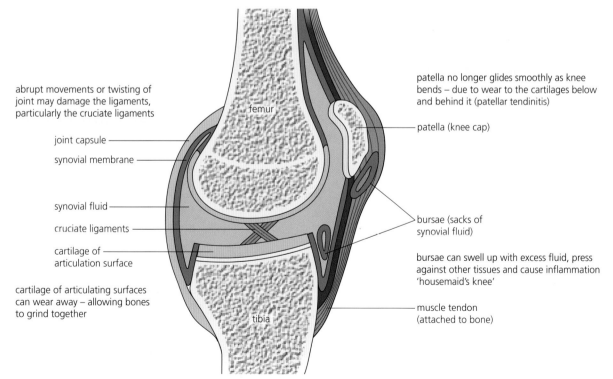

abrupt movements or twisting of joint may damage the ligaments, particularly the cruciate ligaments

joint capsule

synovial membrane

synovial fluid

cruciate ligaments

cartilage of articulation surface

cartilage of articulating surfaces can wear away – allowing bones to grind together

femur

tibia

patella no longer glides smoothly as knee bends – due to wear to the cartilages below and behind it (patellar tendinitis)

patella (knee cap)

bursae (sacks of synovial fluid)

bursae can swell up with excess fluid, press against other tissues and cause inflammation 'housemaid's knee'

muscle tendon (attached to bone)

Figure 7.34 Knee joint – susceptible areas and structures.

19 Bone fractures are common sports injuries, particularly in 'contact sports'. How is it that an apparently inert material such as 'bone' can be repaired by the body, given appropriate medical treatment?

Figure 7.35 Coloured CT scan of a knee joint, showing a meniscus tear – damage to the cartilage discs that provide a smooth surface for movement. This injury is particularly common in athletes.

Injuries are relatively common occurrences among professional athletes and sports people, and these unfortunate events are taken most seriously, lest long-term health is threatened. While the first response to injury may be 'RICE' – rest, ice, compression, elevation – if the pain and immobility are not quickly overcome, then a primary care physician or staff of the available medical team are consulted. Where the symptoms are sufficiently serious, subsequent diagnoses typically involve CT Scans (page 161, and Figure 7.35) or X-ray analysis. Soft tissue damage is analysed by magnetic resonance imaging (MRI, page 162). Following diagnosis and depending upon the injury, appropriate treatments range from further rest and anti-inflammatory medicines, to use of healing supports such as splints or casts, and sometimes surgery.

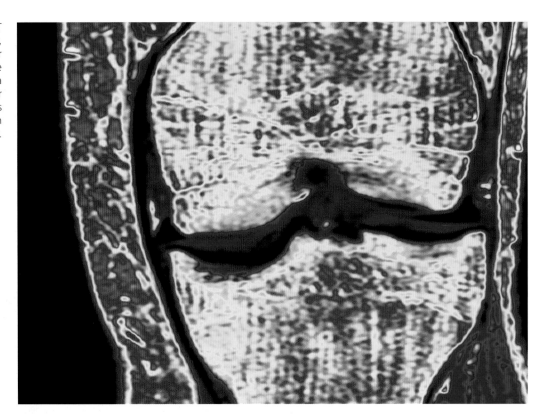

Medical technology applied to sports injury

Specific developments in medical technology have important applications in current treatments of sports injuries. We can illustrate this by the surgical technique of arthroscopy (keyhole surgery) and by the use of prostheses.

Arthroscopy

Arthroscopy is a procedure now used by orthopaedic surgeons to examine, diagnose and treat damage to joints. Although the necessary incisions required are tiny compared with previous, conventional techniques, arthroscopy still requires a hospital operating theatre and an anaesthetic, general or local.

The corrective surgery requires specially designed, miniature instruments. These are inserted through tiny incisions and then operated remotely. The arthroscope is a telescopic camera, equipped to deliver light into the incision by means of fibre optics, and provide a magnified image of the damaged area and its repair. It also enables the whole process to be observed and followed on a television screen.

The improvements this development provides compared with previous surgical techniques, which required a larger, 'open' wound, are highlighted in Table 7.7. Typical damage to knee cartilages and the process of arthroscopy by which it may be repaired are illustrated in Figure 7.36.

Table 7.7 Conventional knee surgery versus keyhole surgery.

Conventional 'open' surgery	Keyhole surgery
■ relatively large incision required – to illuminate whole area of damage, to allow surgeon to see clearly, and for access of surgeon's hands and equipment ■ significant blood-loss likely ■ painful wound as an outcome ■ increased risk of infection ■ prolonged recovery period – procedure may significantly shorten sports person's career	■ incision the size of a buttonhole required to insert arthroscope – other, similar incisions may be needed to view other parts of the joint or for other instruments ■ arthroscope is a pencil-sized instrument, with a small lens and light (via fibre optics) attached to illuminate the site and observe damage and repair ■ television camera attached to display image ■ small dressing required and little or no pain medication

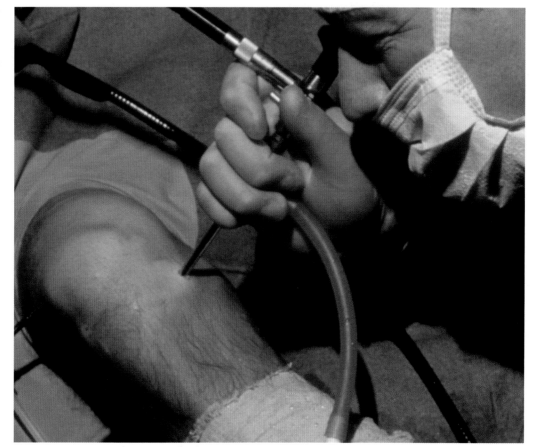

Figure 7.36 Arthroscopy applied in the treatment of damaged knee cartilages. The procedure is carried out under general anaesthetic.

Prostheses

A prosthesis (plural, prostheses) is an artificial substitute, replacing a body part, such as a limb, tooth or heart valve, that has been removed or use of which has been lost by trauma, disease or defect. Dentures are familiar prosthetic devices constructed to replace missing teeth. They have a long history – the first European dentures date from the fifteenth century at least. Today in the UK, surgeons replace many thousands of hip joints damaged by arthritis every year.

We can illustrate the installation and use of prostheses by reference to a knee joint. Knee joint replacement is recommended, for example, where arthritis has severely decreased knee function, or possibly when knee tissues have been invaded by tumours. Under general anaesthetic, the affected knee joint is opened up. The entry is a relatively minor incision in order to avoid cutting the tendon at the front of the knee. Then the patella is moved to one side, and the damaged ends of the femur and tibia cut to fit the prosthesis. The prosthesis is attached using bone cement. The articulating surfaces of the prosthesis may be of metal and plastic, but some models exploit metal–metal surfaces, or ceramic, or ceramic–plastic surfaces (Figure 7.37, overleaf).

Figure 7.37 X-ray photograph of a knee joint prosthesis.

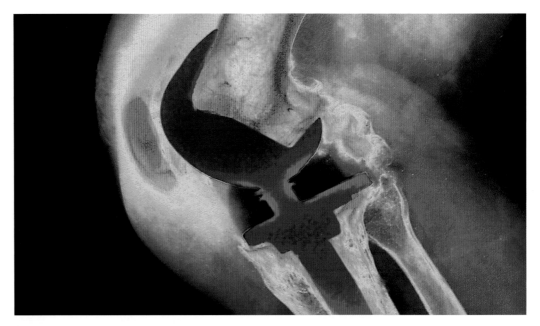

Performance-enhancing substances in athletics

Performance-enhancing substances are those used in the practice of 'doping' in sport. By **doping** we mean the use (or the distribution for use) of certain substances that may have the effect of artificially improving an athlete's performance. These might act directly on muscles, nerves, blood circulation or breathing, or indirectly, via their effects on mental state.

The oath sworn on behalf of Olympic athletes commits all competitors to participation 'without doping and without drugs, in the true spirit of sportsmanship'.

However, not all sports persons keep this promise. For example, at the 2008 Olympic games there were many cases of doping violations recorded. Since the International Amateur Athletic Federation ruled that doping is forbidden, the organisations responsible for individual sports have been placed in control of testing for abuses. Chemists working in dedicated laboratories analyse samples of body fluids, chiefly blood and urine samples, typically collected at random, to check for evidence of use of particular groups of banned substances (Figure 7.38).

The practice of doping probably originated with athletes in ancient Greece who used stimulants to enhance their performances. However, today it seems that drug taking has become a common part of many individuals' training programmes, as well as of competitive sports at national and international levels. Suppliers of such drugs also seek newer substances that, after use, leave little or no detectable trace in the samples taken for analysis – in response, testers strive to quickly find means of detecting their use. However, not all substances taken to enhance performance are banned. For example, creatine (a naturally occurring 'energy reserve', found in our skeletal muscle tissue) is defined as a dietary supplement, and its use is permitted.

Banned substances – risks and benefits

Erythropoietin (EPO)

Some athletes use a synthetic form of the natural hormone **erythropoietin (EPO)**. EPO is normally produced by the kidneys and regulates red blood cell production within the bone marrow. A 12% increase in haemoglobin typically follows a six-week period of pre-performance treatment with EPO. However, the corresponding increase in blood viscosity that occurs is potentially life-threatening. Likelihoods of strokes, heart attacks and pulmonary oedema (swelling due to accumulation of tissue fluid) are increased. For example, it has been alleged that there have been 18 deaths (attributed to heart attacks) among competitors in gruelling cycle races that have been associated with EPO pre-treatments.

20 Outline why the use of EPO may trigger pulmonary oedema.

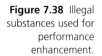

Figure 7.38 Illegal substances used for performance enhancement.

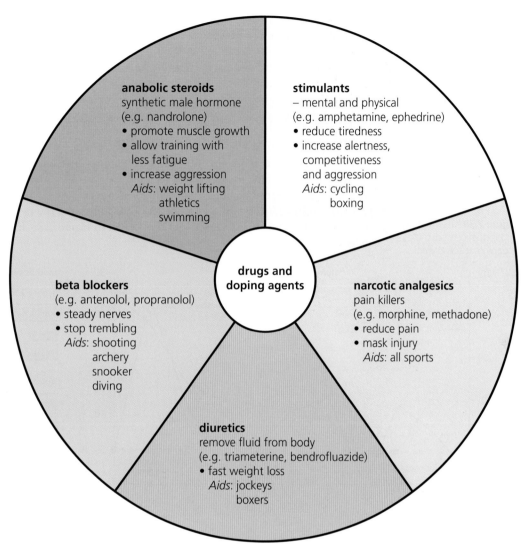

Activity 7.15: Secondary sexual characteristics

EPO abuse has been tested for by detecting abnormally high red blood cell counts, because the drug has proved difficult to detect in the urine. Now, a technique to distinguish between synthetic and natural EPO has been developed.

Anabolic steroids

The naturally occurring sex hormones **testosterone** and **oestrogen** are chemicals known as steroids, and are manufactured in our bodies from cholesterol (*Biology for AS*, page 27). Naturally occurring testosterone is responsible for male secondary sexual characteristics (Activity 7.15).

Testosterone is the more powerful of the steroid hormones in producing pronounced anabolic effects, sought by those who wish to enhance body size and strength in this way. **Anabolism** is the building of large molecules, such as proteins, including muscle protein.

The use of anabolic steroids leads to enlarged muscles and, incidentally, an increased speed of recovery between training sessions. Another anabolic effect that testosterone and the other sex hormones have is on the bones; the natural breakdown and reabsorption of old bone is slowed down, and the deposition of new bone is promoted. The skeleton is strengthened as a result. (Anabolic steroids are prescribed by the medical profession in the treatment of osteoporosis.)

Testosterone also has androgenic effects, summarised as masculising of the body. Facial hair growth increases, the voice deepens – all unfortunate consequences for female athletes who choose to use it.

Testosterone itself has to be administered by injection and even then is short-lived in effects, for it is rapidly broken down in the body and excreted.

A* Extension 7.11:
Two modes of hormone action

HSW 7.2: Criterion 8 – Developments in drug testing

Nandrolone is one example of laboratory-synthesised forms of testosterone, which show only minor changes to the molecule's structure. The effects of these on the body are almost identical to testosterone. Their use is banned by the International Olympic Committee (Figure 7.38). Incidentally, their sale in some countries is a criminal offence. However, it is alleged that sales of anabolic steroids are second only to sales of cannabis among the list of illegal substances. Those who sell them to users (including to some gym users keen to increase muscle size and 'improve' their appearance) are able to import from countries where their sale is legal, including Mexico.

The ethics of using performance-enhancing drugs

The widespread use and abuse of performance-enhancing drugs raises many ethical issues. An alarming number of sports, including baseball, football, track and field athletics, and especially cycling, have experienced doping scandals in recent years.

The relationship between the incidences of doping tests and the numbers of recorded cases of drug use at the Olympic Games, 1968–2008 is shown in Figure 7.39. *Examine this illustration carefully.*

Figure 7.39 Drug testing and incidence of detected doping at the Olympics.

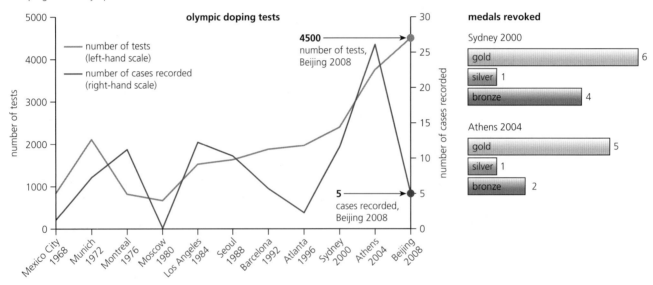

Questions for research and discussion

1. Can you find out how many medals were finally revoked at the 2008 Olympic Games?
2. The relationship between doping tests and detected cases 1968–2008 (graph in Figure 7.39) seems complex. Can you identify any significant trends?
3. If the drugs becoming available to athletes are extremely effective *and* progressively more difficult to detect, what kind of dilemma does this generate for ambitious sports people?
4. When the 'payoffs' for success are high, does the likelihood of 'clean' competitors being cut from teams on the basis of their comparative performances increase? Can you think of solutions to this dilemma?
5. Is there a need to be even more ruthless in the detection and punishment of doping? Alternatively, is it time for a more permissive approach? What are the likely advantages and disadvantages of each of these approaches?
6. Complete the table in Activity 7.16 concerning the ethical issues arising from the use of drugs in sport.

Activity 7.16: Ethical issues with the use of drugs (HSW Criterion 10)

End-of-topic test

An end-of-topic test is provided as part of the accompanying *Edexcel Biology for A2* Dynamic Learning resources, with (separate) answers.

Sample assessment material produced by Edexcel is available via the Edexcel web site: www.edexcel.org.uk.

8 Grey matter

STARTING POINTS

■ Organisms detect changes in their environment and respond to them – a characteristic known as sensitivity. Changes that are detected in cells and organisms and that bring about responses are called stimuli.

■ Organisms have mechanisms of internal communication. In animals, communication involves both the nervous system and hormones from endocrine glands. In plants, communication is via plant growth regulator substances.

■ Our brain receives and integrates incoming information from sensory receptors (for example, in the eye) and sends impulses to effectors (such as muscles and glands), stores information as a memory bank, and initiates activities.

■ Behaviour – the way organisms respond to the environment – is based on feedback, using the control and co-ordination mechanisms of the body.

■ Molecular genetics, based on the development of genetic engineering techniques and on the mapping of the entire human genome, offers huge benefits for society. It also generates challenging ethical issues.

8.1 The nervous system and sense organs

The ability to detect changes and respond appropriately is a life-preserving feature of living things, literally. This characteristic, known as **sensitivity**, is just as much a property of single cells as it is of mammals and flowering plants. We see this when a cell such as a phagocytic white cell (*Biology for AS*, page 53) or an organism such as *Amoeba* detects a suitable 'food' organism immediately outside its plasma membrane and moves to take it into a vacuole by phagocytosis. In this examination of sensitivity, we first focus on this feature in animals, particularly in mammals.

Changes that bring about responses are called **stimuli**. The stimulus is detected by a **receptor**, and an **effector** brings about a response. Since the receptor and effector are often in different places in a multicellular organism, mechanisms of internal communication are essential. In animals, internal communication involves both the **nervous system** and **endocrine system** (hormone-producing, page 179). We start by examining the nervous system, focusing in particular on the human.

Neurones – structure and function

The nervous system is built from specialised cells called **neurones**. Each neurone has a substantial cell body containing the nucleus and the bulk of the cytoplasm, from which extremely fine cytoplasmic nerve fibres run. The nerve fibres are specialised for the transmission of information in the form of impulses. Most fibres are very long indeed. Impulses are transmitted along these fibres at speeds between 30 and 120 metres per second in mammals, so nervous co-ordination is extremely fast, and responses are virtually immediate. The three types of neurones are shown in Figure 8.1 (overleaf).

■ **Motor neurones** have many fine **dendrites,** which bring impulses *towards* the cell body, and a single long **axon,** which carries impulses *away* from the cell body.

■ **Interneurones** (also known as **relay neurones**) have numerous, short fibres.

■ **Sensory neurones** have a single long **dendron**, which brings impulses *towards* the cell body, and a single long axon, which carries impulses *away*.

Activity 8.1:
Comparing neurones

Surrounding the neurones there are different types of supporting cells called **neuroglia cells** (sometimes shortened to 'glial cells') – also an important part of the nervous system. One type of neuroglia cell is called a **Schwann cell**. Many of the long fibres (dendrons and axons) are protected by Schwann cells. These wrap themselves around the fibres, forming a structure called a **myelin sheath**. Between each pair of Schwann cells is a junction in the myelin sheath, called a **node of Ranvier**. The myelin sheath and its junctions help increase the speed at which impulses are conducted (page 144).

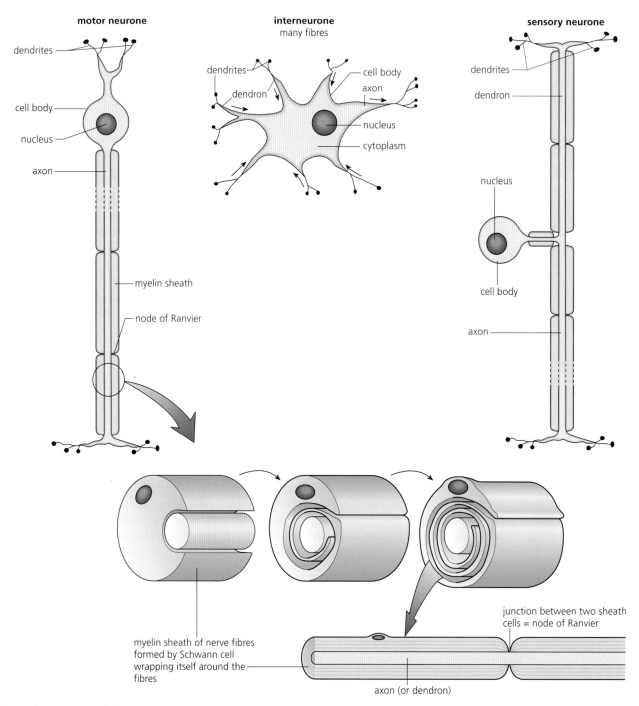

Figure 8.1 Neurones of the nervous system.

Organisation among neurones – reflex arcs and reflex action

The transmission of nerve impulses is not a haphazard process. It involves organised pathways among the neurones. These pathways are called **reflex arcs**. The reflex arc connects a sense organ (receptor) with a muscle or gland (effector), via neurones. A generalised reflex arc is shown in Figure 8.2.

Figure 8.2 The layout of a reflex arc – the structural basis of reflex action.

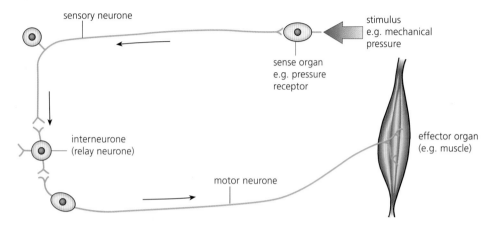

How does a reflex arc work?

The action begins when a sense organ detects a stimulus, which is a form of energy such as sound, light, or mechanical movement (causing pressure). This is converted into an impulse in the nerve fibre of a neurone serving that sense cell. Some of our receptors are elaborate organs containing many receptor cells, like the eye. Others are single cells, or merely sensitive endings of nerve fibres. Once generated, the impulse is transmitted along the fibres of a sequence of neurones in the reflex arc to an effector organ. When it arrives at the effector, the impulse causes a response – for example, it may cause a muscle to contract or a gland to secrete.

What has just been described is the simplest form of response in the nervous system. It is called a **reflex action**, and is a rapid, automatic but short-lived response to a stimulus. It is an involuntary response, not generally controlled by the brain's decision-making centres and not involving the rest of the nervous system. Also, a particular stimulus tends to produce the same response, every time. In humans, examples of reflex actions are the 'knee-jerk' reflex and the jerking away of your hand from scalding hot water.

We will discuss the impulse itself, and how it is transmitted, next.

Transmission of an impulse

An impulse is transmitted along nerve fibres, but it is *not* an electrical current that flows along the 'wires' of the nerves. Rather, the impulse is a momentary reversal in electrical potential difference in the membrane. That is, it is a change in the amounts of positively and negatively charged ions between the inside and outside of the membrane of a nerve fibre (Figure 8.3, overleaf). This reversal travels from one end of the neurone to the other in a fraction of a second. Between conduction of one impulse and the next, the neurone is said to be resting. Actually, this not the case. During the 'resting' interval between impulses, the membrane of a neurone actively creates and maintains an electrical potential difference between the inside and the outside of the fibre.

How is this done?

The resting potential

Two processes together produce the resting potential difference across the neurone membrane.

■ There is **active transport** of potassium (K^+) ions *in* across the membrane, and of sodium (Na^+) ions *out* across the membrane. The ions are transported by a Na^+–K^+ pump, with transfer of energy from ATP (page 6). So potassium and sodium ions gradually concentrate on opposite sides of the membrane. However, this in itself makes *no change* to the potential difference across the membrane.

■ There is also **facilitated diffusion** of K$^+$ ions *out* and Na$^+$ ions back *in* (*Biology for AS*, page 52). The important point here is that the membrane is *far more permeable* to K$^+$ ions flowing out than to Na$^+$ ions returning. This causes the tissue fluid outside the neurone to contain many more positive ions than are present in the cytoplasm inside. As a result, the inside becomes more and more negatively charged compared with the outside; the resting neurone is said to be **polarised**. The difference in charge, or **potential difference**, is about -70 mV. This is known as the **resting potential**. Figure 8.3 summarises how it is set up.

Figure 8.3 The establishment of the resting potential.

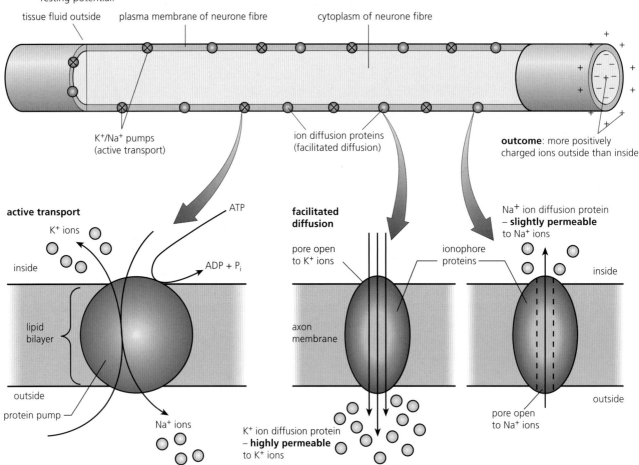

The action potential
The next event, sooner or later, is the passage of an impulse. An impulse, or **action potential**, is triggered by a stimulus received at a receptor cell or sensitive nerve ending. The energy transferred by this stimulus causes a temporary and local reversal of the resting potential. The result is that the membrane is briefly **depolarised** at this point (Figure 8.4).

How does this happen?

The change in potential across the membrane occurs through pores in the membrane, called **ion channels** because they can allow ions to pass through. One type of channel is permeable to sodium ions, and another to potassium ions. These channels are globular proteins that span the entire width of the membrane. They have a central pore with a gate, which can open and close. During a resting potential, these channels are all closed.

The energy of the stimulus first opens the gates of the sodium channels in the plasma membrane. This allows sodium ions to diffuse in, down their electrochemical gradient. So the cytoplasm inside the neurone fibre quickly becomes progressively more positive with respect to the outside. This charge reversal continues until the potential difference has altered from -70 mV to $+40$ mV. At this point, an action potential has been created in the neurone fibre.

The action potential then travels along the whole length of the neurone fibre. At any one point it exists for only two thousandths of a second (2 milliseconds), before the membrane starts to re-establish the resting potential. So action potential transmission is exceedingly quick – an example of **positive feedback**, in fact.

Almost immediately after an action potential has passed, the sodium channels close and potassium channels open. So potassium ions can exit the cell, again down an electrochemical gradient, into the tissue fluid outside. This causes the interior of the neurone to start to become less positive again. Then the potassium channels also close. Finally, the resting potential of $-70\,mV$ is re-established by the sodium–potassium pump, and the process of facilitated diffusion.

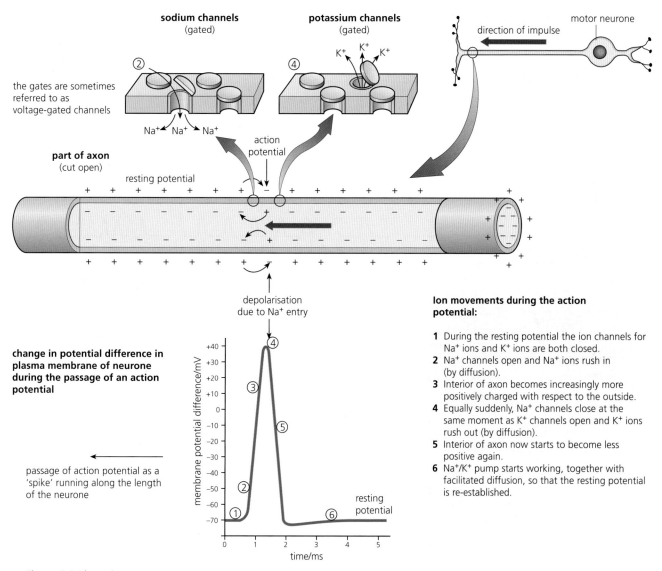

the gates are sometimes referred to as voltage-gated channels

change in potential difference in plasma membrane of neurone during the passage of an action potential

passage of action potential as a 'spike' running along the length of the neurone

Ion movements during the action potential:

1 During the resting potential the ion channels for Na^+ ions and K^+ ions are both closed.
2 Na^+ channels open and Na^+ ions rush in (by diffusion).
3 Interior of axon becomes increasingly more positively charged with respect to the outside.
4 Equally suddenly, Na^+ channels close at the same moment as K^+ channels open and K^+ ions rush out (by diffusion).
5 Interior of axon now starts to become less positive again.
6 Na^+/K^+ pump starts working, together with facilitated diffusion, so that the resting potential is re-established.

Figure 8.4 The action potential.

The refractory period

For a brief period following the passage of an action potential, the neurone fibre is no longer excitable. This is the **refractory period**. It lasts only 5–10 milliseconds in total. During this time, firstly there is a large excess of sodium ions inside the neurone fibre and further influx is impossible. As the resting potential is progressively restored, however, it becomes increasingly possible for an action potential to be generated again. Because of this refractory period, the maximum frequency of impulses is between 500 and 1000 per second.

The 'all or nothing' principle

Obviously, stimuli are of widely different strengths – for example, the difference between a light touch and the pain of a finger hit by a hammer! A stimulus must be at or above a minimum intensity, known as the **threshold of stimulation**, in order to initiate an action potential at all. Either a stimulus depolarises the membrane sufficiently to reverse the potential difference ($-70\,mV$ to $+40\,mV$), or it does not. If not, no action potential is generated. With all sub-threshold stimuli, the influx of sodium ions is quickly reversed, and the resting potential is re-established.

For stimuli above the threshold, as the intensity of the stimulus increases the frequency at which the action potentials pass along the fibre increases (the individual action potentials are all of standard strength). For example, with a very intense stimulus, action potentials pass along a fibre at an accelerated rate, up to the maximum possible, permitted by the refractory period. This means the effector (or the brain) recognises the intensity of a stimulus from the *frequency* of action potentials (Figure 8.5).

Figure 8.5 Weak and strong stimuli and the threshold value.

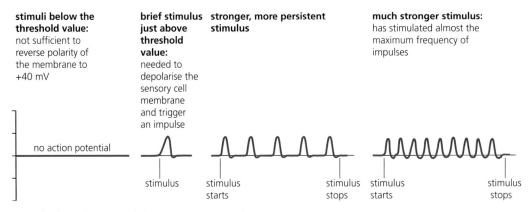

Speed of conduction of the action potential

The presence of a myelin sheath affects the speed of transmission of the action potential. The junctions in the sheath, known as the nodes of Ranvier, occur at 1–2 mm intervals. Only at these nodes is the axon membrane exposed. Elsewhere along the fibre, the electrical resistance of the myelin sheath prevents depolarisations. Consequently, the action potentials are forced to jump from node to node (Figure 8.6). This is called **saltatory conduction** ('saltation' meaning 'leaping'), and is an advantage, as it greatly speeds up the rate of transmission.

A* Extension 8.1: Laboratory investigation of an impulse (HSW Criteria 3 and 5b)

Figure 8.6 Saltatory conduction.

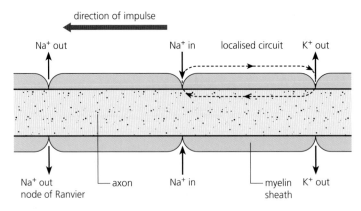

Not all neurones have myelinated fibres. In fact, non-myelinated dendrons and axons are common in non-vertebrate animals. Here, transmission is normally much slower, because the action potential flows steadily, right along the fibres. However, among non-myelinated fibres it is a fact that large diameter axons transmit action potentials much more speedily than do narrow ones. Certain non-vertebrates like the squid and the earthworm have giant fibres, which allow fast transmission of action potentials (although not as fast as in myelinated fibres). Experimental investigation of action potentials has been carried out on such giant fibres (A* Extension 8.1).

3 Why do myelinated fibres conduct faster than non-myelinated fibres of the same size?

Synapses – the junctions between neurones

Where two neurones meet they do not actually touch. A tiny gap, called a **synapse**, is the link point between neurones (Figure 8.7). Synapses consist of the swollen tip (synaptic knob) of the axon of one neurone (pre-synaptic neurone) and the dendrite or cell body of another neurone (post-synaptic neurone). Between these is the **synaptic cleft**, a gap of about 20 nm.

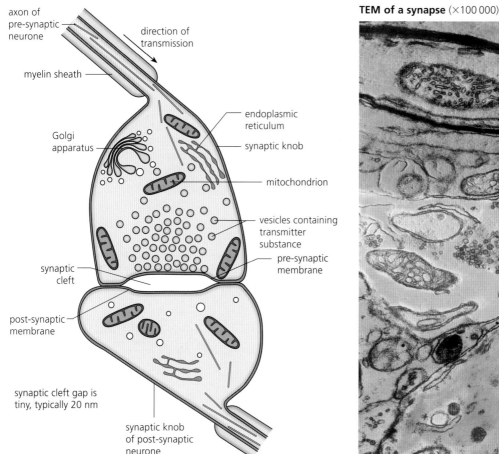

TEM of a synapse (×100 000)

Figure 8.7 A synapse in section.

The practical effect of the synaptic cleft is that an action potential cannot cross it. Here, transmission occurs by specific chemicals, known as **transmitter substances**. These substances are all relatively small, diffusible molecules. They are produced in the Golgi apparatus in the synaptic knob, and held in tiny vesicles prior to use.

Acetylcholine (ACh) is a commonly occurring transmitter substance; the neurones that release acetylcholine are known as **cholinergic** neurones. Another common transmitter substance is **noradrenalin** (released by **adrenergic** neurones). In the brain, the commonly occurring transmitters are glutamic acid and dopamine (page 175). Other neurotransmitter substances, including those active at synapses in the brain, are discussed later in this chapter.

Steps involved in synapse transmission
You may find it helpful to follow each step in Figure 8.8 (overleaf).

1   The arrival of an action potential at the synaptic knob opens calcium ion channels in the pre-synaptic membrane. Calcium ions flow in from the synaptic cleft.

2 The calcium ions cause vesicles of transmitter substance to fuse with the pre-synaptic membrane and they release a transmitter substance into the synaptic cleft. The transmitter substance diffuses across the synaptic cleft.

3 The transmitter substance binds with a receptor protein on the post-synaptic membrane.

In the post-synaptic membrane, there are specific receptor sites for each transmitter substance. Each of these receptors also acts as a channel in the membrane that allows a specific ion (such as Na^+ or Cl^-, for example) to pass. The attachment of a transmitter molecule to its receptor instantly opens the ion channel.

When a molecule of ACh attaches to its receptor site, a Na^+ channel opens. As the sodium ions rush into the cytoplasm of the post-synaptic neurone, depolarisation of the post-synaptic membrane occurs. As more and more molecules of ACh bind, it becomes increasingly likely that depolarisation will reach the threshold level. When it does, an action potential is generated in the post-synaptic neurone. This process of build-up to an action potential in post-synaptic membranes is called **facilitation**.

4 The transmitter substance on the receptors is quickly inactivated. For example, the enzyme cholinesterase hydrolyses ACh to choline and ethanoic acid. These molecules are inactive as transmitters. This reaction causes the ion channel of the receptor protein to close, and so allows the resting potential in the post-synaptic neurone to be re-established.

5 Meanwhile, the inactivated products of the transmitter re-enter the pre-synaptic neurone, are re-synthesised into transmitter substance, and packaged for re-use.

Figure 8.8 Chemical transmission at the synapse.

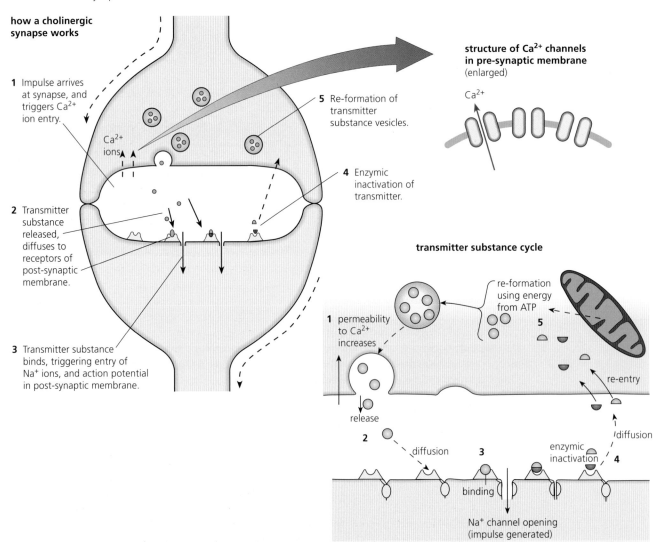

how a cholinergic synapse works

1 Impulse arrives at synapse, and triggers Ca^{2+} ion entry.

Ca^{2+} ions

2 Transmitter substance released, diffuses to receptors of post-synaptic membrane.

3 Transmitter substance binds, triggering entry of Na^+ ions, and action potential in post-synaptic membrane.

5 Re-formation of transmitter substance vesicles.

4 Enzymic inactivation of transmitter.

structure of Ca^{2+} channels in pre-synaptic membrane (enlarged)

Ca^{2+}

transmitter substance cycle

re-formation using energy from ATP

5

1 permeability to Ca^{2+} increases

re-entry

release

2

diffusion

3

enzymic inactivation

4

diffusion

binding

Na^+ channel opening (impulse generated)

4 What are the roles of:
a the Golgi apparatus
b mitochondria in the synaptic knob?

An alternative type of synapse

In this introduction to the synapse, it is an **excitatory synapse** that has been described. That is, the incoming action potential *excites* the post-synaptic membrane and generates an action potential that is then transmitted along the post-synaptic neurone. We should note at this stage that some synapses have the opposite effect. These are known as **inhibitory synapses**.

■ Extension: Why have synapses between neurones?

Since synapses have the disadvantage of very slightly slowing down the transmission of action potentials, we may assume they also provide distinct advantages to the operation of nervous communication in organisms, too. In fact there are a number of advantages. Synapses allow:

- the filtering out of low-level stimuli of limited importance
- the protection of effectors (muscles and glands) from over stimulation, since continuous transmission of action potentials eventually temporarily exhausts the supply of transmitter substances (that is, it causes synapse fatigue)
- flexibility of response by the central nervous system, particularly by the brain
- integration of information, since the post-synaptic neurone may receive action potentials from both excitatory and inhibitory pre-synaptic neurones – the post-synaptic neurone summates all the action potentials, thereby integrating impulses from more than one source neurone or sense organ, for example.

These latter points are illustrated in Section 8.2, page 157.

DL
www
A* Extension 8.2: Motor nerve endings make connection with muscle

Activity 8.3: The neurone as a specialised animal cell

Activity 8.4: Simulation of neurones in action

Receptors – the sensory system

Receptors are the sense organs that detect change. It is a property of all receptors that, in response to appropriate stimuli, they generate action potentials in a sensory nerve fibre. Receptors are typically sensitive to **one** type of stimulation only, such as differences in temperature, light, touch or chemicals. Some sense organs consist simply of a sensitive nerve ending, such as the Pacinian corpuscle, a commonly occurring pressure receptor, found below the skin and at joints in the body. Others sense organs consist of an individual cell or small groups of cells, while some are large, specialised organs like the eye and the ear, containing elaborate receptor cells within a complex supporting structure. As an example of the latter, we shall examine how certain of the specialised cells of the retina of the eye form action potentials in the optic nerve in response to light stimulation.

We have already noted that the intensity of a stimulus determines the frequency of the action potentials – the stronger a stimulus, the more frequently action potentials flow in neurones (Figure 8.5, page 144). This is the situation in sense cells, too, *at least initially*. However, if a stimulus is maintained at a high level, then sooner or later the permeability of the membrane of the sense cell to Na^+ ions decreases. As a result, the frequency of action potentials slows and may eventually stop. The sense organ is said to have **adapted**.

Sense organs adapt to varying degrees. Fine touch receptors in the skin adapt quickly; after dressing we soon cease to notice the touch of clothing on skin. Pain receptors all over our bodies, and stretch receptors in our muscles, adapt hardly at all.

The sense of sight

The eyes of mammals are protected in deep, bony sockets called orbits. The eyes supply information from which the brain perceives the size, shape, movement, and (sometimes) the colour of objects in the environment, and the direction and intensity of light. In those mammals with eyes directed forwards, so that their visual fields overlap (as in all primates), the brain also resolves the slightly different information from the two retinas into a three-dimensional image. This is known as stereoscopic vision. The structure of the eye and the focusing of an image on the retina are illustrated in Figure 8.9 (overleaf). Dilation and contraction of the pupil – regulating how much light is received on the retina – are discussed on page 155.

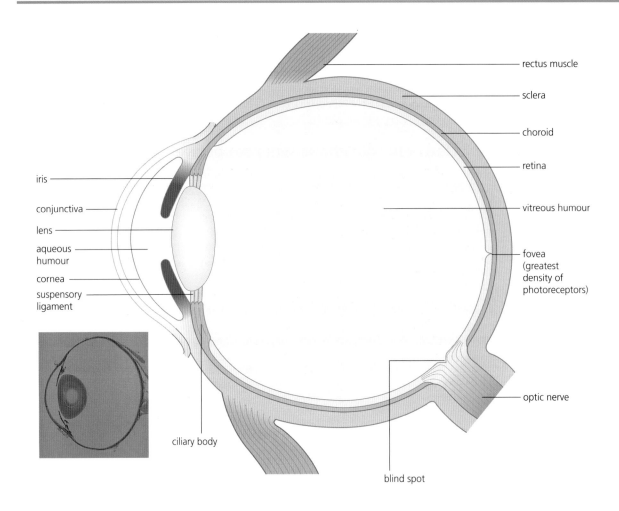

iris
conjunctiva
lens
aqueous humour
cornea
suspensory ligament

ciliary body

rectus muscle
sclera
choroid
retina
vitreous humour
fovea (greatest density of photoreceptors)

optic nerve

blind spot

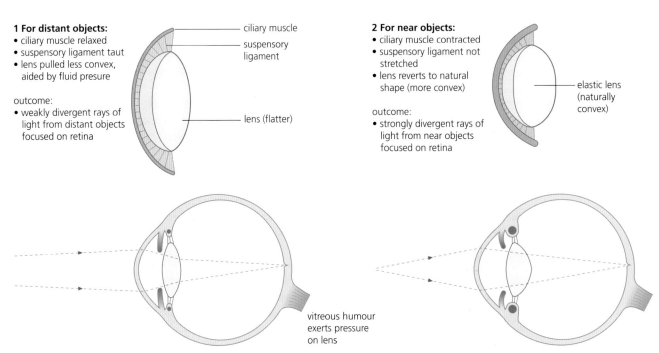

1 For distant objects:
- ciliary muscle relaxed
- suspensory ligament taut
- lens pulled less convex, aided by fluid presure

outcome:
- weakly divergent rays of light from distant objects focused on retina

ciliary muscle
suspensory ligament
lens (flatter)

2 For near objects:
- ciliary muscle contracted
- suspensory ligament not stretched
- lens reverts to natural shape (more convex)

outcome:
- strongly divergent rays of light from near objects focused on retina

elastic lens (naturally convex)

vitreous humour exerts pressure on lens

Figure 8.9 The eye, and the formation of an image on the retina.

The working retina

The **retina** of each eye is sensitive to light in the wavelength range 380–760 nm – that is, the visible range of the electromagnetic spectrum (the radiation from the Sun). The retina has two types of light-sensitive cell, the **rods** and **cones**, shown in Figure 8.10. These very elongated cells have an outer part called the outer segment. This consists of flattened membranous vesicles housing a light-sensitive pigment. An inner segment contains many mitochondria (the site of ATP formation).

Rods are far more numerous than cones; the human retina contains about 120 million rods compared with 6 million cones. Rods are distributed evenly throughout the retina, while cones are concentrated at and around a region called the **fovea**. This is an area where vision is most accurate – here there is the greatest density of photoreceptors. (Note that light passes through the neurones synapsing with the rod and cone cells *before* reaching the outer segments of these cells. Because of this feature, the retina is described as 'inverted' – Figure 8.10.)

Figure 8.10 The structure of the retina.

photomicrograph of a thin section of retina, stained to show cellular structure

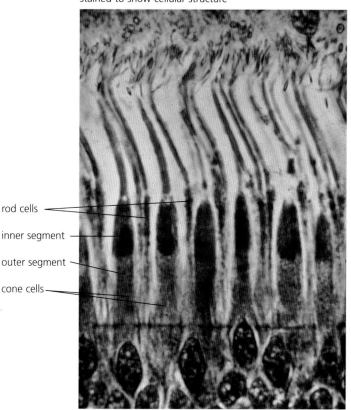

rod cells

inner segment

outer segment

cone cells

interpretive drawing of section of the retina

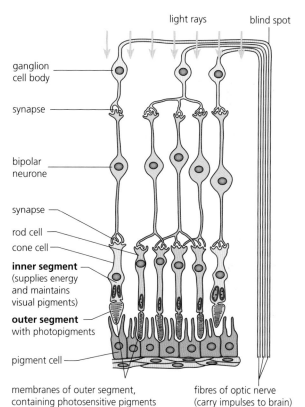

light rays   blind spot

ganglion cell body

synapse

bipolar neurone

synapse

rod cell

cone cell

inner segment (supplies energy and maintains visual pigments)

outer segment with photopigments

pigment cell

membranes of outer segment, containing photosensitive pigments

fibres of optic nerve (carry impulses to brain)

Rod cells are extremely sensitive to light, much more sensitive than the cones, but rod cells do not discriminate colours. Since they respond to lower light intensities than cones, they are principally used for dim light and night vision. The type of visual pigment molecules housed in the rods is called 'visual purple' or **rhodopsin**. This molecule is a combination of a protein (opsin) and a light-absorbing compound derived from vitamin A, called retinal. Remember, a diet deficient in vitamin A cause 'night blindness' – the inability to see in low light intensities.

The ways a rod cell responds to stimulation by light, and to its absence, are detailed in the labelled diagram in Figure 8.11.

Look carefully at this illustration as you follow the numbered steps.

In the dark, there is a steady flow of sodium ions into the outer segment, through open cation channels, located in the plasma membrane here. At the same time, the plasma membrane of the inner segment reverses this movement of ions – sodium ions are continuously pumped out of the cell at this point. This efflux occurs at the expense of ATP formed in the mitochondria of the inner segment. Consequently a concentration gradient is maintained between outer and inner segments, down which the sodium ions flow. Meanwhile, the influx of sodium ions at the inner segment slightly depolarises the cell, and the potential difference across the plasma membrane is about $-40\,mV$ (compared with a resting potential of $-70\,mV$).

Under these conditions, the rod cell releases a neurotransmitter substance (glutamate) that binds to the bipolar cell and prevents its depolarisation. The consequence is that no action potential is generated in the optic nerve that synapses with that bipolar cell.

When light falls on the retina, it causes reversible structural change in rhodopsin (called 'bleaching'), breaking it down into retinal and opsin. Opsin now functions as an enzyme that activates a series of reactions resulting in the closing of the cation channels of the outer segment, and so the influx of sodium ions is blocked. Meanwhile the inner segment continues to pump out sodium ions. This causes the interior of the rod cell to become *more* negative – a state described

5 What is the difference in structure between the fovea and the blind spot?

Figure 8.11 The working rod cell.

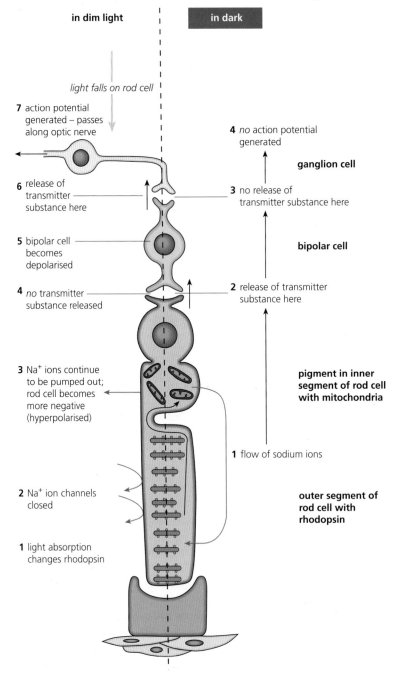

in dim light | **in dark**

light falls on rod cell

7 action potential generated – passes along optic nerve

4 *no* action potential generated

ganglion cell

6 release of transmitter substance here

3 no release of transmitter substance here

5 bipolar cell becomes depolarised

bipolar cell

4 *no* transmitter substance released

2 release of transmitter substance here

3 Na^+ ions continue to be pumped out; rod cell becomes more negative (hyperpolarised)

pigment in inner segment of rod cell with mitochondria

1 flow of sodium ions

2 Na^+ ion channels closed

outer segment of rod cell with rhodopsin

1 light absorption changes rhodopsin

as **hyperpolerisation**. In this condition, no neurotransmitter is released by the rod cell, and the bipolar cell becomes depolarised.

The bipolar cell releases a transmitter substance. An action potential is generated in a neurone of the optic nerve serving the rod cell. This action potential is transmitted to the visual cortex of the brain.

Meanwhile, the structure of rhodopsin is rebuilt, using energy from ATP. In very bright light, all the rhodopsin is bleached. In these conditions we are using cone cells, and the state of the visual pigment in rod cells is not of immediate consequence. In fact, we are not aware our rods cells are temporarily non-functional. But if we move suddenly from bright to very dim light it takes time for sufficient reversing of bleaching to occur, and we are temporarily blinded. We say our eyes are 'adapting to the dark'.

Processing action potentials from the retina

Observations of the three-dimensional world about us are reduced to two-dimensional images on the surface of the retina. As a consequence, action potentials generated in the rods and cones are carried by neurones of the optic nerves to the visual cortex of the brain (page 158). While each eye views left and right sides of the visual field, the brain receives and interprets action potentials from the right and left visual fields on the opposite side of the visual cortex. This is known as contralateral processing (Figure 8.12).

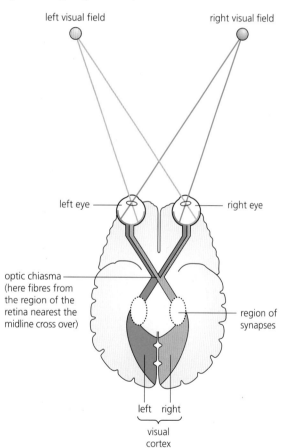

Figure 8.12 The eyes and the visual cortex – the pathways of impulses.

The messages from interpretation of these action potentials are combined by the brain to produce a single impression – our sight. 'Seeing', therefore, occurs largely in the brain, and the seeing process, known as **perception**, is complex. This is because perception involves the interpretation of sense data from the retina in terms of existing and past experiences and our expectations. The phenomenon of perception has implications for the nature and reliability of visual sense data, too (and, therefore, for the processes of science).

6 Explain the difference between a nerve and a neurone.

Nerves in control and integration

It is most likely that you are already familiar with the gross structure of our nervous system, consisting as it does of the **central nervous system** (CNS – brain and spinal cord) and all the peripheral nerves (Figure 8.13).

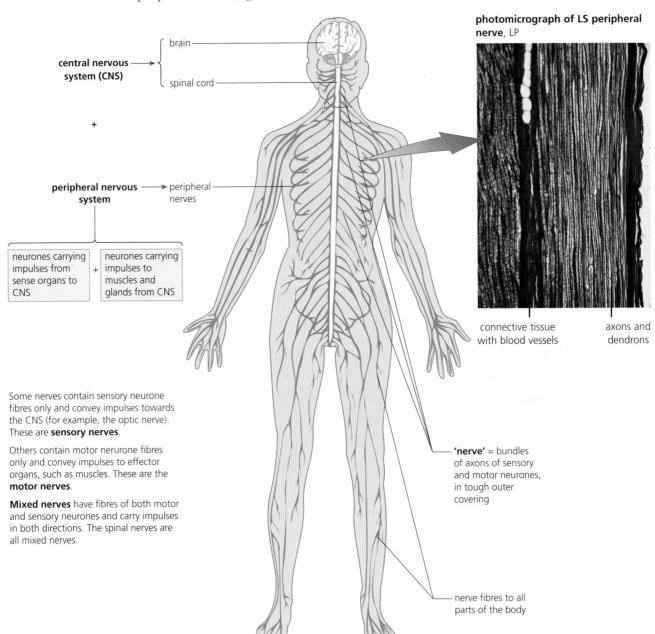

photomicrograph of LS peripheral nerve, LP

central nervous system (CNS) →
- brain
- spinal cord

+

peripheral nervous system → peripheral nerves

| neurones carrying impulses from sense organs to CNS | + | neurones carrying impulses to muscles and glands from CNS |

connective tissue with blood vessels

axons and dendrons

Some nerves contain sensory neurone fibres only and convey impulses towards the CNS (for example, the optic nerve). These are **sensory nerves**.

Others contain motor nerurone fibres only and convey impulses to effector organs, such as muscles. These are the **motor nerves**.

Mixed nerves have fibres of both motor and sensory neurones and carry impulses in both directions. The spinal nerves are all mixed nerves.

'nerve' = bundles of axons of sensory and motor neurones, in tough outer covering

nerve fibres to all parts of the body

Figure 8.13 The organisation of the mammalian nervous system.

The role of the brain in co-ordination and control of the body's responses is summarised in Figure 8.14. Brain structure, development and function are discussed in Section 8.2, below.

The role of the spinal cord is to relay action potentials between sensory organs and effector organs of the body (by reflex action), and between them and the brain. The layout of a reflex arc – the structural basis of reflex action – is introduced in Figure 8.2, page 141. In Figure 8.15, we see how a reflex action may be overridden by impulses sent from the brain. However, some pathways are relatively simple and cannot be overridden (they consist of two neurones only – a sensory neurone and a motor neurone – see SAQ 7, page 154).

Figure 8.14 Co-ordination and control by the nervous system.

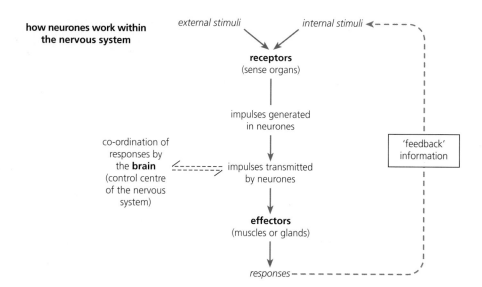

how neurones work within the nervous system

external stimuli → internal stimuli

receptors
(sense organs)

impulses generated in neurones

co-ordination of responses by the **brain** (control centre of the nervous system) ⇐ impulses transmitted by neurones

'feedback' information

effectors
(muscles or glands)

responses

Figure 8.15 The spinal cord and the roles of its neurones.

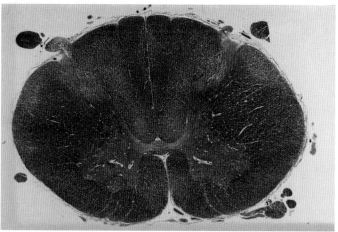

photomicrograph of the spinal cord in TS – note that the lipid-rich tissue (white matter) is stained with a dye

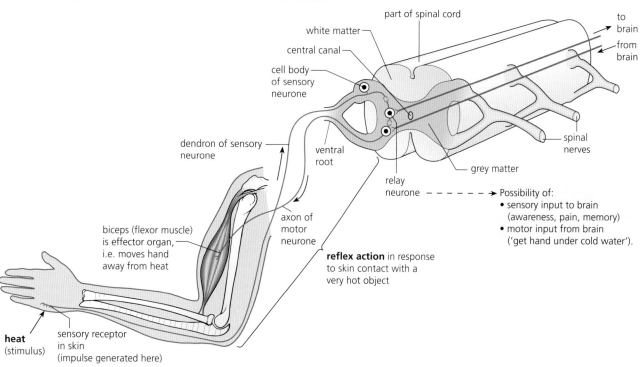

part of spinal cord

white matter

central canal

cell body of sensory neurone

dendron of sensory neurone

ventral root

axon of motor neurone

biceps (flexor muscle) is effector organ, i.e. moves hand away from heat

heat (stimulus)

sensory receptor in skin (impulse generated here)

to brain

from brain

spinal nerves

grey matter

relay neurone ⟶ Possibility of:
• sensory input to brain (awareness, pain, memory)
• motor input from brain ('get hand under cold water').

reflex action in response to skin contact with a very hot object

7 When the tendon that secures the patella is tapped, a knee jerk is observed. Sketch a diagram and annotate it to show the structures and the events involved in the knee jerk response.

The nerves of the **peripheral nervous system (PNS)** consist of the nerve fibres (axons and dendrons) arranged in bundles, protected by connective tissue sheaths (Figure 8.16). These nerves consist of:

- sensory neurones carrying impulses to the central nervous system
- motor neurones carrying impulses to muscles and glands.

Figure 8.16 A peripheral nerve in TS (×250) – the vagus nerve, which is mixed, containing axons of motor neurones and dendrons and axons of sensory neurones, each surrounded by a myelin sheath (dark).

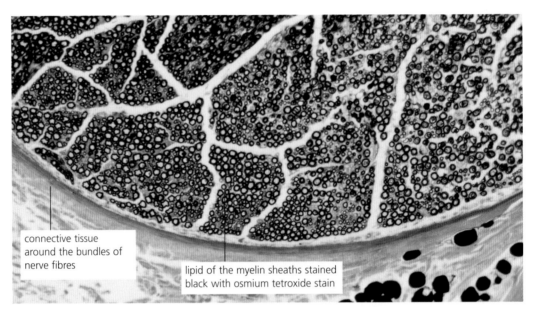

connective tissue around the bundles of nerve fibres

lipid of the myelin sheaths stained black with osmium tetroxide stain

Many of the motor neurones serve the muscles we use in conscious actions to produce voluntary movements, and they form the **somatic nervous system**.

On the other hand, the **autonomic nervous system (ANS)** controls activities inside the body that are mostly under unconscious (involuntary) control. It consists of motor neurones running to the smooth muscle of the internal organs and to various glands.

The autonomic nervous system acts to maintain the body's internal environment constant (autonomic means 'self-governing'). The ANS was first introduced in discussing control of heart and breathing rates in Chapter 7 (page 126) – *remind yourself of these examples, now.*

Table 8.1 The autonomic nervous system – roles and responses.

Sympathetic nervous system (SNS)	Parasympathetic nervous system (PNS)
more active in times of stress to produce 'flight or fight' responses	concerned in conservation of energy and the replacement of body reserves
at their junctions with effector tissues (muscles or glands) the neurones release noradrenaline	at their junctions with effector tissues the neurones release acetylcholine
Some of the responses of the two systems	
increases ventilation rate	decreases ventilation rate
causes widening (dilation) of the pupils	causes narrowing (constriction) of the pupils
has no effect on the tear glands	causes the secretion of tears
has no effect on salivary glands	causes secretion of saliva from salivary glands
peristalsis slowed	peristalsis accelerated
constricts bladder sphincter muscles	causes relaxation of the sphincter muscle of the bladder and contraction of the muscular wall of bladder (under overall control of conscious part of brain)

Actually, there is a further complication to the ANS, for it is divided into two parts:

- the sympathetic nervous system (SNS)
- the parasympathetic nervous system (PNS).

The layout of the peripheral nervous system as a whole is shown in Figure 8.17. In Table 8.1, the key differences between the SNS and the PNS are listed. Note that in some of the functions the two systems are antagonistic in their effects (for example, the SNS causes the heart rate to increase and the PNS causes it to decrease). However, in other cases they may have the same effect on a gland or muscle.

Figure 8.17 Peripheral nerves and conscious/unconscious control.

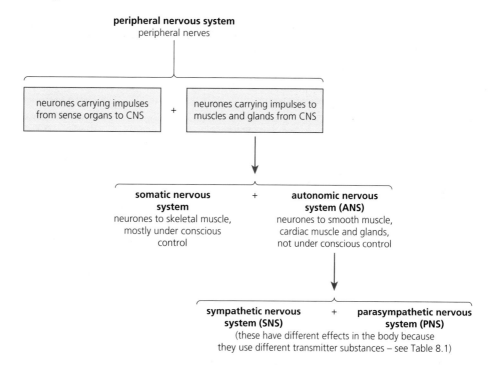

The pupil reflex – SYS and PNS in action

Look again at the structure of the eye seen in section (Figure 8.9, page 148).

Immediately in front of the lens is the iris. This is a circular disc of tissue containing radial and circular muscle fibres with a central hole, the pupil (Figure 8.18, overleaf). Incidentally, the iris contains the pigment responsible for 'eye colour'. When we move from the low light intensity of a shaded position or from any darkened environment, out into bright sunlight, a reflex arc instantly causes the diameter of the pupil to reduce in size. The amount of light entering the eye is immediately reduced. Excessive light is prevented from reaching the retina.

The iris muscles are controlled by the ANS; the radial muscle fibres are served by the SNS, and the circular muscle fibres are served by the PNS. The reflex arc of the iris diaphragm mechanism is shown in Figure 8.18 (overleaf).

8 What are the roles of sympathetic and parasympathetic nerve fibres in controlling heart rate?

Figure 8.18 The iris diaphragm and the pupil reflex.

iris diaphragm mechanism
in bright light   in dim light

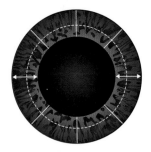

▶ circular muscle fibres of iris contract
▶ radial muscle fibres relax
▶ pupil diameter decreases
▶ less light enters the eye
  (preventing damage to the retina)
▶ depth of focus is increased

▶ radial muscle fibres of iris contract
▶ circular muscle fibres relax
▶ pupil diameter increases
▶ more light enters the eye
  (enabling vision at low light intensity)
▶ depth of focus is decreased

reflex action
Change of pupil size is a reflex action, controlled by the automonic nervous system. The radial muscle fibres are served by the sympathetic nervous system, the circular muscle fibres are served by the parasympathetic nervous system.

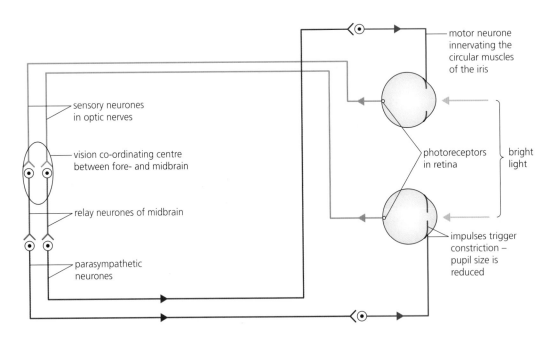

A* Extension 8.6: Atropine and the pupil reflex

Activity 8.8: The layout of the nervous system – test yourself!

The **reflex arcs** responsible for **dilation** of pupils (involving **sympathetic nerves**) are similar – but they are not shown here.

9 Which of the antagonistic muscles of the iris diaphragm cause the pupils to constrict and in what conditions will this reflex response occur?
10 How does variation of pupil size influence accommodation (focusing of an image)?

8.2 The brain and learning

The brain, a highly organised mass of interneurones connected with the rest of the nervous system by numerous motor and sensory neurones, is responsible for complex patterns of behaviour, in addition to many reflex actions. Much activity is initiated by the brain, rather than being mere response to external stimuli. In summary, the human brain controls all body functions apart from those under the control of simple spinal reflexes. This is achieved by:

- receiving impulses from sensory receptors
- integrating and correlating incoming information in association centres
- sending impulses to effector organs (muscles and glands) causing bodily responses
- storing information and building up an accessible memory bank
- initiating impulses from its own self-contained activities (for the brain is also the seat of 'personality' and emotions, and enables us to imagine, create, plan, calculate, predict and reason abstractly).

The vertebrate brain develops in the embryo from the anterior end of a simple tube, the **neural tube**. This tube enlarges to form three primary structures, known as the **forebrain, midbrain** and **hindbrain** (Figure 8.19, overleaf). The various parts of the mature brain develop from these by selective thickening and folding processes of their walls and roof.

These enlargement processes are most pronounced in mammals, and a striking feature of this group is the enormous development of the **cerebral hemispheres**, which are an outgrowth of the forebrain. The human brain contains about 10^{11}–10^{12} interneurones and the same number again of neuroglia cells. The majority of these neurones occur in the cerebral hemispheres. There, it is estimated, each interneurone forms synapses with a thousand other neurones. Mammals are the most intelligent of all animals, and their long memory, complexity of behaviour and subtlety of body control are also linked to the development of this brain structure.

When tissue inside the CNS is examined, parts where cell bodies are grouped together appear grey, so these are known as **grey matter**. Areas where myelinated nerve fibres occur together appear whiter, and so are called **white matter**. White and grey matter are present in the brain and in the spinal cord. Grey matter makes up the interior of the brain, and white the exterior. However, in the cerebral hemispheres and cerebellum (see below) there are additional layers of grey matter (that is, extra neurones).

Extension: Blood–brain barrier

Blood capillaries are also present throughout the nervous tissue. However, in the brain, the capillary walls form a barrier against many of the dissolved substances in the blood. This means that only the essential substances, such as oxygen and glucose, can cross into the brain. This is called the **blood–brain barrier**, and it is important for maintenance of normal brain function. For instance, some amino acids also act as neurotransmitters in brain synapses, so they must be excluded.

Brain – localisation of roles and duties

Within the brain as a whole, certain tasks and roles are localised (Figure 8.19, overleaf). For example, the **hypothalamus** – part of the floor of the forebrain, and exceptionally well supplied with blood vessels – is the control centre for the autonomic nervous system. Here the body monitors and controls body temperature and the levels of sugars, amino acids and ions (page 117). Feeding and drinking reflexes, and aggressive and reproductive behaviour, are also controlled here. The hypothalamus works with a 'master gland' called the **pituitary gland**, to which it is attached, monitoring hormones in the blood, and controlling the release of hormones. So the hypothalamus is the main link between nervous and endocrine systems (page 179).

Near the hypothalamus are the **thalamus** (the 'relay station' for impulses to the cerebral cortex from the rest of the brain and the spinal cord), and the **hippocampus** (responsible, together with parts of the cerebral hemispheres, for long-term memory).

the neural tube of an embryo

forebrain

hindbrain

midbrain

remainder of
tube forms
the spinal cord

**brain in section (formed by enlargement and
folding of fore-, mid- and hindbrain regions)**

cerebral
hemispheres

fluid-filled space
(ventricles)

hypothalamus

pituitary body

cerebellum

medulla

**brain *in situ* (protected
within the cranium)**

cranium

space filled with fluid

membranes
(meninges)

fluid-filled space
(ventricles)

choroid plexus – cerebrospinal
fluid formed here, and circulated
in the brain (in ventricles) and
around the brain in the cranium

Note: meningitis is an illness in
which the meninges become
infected and inflamed, either
owing to a virus, or to a
bacterium (the more dangerous).

brain from left side, with roles of some areas identified

frontal lobe (higher centres of the brain)
– personality (many aspects), thought and
reasoning, decision making, and making
association by combining inputs from
rest of cortex; also motor cortex, directly
linked to spinal cord, sending impulses
that trigger movements

parietal lobe – sensory association
areas, concerned with orientation,
movement, aspects of memory and
recognition, calculation and sensation

occipital lobe – visual sensory area,
concerned with processing inputs
from the eyes

olfactory (smell) area

cerebellum – posture, balance
and fine motor control

temporal lobe – hearing sensory area,
concerned with processing inputs from
the ears, sound recognition and speech
(left side lobe), plus aspects of memory

medulla oblongata

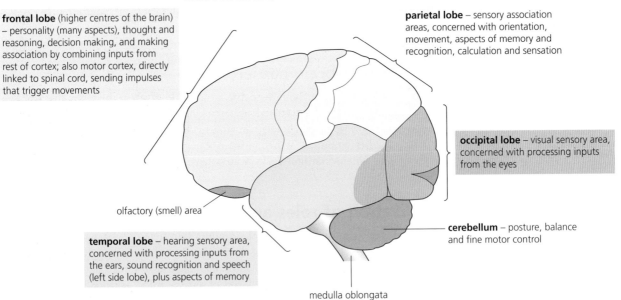

Figure 8.19 The human
brain.

The **cerebral hemispheres**, an extension of the forebrain, form the bulk of the human brain.
They are positioned above and around the remainder of the brain. Here the body's voluntary
activities are co-ordinated, together with many involuntary ones. The hemispheres have a vastly
extended surface, which is achieved by extensive folding so that it forms deep groves. The
surface, called the **cerebral cortex**, is covered by grey matter to a depth of 3 mm, and is densely
packed with non-myelinated neurones.

The cerebral cortex is divided into right and left halves, each of which is responsible for the opposite half of the body. This means that the right side of the cortex receives information (impulses from sensory neurones) from, and controls movements and other responses in, the left side of the body. (Communication between right and left cerebral cortices occurs via a substantial band of axons called the **corpus callosum**.) Within the hemispheres are the basal ganglia, consisting of discrete groups of neurones. They receive inputs and provide outputs to the cerebral cortex, thalamus and hypothalamus, and they control automatic movements of skeletal muscle and muscle tone.

Each side of the cerebral cortex is, by convention, divided into four lobes (frontal, parietal, temporal and occipital lobes). You can see from Figure 8.19 (lower image) that the areas of the cortex with special sensory and motor functions have been mapped out.

The **cerebellum**, part of the hindbrain, has an external surface layer of grey matter. It is concerned with the control of involuntary muscle movements of posture and balance. Here, the precise, voluntary movements involved in hand manipulations, speech and writing are co-ordinated (rather than initiated).

The **medulla**, the base of the hindbrain, is a continuation of the uppermost part of the spinal cord. It houses the regulatory centres concerned with maintaining the rate and force of the heart beat and the diameter of the blood vessels. Also it is here that a respiratory centre adjusts the basic rate of breathing. It is in the medulla that the ascending and descending pathways of nerve fibres connecting the spinal column and brain cross over (resulting, as already noted above, in the left side of our body being controlled by the right side of the brain, and vice versa).

■ Extension: The brain and decision making – an introduction

The brain consists of vast numbers of interconnected neurones – typically, at least 10^{11} neurones (that is 100 000 000 000) linked by 10^{14} synapses. The latter are highly significant in brain function.

The synapse introduced on page 145 was an excitatory synapse. That is, the incoming action potential excited the post-synaptic membrane and contributed to the generation of an action potential to be transmitted along the post-synaptic neurone. Other synapses have an opposite effect. These are known as inhibitory synapses (Figure 8.20). Here, release of the transmitter into the synaptic cleft triggers the opening of ion channels in the post-synaptic membrane through which chloride ions enter, or channels through which potassium ions leave. In either

Figure 8.20
Integration of multiple synaptic inputs.

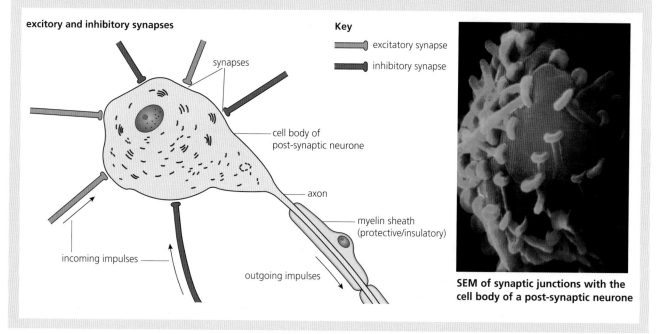

excitory and inhibitory synapses

Key
excitatory synapse
inhibitory synapse

synapses

cell body of post-synaptic neurone

axon

myelin sheath (protective/insulatory)

incoming impulses

outgoing impulses

SEM of synaptic junctions with the cell body of a post-synaptic neurone

case, the interior of the post-synaptic neuron becomes more negative (we say it is hyperpolarised). This makes it more difficult for the post-synaptic cell to generate a nerve impulse in response to excitation by other synapses (excitatory synapses).

In general, at a synapse, an action potential will be generated in the post-synaptic neurone only if the combined effects of action potentials arriving at excitatory synapses and at inhibitory synapses cause the depolarisation of the post-synaptic membrane to exceed the threshold level (Figure 8.20). This additive effect of post-synaptic potentials is known as **summation**. When several impulses arrive at a synapse in quick succession from a *single* axon and cause an action potential in the post-synaptic neurone, this is temporal summation. Alternatively, impulses from *several different axons* may contribute to the total, which we call spatial summation. Summation contributes to decision-making processes of the brain, as we see next. In brain function, in addition to impulses being received and generated, there is an ongoing process which we call **integration**. In effect, decisions are being taken in various centres in the brain, based upon integration of incoming data with memory data, at least in many cases.

How is this brought about?

One factor is *physiological* – the integration of the activities of excitatory and inhibitory pre-synaptic neurones at synapses described above, but operating within the unimaginably numerous connections that occur between the vast numbers of neurones present.

The other factor is *structural*. Different types of connection pathways are found between neurones. Some of these relay impulses to other pathways, some trigger a single response from many inputs, some ensure persistence of an original input, and some produce a strong, persistent result. The form and significance of each of these connections is introduced in Figure 8.21.

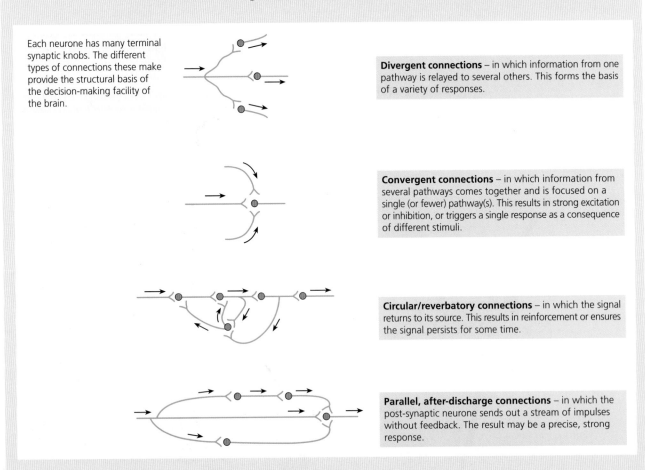

Each neurone has many terminal synaptic knobs. The different types of connections these make provide the structural basis of the decision-making facility of the brain.

Divergent connections – in which information from one pathway is relayed to several others. This forms the basis of a variety of responses.

Convergent connections – in which information from several pathways comes together and is focused on a single (or fewer) pathway(s). This results in strong excitation or inhibition, or triggers a single response as a consequence of different stimuli.

Circular/reverbatory connections – in which the signal returns to its source. This results in reinforcement or ensures the signal persists for some time.

Parallel, after-discharge connections – in which the post-synaptic neurone sends out a stream of impulses without feedback. The result may be a precise, strong response.

Figure 8.21 Neural connections observed between brain cells.

11 Suggest what advantages may result from the convergence of axon endings from several neurones on one post-synaptic neurone.

How the functions of brain regions have been discovered

Activity 8.9: Early detective work on brain function

The earliest known reference to the human 'brain' is on an Egyptian papyrus, dated to approximately 3800 years ago. It records the treatment of a sword wound to the head. By investigating brain-damaged patients, it has sometimes been possible to precisely correlate specific areas of the brain with the performance of particular functions. The sites of control of various facilities have been located (Activity 8.9).

In fact, external wounds that penetrate to the brain are often quickly fatal. On the other hand, cerebrovascular accidents ('strokes' – *Biology for AS*, page 25) are relatively common events, particularly in older people – and many strokes are not immediately fatal. The outcome may be paralysis in a part of the body, or loss of a specific sensation or facility. In subsequent post-mortem investigations, it has sometimes been possible to discover the specific area of the brain involved in a patient's particular loss of function.

Another source of information on brain function has been animal experiments. These have involved mammals and other vertebrates, and the removal of parts of a healthy brain or the severing of connections within the brain. The resulting altered behaviour has provided insights into the roles of parts of the brain. For example, the severing of the fibres that cross over in the centre of the brain below the two halves of the cerebral hemispheres gave clues to the interaction of left and right halves of the brain. Cats were used for that investigation.

Many of these approaches, using animals, would be unacceptable today (unethical and unnecessary – see below); as a society we are reluctant to sanction non-essential surgery that may cause pain.

In a **computerised axial tomography (CT or CAT)** scan, a series of narrow-beam X-ray impressions are taken of the body at slightly different angles and a computer puts them together to produce a detailed picture in which different soft tissues are detected. The result is a cross-sectional view of the interior of the area of body being studied. (Standard, broad-beam X-ray machines detect only dense body materials such as bone.) The picture is taken while the subject lies on a couch that moves backwards and forwards through a doughnut-shaped hole in the special X-ray equipment. In the process, numerous X-ray beams and a set of electronic X-ray detectors are rotated around the body, measuring the radiation being absorbed. Modern scanners are extremely fast – they can scan a large section of the body in a few seconds. CAT scans are commonly performed on the head or abdomen (Figure 8.22).

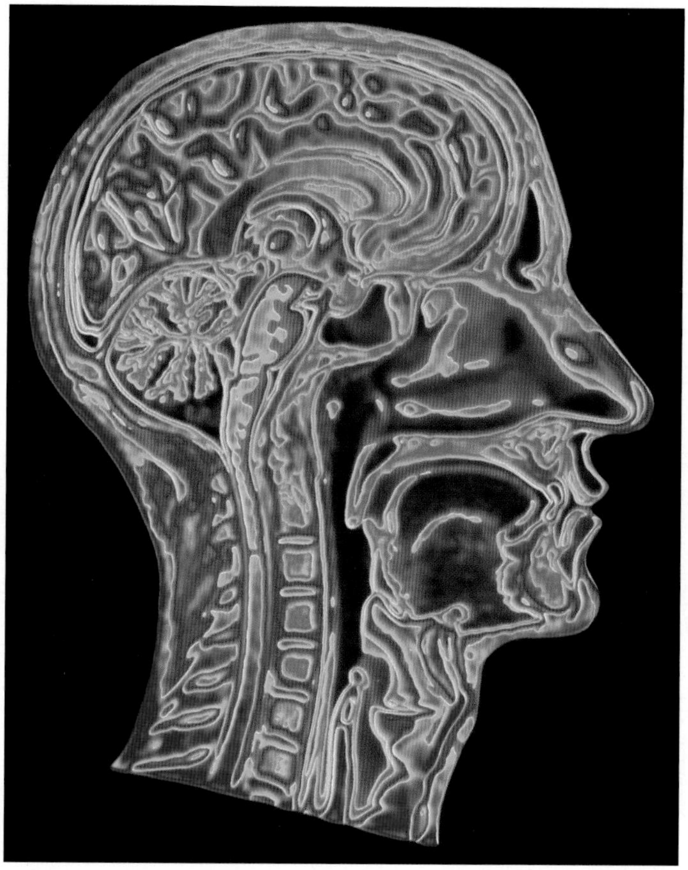

Figure 8.22 A CAT scan of the human head in sagittal section, showing a healthy brain. The folded appearance of the cerebrum and cerebellum are clear, as well as the forms of other soft-tissue structures.

A* Extension 8.7: CAT scanning and human origins – an unusual application (HSW Criteria 1 and 3)

Head scans are used to detect brain tumours or areas damaged by a stroke, for example. A picture of structures present is provided, rather than a diagnosis of functions. The patient is exposed to a dose of X-rays equivalent to that received from background radiation in a period of about three years. Since the information provided is obtained non-invasively, the benefits far outweigh the risks, in the circumstances in which a CAT scan is recommended. For example, they are used to detect various cancers, detecting the precise location of a tumour and the extent of the involvement of surrounding tissues. Serious internal injuries in cases of trauma can also be identified. Alternatively, a CAT scan can provide data on bone density in the detection of osteoporosis.

Using **magnetic resonance imaging (MRI),** the precise parts of a living, healthy, functioning brain that are *activated* when a particular body activity occurs, can be accurately mapped. This technique is also entirely non-invasive. Furthermore, it can detect activity anywhere in the brain, with high resolution, and provide results quickly.

MRI uses a strong magnet to produce detailed images. It works by measuring the way the vast number of hydrogen atoms present in the body absorb and then emit electromagnetic energy. The nucleus of each hydrogen atom is, in effect, a tiny magnet; in a strong magnetic field, these nuclei line up – as compass needles do in a magnetic field. In the process of a scan, a pulse of radio waves is then applied, sufficient to cause hydrogen nuclei to change orientation. When the pulse is switched off the nuclei revert to their original orientation and each nucleus gives off energy (at radio frequencies). From this signal, the scanner can work out the location of each nucleus.

fMRI images of volunteer undertaking a specific thinking task – scans of the brain show the right and left hemispheres (side views) and the brain from the midline, looking at left hemisphere (upper) and right hemisphere (lower image)

subject undergoing a series of brain scans while occupied on particular tasks – the regions of the cerebral hemispheres that are momentarily the sites of special neural activity are observed and recorded via the computer screen

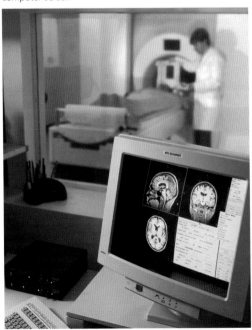

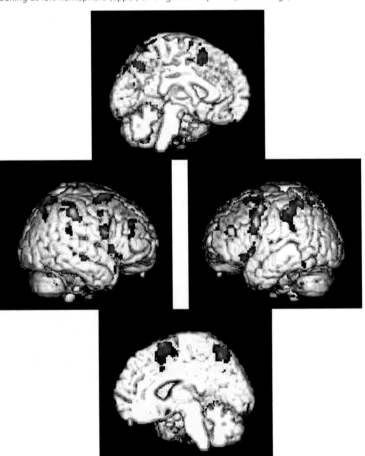

Figure 8.23 An advanced fMRI scanner in use.

Functional Magnetic Resonance Imaging (fMRI) is an advanced form of MRI that can be used to detect the parts of the brain that are active when the body performs particular tasks. Brain cells require energy and a good supply of oxygen at all times, but during periods of intense activity demand for these resources increases locally. The scanner can detect an increase in red blood cell oxygenation at the site of special neural activity, in a technique known as blood oxygen level dependent (BOLD) contrast. The increase in blood flow to the most active areas is disclosed by the difference between signals arising from hydrogen nuclei in water molecules in the neighbourhood of oxyhaemoglobin, compared with those close to deoxyhaemoglobin. When the concentration of oxyhaemoglobin increases, the MRI signal rises. The data obtained are transformed into three-dimensional images in which the brightest parts of the image are those that are most active.

In Figure 8.23, the scanner is in use with a volunteer who is involved in a thinking task (generating random numbers between 1 and 9, at a given pace). It can be seen that particular parts of cerebral hemispheres show increased blood flow, confirming the role of these areas. In fact, this brain mapping technique discloses the spatial organisation of human brain function down to a submillimetre level. Monitoring of healthy brain activity using fMRI has enabled researchers to precisely locate decision-making activities in areas of the brain associated with particular skills and body functions.

Activity 8.10: Viewing CAT and MRI scans

Development of human brain function – studies and outcomes

An early embryo consists of a vast number of very similar cells, the product of countless mitotic divisions. For example, at times during brain development alone, some 250 000 neurones are created every 60 seconds. Another feature of these embryonic cells is that they are in constant communication. Everything that happens in the developing organism (and in the adult body, too) relies upon the ability of cells to 'talk to each other'. During development, this communication is necessary for cells to know where to migrate to, what to develop into, and when to divide, for example.

We shall illustrate the process of development by reference to the human brain and, in particular, by the processes in which our visual capacities are formed. However, we should first note that, during development, literally billions of our cells die for the good of the whole organism, too. It is a mass of superfluous cells, together with any infected or damaged cells, that are destroyed in the process of development and in the functioning of healthy tissues and organs. This cell death is not a process of disorganised breakdown, but rather it is a finely controlled process – it is described as **programmed cell death**.

Growth of the brain

At birth, a baby's brain is about 25% of its approximate adult weight. Before birth, the brain has produced approximately *twice* as many neurones as it will ultimately need, and is estimated to contain some 10 000 million neurones at this early stage (Figure 8.24).

Figure 8.24 The structure of a brain neurone.

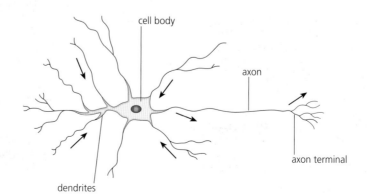

In post-natal brain development, existing neurones grow in size, axons elongate, and vast numbers of synaptic 'connections' are formed. Each individual neurone may become connected to 15 000 other neurones in this way. Specific neurotransmitters then start to facilitate the passage of impulses across these synapses. Meanwhile, the numbers of *additional* neurones formed in this post-natal period is not large. However, the developments described here account for a phenomenal degree of growth in the size of the brain during childhood – at the end of our first six months it is about half its adult size, and our brain is fully 80% of its final weight by the time we are two years of age.

Critical periods in growth?

There is good evidence of the existence of relatively brief critical periods in the development of the brain, known as 'windows of opportunity'. During these restricted times, specific types of development and learning take place. If the critical period is missed, such developments are slower or absent. Evidence for the existence of a critical period in visual development comes from both studies of humans and studies on animals, and is summarised in Table 8.2.

Table 8.2 Evidence of a critical period in visual development in mammals.

Human (clinical) studies	
1 Effect of a congenital cataract*	If a cataract present at birth is not diagnosed and removed early in life, the child may remain permanently blind in the affected eye, after its later correction. Adults who develop a cataract revert to entirely normal vision, once the cataract is removed, even when removal has been delayed.
2 Temporary eye-bandages, applied during childhood	Children who have one eye covered by a bandage (as treatment for a minor eye infection) for periods of just two weeks have sustained permanent impairment of vision in that eye, subsequently.
*Animal experiments***	
1 With newborn monkeys	Post-natal deprivation of light in one eye for six months (known as monocular deprivation) resulted in blindness in that eye. Subsequently, rods and cones in the deprived retina stimulated by light rays despatched impulses to the brain via the optic nerves, but the visual cortex did not respond to these. Similar deprivation, applied for a single week in the 'critical period' had the same effect. The vision of adult monkeys, treated similarly, was not impaired.
2 With newborn kittens	Kittens are born 'blind' and remain so for about three weeks. Monocular deprivation at week 4 resulted in the kittens remaining blind in the treated eye, subsequently. Similar deprivation in weeks I–3 and at the three-month stage of development had no harmful effects.

* A cataract is a medical condition in which the lens of an eye becomes progressively opaque.
** These studies with animals were conducted in the 1960s and 1970s by David Hubel and Torsten Wiesel. They were awarded a Nobel Prize in 1981. *Today, animal experiments raise ethical issues, which are discussed below* (page 174).

HSW 8.2: Criterion 7 – Contrasting forms of evidence

12 State, as accurately as you are able, the critical period in development of vision of kittens, based on the evidence presented in Table 8.2.

Development of vision prior to birth and the critical period

The visual cortex is located in the occipital lobes of the cerebral hemispheres (Figure 8.19, page 158) – it is here that our visual images will be created. In the growth and development of the brain, immature neurones migrate to specific brain regions and start the maturation process. Axons of neurones from the retina grow to the thalamus, and there they form synapses with specific neurones. Remember, the thalamus is the relay station for sensory impulses on their way to the cerebral cortex. In fact, the thalamus consists of groups of special neurones known as 'bodies'. One of these bodies receives sensory inputs specifically from the retinas (lateral geniculate body). Then, from the thalamus, neurones grow towards the visual cortex in the occipital lobes in an orderly, co-ordinated way.

It has been shown that isolated within the visual cortex are alternating columns of neurones that process information sent from either the left or right eye. These columns are called **ocular dominance columns**. Axons from the thalamus form synapses with the neurones of specific columns – adjacent columns receive impulses from the same area of the retina in the right and left eyes (Figure 8.25).

This early development of the brain follows a consistent and inherited pattern, quite independent of environmental influences. In effect, it has been discovered that this feature of brain structure is genetically determined, as indeed are most. Another (short-hand) way to describe this process is as 'nature' at work (genetically determined), rather than 'nurture' (driven by experience or environmental influences).

13 Explain the terms 'nature' and 'nurture' as they relate to growth and development, in your own words.

Figure 8.25 Nerve connections from eyes to ocular dominance columns of the visual cortex.

brain in LS, showing centrally placed thalamus and neurone connections with visual cortex

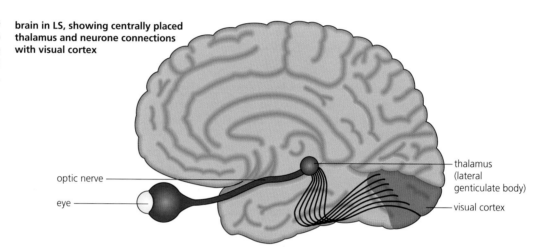

optic nerve

eye

thalamus (lateral geniculate body)

visual cortex

axons connecting retinas with ocular dominance columns of visual cortex

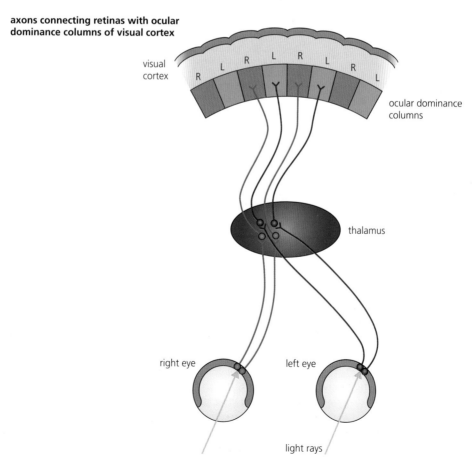

visual cortex

ocular dominance columns

thalamus

right eye

left eye

light rays

The visual cortex in the critical period

In Figure 8.26a, we see part of the visual cortex, and the axons of neurones that have grown in. The cortex is organised into alternating columns, to be served by visual information from one eye or the other. Note that the axons of neurones terminate in several synaptic contacts with the cell bodies of neurones of the visual cortex. There is a degree of overlap – in effect, the boundaries of the columns are not sharply delineated. This pattern occurs because of the innervations that formed during the earliest growth of the brain, prior to a critical period.

What developmental changes may follow in the critical period?

Experiments on the changes that may occur during the critical period indicate that:

1 refinements of the innervation pattern of the visual cortex reduce and eliminate overlapping by dendrites of neurones from left and right eyes within individual columns, as shown in Figure 8.26b

2 if columns are deprived of neurone stimulation – as when innervated by a light-deprived eye, during **monocular deprivation** – they become progressively smaller, with fewer synaptic connections established and maintained, as shown in Figure 8.26c.

These developments that occur to the 'wiring' of the visual cortex during the critical period are believed to be the product of 'competition' between axons for target cells in the column of the cortex. Where an axon makes synaptic contact and impulses arrive as a result, the 'connection' appears to be strengthened. Furthermore, this strengthening is at the expense of neighbouring neurones and their synaptic connections, *if they are not similarly stimulated*. Neurones that are innervated but not in receipt of stimulation by receipt of neurotransmitters at their synaptic connections with axons from the thalamus (and indirectly from an eye) tend to be progressively lost. Programmed cell death of unstimulated neurones eventually takes over – unstimulated columns are diminished as inactive axons and their synapses are pruned back.

The experimental evidence for the formation and existence of ocular dominance columns, their innervation in the visual cortex, and the fate of neurones there when deprived of stimulation, comes from various animal studies. These are summarised in Table 8.3.

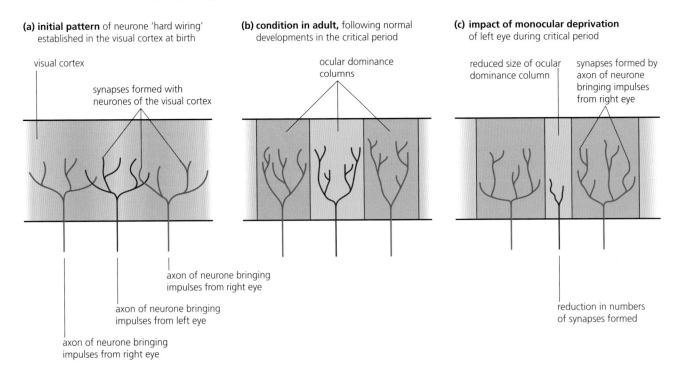

(a) initial pattern of neurone 'hard wiring' established in the visual cortex at birth

visual cortex

synapses formed with neurones of the visual cortex

axon of neurone bringing impulses from right eye

axon of neurone bringing impulses from left eye

axon of neurone bringing impulses from right eye

(b) condition in adult, following normal developments in the critical period

ocular dominance columns

(c) impact of monocular deprivation of left eye during critical period

reduced size of ocular dominance column

synapses formed by axon of neurone bringing impulses from right eye

reduction in numbers of synapses formed

Figure 8.26 Development of the ocular dominance columns in the visual cortex.

Table 8.3 The evidence for the formation and operation of ocular dominance columns.

Observation or investigation	Source
The appearance of ocular dominance columns in the visual cortex of cats was demonstrated 6–13 weeks after their birth. The segregation of synaptic inputs within this cortical layer depended upon post-natal 'visual experiences'.	C.J. Shatz *et al* (1978) *Journal of Comparative Neurology*
Rats reared in visually complex environments develop greater numbers of visual cortex synapses than those in control groups reared in 'standard' animal laboratory cages.	W.T. Greenough *et al* (1985) *Proc. Natl. Acad. Sci. USA.*
Changes in the neurones of the visual cortex of primates (monkeys) at the time of birth result in the formation of ocular dominance 'stripes'. In animals subjected to monocular deprivation subsequently, the stripes are no longer regularly spaced – many were observed to 'corrode'.	J.R. Thomson *et al* (1990) McGill University, Quebec, Canada
The formation of the visual cortex in the brains of ferrets was followed by tracer injections. These studies revealed the formation of ocular dominance columns in the visual cortex about 7 days after birth, *prior to the critical period*. During the critical period, the pattern of columns was altered in cases of monocular deprivation. Current studies centre on the structure and electrical activities of individual neurones, using multi-photon imaging, among other things.	J.C. Crowley *et al* (2000) Duke University Medical Centre, USA

Remember, post-natal deprivation of light in one eye for a significant experimental period is known as monocular deprivation.

'Nature' versus 'nurture' in brain development – other sources of evidence

We have seen how information on brain development and function may be obtained from studies on individuals with brain damage (due to an accident, or a stroke) and from various experiments involving animals, discussed above. This issue of the contributions of 'nature' versus 'nurture' in the development and functioning of our brains has also been tackled in other ways, too. These are illustrated next.

Twin studies

Identical twins (known as 'monozygotic twins') are genetically identical. By comparison, non-identical twins are the product of two separate eggs, simultaneously fertilised. So, while non-identical twins also share the same early *in utero* environment – the earliest environmental factor – they are no more alike than any other two siblings, genetically. Currently, twin studies are used to investigate the genetic basis of complex diseases, including Alzheimer's disease. This is a progressive neurodegenerative disorder involving loss of memory and personality change. The cause of the disease is complex and not fully understood, but all sufferers accumulate amyloid plaques (a particular protein) in the brain.

If one identical twin contracts late-onset Alzheimer's disease, it has now been shown there is a 40% chance the other twin will also do so. However, amongst non-identical twins the likelihood of the other twin also contracting the disease is only 10%. The conclusion of this data is that there is a genetic basis to Alzheimer's disease, but that both genes and environment play a part in triggering onset of the condition.

As a spin-off from the Human Genome Project (page 186), certain genes have been found to be specifically linked with an increased risk of developing late-onset Alzheimer's disease. With an ageing population, the incidence of this condition is likely to continue to rise. Both twin studies and medical research into the human genome will continue to be of importance until the underlying mechanism responsible for this disorder is understood.

Abilities of newborn babies

A newborn baby's earliest reflexes, of which there are several, are present as a result of the brain growth and development that has occurred *in utero*, rather than due to earliest 'life' experiences. In today's parlance, we say these reflexes are 'hard wired'. A selection of newborn reflexes is listed in Activity 8.11.

HSW 8.3: Criteria 10, 11 and 12 – Francis Galton and the eugenics movement

Activity 8.11: Reflexes of the newborn

Another apparent ability that is manifested very early in life is the judgement of 'depth' within our immediate surroundings. So, for example, an infant may accurately move arms and hands to pick up food or other items within easy reach, more-or-less unaided, as soon as he or she is able to sit up and reach out.

The facility to judge depth was investigated by means of a 'visual cliff experiment', as it has come to be known (Figure 8.27). Children, with carers on hand and in sight, were placed on a raised area covered by Perspex or glass, which overlaid a chequered pattern of black and white squares. In one half of the area, the pattern was recessed about one metre below the glass, creating an impression of a chasm and cliff-face. Babies of six months, able to crawl, were encouraged to cross the chasm. The children all declined – apparently sensing the potential danger of the 'cliff'.

Is this facility hard wired, or has it been learned in the period of time in which the baby has also learned to crawl?

14 What do we mean by 'hard wired' in the context of a baby's early reflexes?

Either is possible – as presented here. In an attempt to resolve this uncertainty, the experiment was repeated with various animals – chicks, kids (baby goats) and lambs, all selected because they walk as soon as they are born. All these animals stopped at the cliff face, refusing to move out over the 'chasm'. *Does this permit us to draw conclusions about human babies and the judgement of distance or depth?*

the experimental environment designed by E.J. Gibson and R.D. Walk (1960), known as the 'visual cliff'

a child hesitates to cross the visual 'cliff', despite encouragement from a trusted parent

Figure 8.27 The visual cliff experiment.

Cross-cultural studies

Optical illusions are more than party tricks! For one thing, they demonstrate that we 'see' in our brains, rather than in our eyes. So, for example, in Figure 8.28a, the stark outlines we observe appear to alternate between being a solid black vase on a white background, and then opposed faces, perhaps engaged in some conflict! In Figure 8.28b, we readily see lines that are absent. Clearly, the interpretation of the impulses received via the optic nerves in the brain involves memory and imagination.

Also, from the field of optical illusion we can gain insights into the conundrum of the visual cliff experiment, described above – is depth perception hard wired or learned? In Figure 8.28c, the illusion of depth is created by the converging lines and we find these clues impossible to ignore. The 'distant' cylinder must clearly be much the largest! But is it?

In Figure 8.28d, the Müller-Lyer illusion is presented – it comprises two arrow-like figures, one with ends pointing in and the other with ends pointing out. The former line is seen as longer.

Figure 8.28 Examples of visual illusions.

a vase or faces?

b seeing edges that do not exist

c illusions of depth (distance) and size

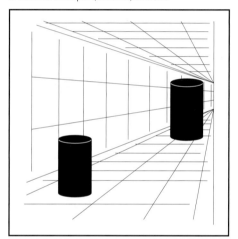

d Müller-Lyer illusion – culturally dependent?

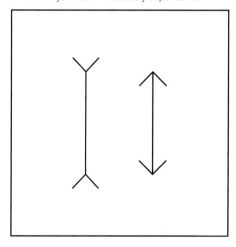

Why?

Do the inward-pointing arrows seem as extensions to the line? Do we see these as corners of rooms or buildings – the one on the left as the outgoing corner (so, 'angles pointing in' corresponds to an object that is closer), and that on the right as the ingoing corner (so, 'angles pointing out' signifies an object that is further away)?

Of special interest here is that our response to the Müller-Lyer illusion is not cross-cultural. Those of us who grow up and live in the built environment, full of horizontal and vertical lines are so 'fooled'. We see the right-hand image as shorter. Meanwhile, Zulu people brought up to live in circular thatched huts without angular walls, within a landscape without a wealth of vertical lines, are unlikely to see these images as we do. If this is correct, then our perception of depth has a strong environmental element – based on cultural differences.

Activity 8.12: Müller-Lyer illusion

The brain, learning and memory

Behaviour is defined as the way organisms respond to the environment and to other members of the same species. The study of behaviour is known as **ethology**, and it is closely related to the disciplines of ecology, genetics and physiology. Psychology has close connections with animal behaviour, too.

The activities of animals enable them to survive, to seek out favourable environments, and to reproduce. As an integral part of these activities, an organism receives information (sense data), allowing continuous adjustments of its responses. So, behaviour is based on 'feedback', using the control and co-ordination machinery of the body (this includes the sense organs and nervous system) and the effector organs. Behaviour is sometimes said to be either 'innate' or 'learned'.

Innate behaviour is instinctive, and automatically triggered in certain circumstances. It includes behaviour that is due to a reflex action. You may have observed the response of woodlice found sheltering under stones in a damp place – when exposed to light, they scatter and disappear under available cover.

Learned behaviour occurs when experiences are retained and used to modify behaviour on future occasions. Learning permits quick adaptations to changing circumstances; it is acquired by experience and modified in the light of further experience. We will discuss some aspects of learning next. However, in the natural world, the differences between 'innate' and 'learned' behaviour are not always clear cut, as the above introduction may suggest. Rather, many animals display a range of behaviours, some with innate features, and some which is clearly learned, in part at least.

A* Extension 8.8: Interpreting animal behaviour – a word of caution

Learned behaviour

Various forms of learned behaviour are shown by animals. We look at these next, starting with habituation and classical conditioning, prior to a discussion of the phenomenon of 'memory'.

Habituation

15 Describe *two* examples of habituation learning you may have experienced.

Habituation is illustrated when a crawling snail is touched with a leaf and retreats into its shell. Soon it re-emerges – unharmed. Every time the snail is touched in this way it withdraws, but for a shorter period. Eventually it does not respond protectively at all. Thus, a repeated stimulus that brings no danger can safely be ignored, so saving loss of feeding time and thereby increasing the chances of survival and reproduction for the snail. Similarly, a flock of birds, such as pigeons, are driven away from agricultural crops when a 'gunshot' bird-scaring device is first installed, but later the birds feed undisturbed, despite the continuing noises!

Activity 8.13: An investigation of habituation to a stimulus (HSW Criteria 2, 3, 4, 5, 6, 8 and 10)

So by definition, habituation is a type of learning involving the repeated application of a stimulus that results in decreased responsiveness. This is the simplest form of learned behaviour. In Activity 8.13, a practical investigation of habituation to a stimulus is presented. We will return to the issues of habituation in a discussion of cellular mechanism in learning, shortly.

Conditioning

Conditioning is a form of learning in which an animal forms an association between a previously significant stimulus and a previously neutral stimulus or response. Two types are recognised – classical conditioning (Figure 8.29) and operant conditioning.

Experiments on animals
Pavlov's experimental procedure would not be acceptable to most biologists today, but it is described here in acknowledgement that much of our understanding of human physiology has been derived from experiments on animals.

In these experiments Pavlov devised this complex arrangement so that the investigator was not present, and so that stimuli presented to the dog were precisely controlled.

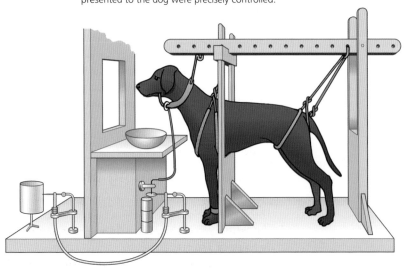

Figure 8.29 Pavlov's 1902 experiment on conditioned reflexes.

Classical conditioning was demonstrated by the work of the Russian experimental physiologist, Ivan Pavlov (1849–1936) in St Petersburg. This demonstration was part of an investigation of digestion. It is a common observation that a hungry dog may salivate (saliva drips from the mouth) on sight or smell of food. Pavlov studied this response under laboratory conditions that ensured the dog received no unintended additional stimulus (Figure 8.29). In his experiment, a second stimulus (the ringing of a bell), not directly related to food or feeding, was then introduced. The sound of the bell produced no response initially – the dog continued to salivate only on sight or smell of food. However, after several experiences of consistently hearing the ringing of a bell at the same time as food was seen or smelled, the dog became conditioned to salivate whenever the bell was rung, even without the food stimulus. This response was described as a conditioned response (Table 8.4). Pavlov called the salivation at the sound of the bell a conditioned reflex.

Activity 8.14: Demonstrate Pavlov's reflex

Table 8.4 Stimuli and responses in Pavlov's experiment.

	Stimuli	**Responses**
Unconditioned	sight or smell of food	salivation
Conditioned	bell sound	salivation without food stimulus

■ Extension: Operant conditioning

Operant conditioning involves the establishment of an association between a particular response and some reinforcement situation. So, for example, in a laboratory experiment a rat may associate pressing a bar with delivery of food. In the wild, a bird may associate turning over a dead leaf with the discovery of edible minibeasts. Reinforcements can also be negative, as in the case of farm stock (cows or pigs) that experience an electric shock from a live fence, when attempting to browse among lush grass beyond the barrier.

A* Extension 8.9: Other forms of learning – an introduction

What is memory?

Memory is the ability to express or perform some previously learned piece of information or skill. Memory involves learning, storage, retention and retrieval processes. We recognise that we have short-term memory and long-term memory. Short-term memory lasts seconds and is located in the frontal lobes of the brain, whereas long-term memory lasts at least 24 hours and usually very much longer. Long-term memory is established by processes involving the hippocampus (page 157). Stored information may be retrieved, and brought back into short-term memory. Associations of new data with previously learned 'memory' tend to make the new information easier to recall.

It may be that short-term memory is held in inter-connected neurones and exists in the form of impulses passing around circuits. If so, the loss of short-term memory could be by decay of the impulses, of by interference with newer memory circuits acquired subsequently. On the other hand, long-term memory is likely to take the form of permanent changes to brain cell circuitry and, perhaps to a lesser extent, chemistry.

As with any storage system, *retrieval* of information is as important a process as acquisition and retention. An adequate theory of memory has to account for the vagaries of our retrieval process. And the reliability of memories recalled is an issue of importance in many situations (Figure 8.30, overleaf).

Meanwhile, studies of habituation in the sea slug (*Aplysia* sp.), looking at the neural pathways involved in the gill-withdrawal reflex, have demonstrated one of the mechanisms implicated in the establishment of 'memory'.

Activity 8.15: Short-term memory tests

The sea slug and the cellular basis of learning

The sea slug, *Aplysia californica* is a giant marine mollusc with a diet of large seaweeds. It grows to a length of 1 m and achieves a body weight of 7 kg (Figure 8.31, overleaf). Oxygen is continuously extracted from sea water at the gills, which are within the mantel cavity. A respiratory current is pumped through the cavity by the action of a siphon, especially when it is extended.

Figure 8.30 The reliability of memory is a problem in courts of law.

THE TIMES Friday July 11 2008

You can't trust a witness's memory, experts tell courts

Psychologists call for action to avoid risk of wrongful convictions

Frances Gibb Legal Editor

The memories of witnesses are flawed, marred by gaps or inventions and should not be relied upon in court cases, researchers say.

Memories are a record of people's experiences of events – not a record of those events themselves, their report concludes. People also "remember" events that they have not in reality experienced and such recollections could – if heavily relied upon – lead to wrongful convictions.

Memory and the Law is being published today by the British Psychological Society, along with guidelines to help those in the legal system to evaluate evidence based on memory. It recommends that courts use memory experts to help juries to evaluate memory-based evidence, where, for instance, given by a child or elderly person.

Martin Conway, of the University of Leeds, the report's main author, said "Without corroborating evidence, witness testimony based on memory should not be relied on. In many legal cases, memory may feature as the main or only source of evidence, and it is nearly always critical."

It was difficult, if not impossible, for jurors to know how accurate a memory was likely to be and how much it could be relied on, he said. "What we say is that there is really not such a thing as a true memory. It is a record of experience – but is your experience a true record of reality?"

The memory was also defective in that it would lose details and have gaps, would be modified and changed by subsequent recall and could conflate events or experiences.

The report says that memories dating from below the age of 7 cannot be relied upon without independent evidence. Memories of specific events experienced after the age of 10 can be highly accurate, highly inaccurate and sometimes wholly false.

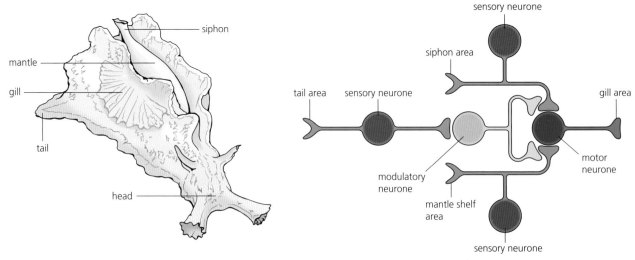

Figure 8.31 The sea slug and the neurones serving the gills.

16 How do the structure and function of myelinated and non-myelinated neurones differ? Tabulate the points in your answer.

The body of the slug contains about 20 000 neurones, which represents a nervous system infinitely less complex than that in the human body. However, the neurones in both are of comparable function, although those of the slug have fibres that are not myelinated.

Within its marine environment, the body of the slug experiences the constant pull and push of currents and waves, and frequent contacts with bulky seaweed fronds and stipes, among which it lives. To be effective, the nervous and sensory system has to be able to differentiate between these harmless, trivial tactile stimulations and any occasional, aggressive moves by a predator. Under such an external attack, the gills are withdrawn into the mantle cavity as an immediate, reflex reaction response. However, *habitual*, harmless environmental contacts are beneficially ignored in this respect. Consequently, it is no surprise that experimenters have demonstrated **habituation** in the responses of *Aplysia* to those mild and harmless stimulations of the body. Habituation is a type of learning.

How does a violent or painful stimulation of the body alter this response?

This issue was the subject of an intensive investigation by E.R. Kendel and team. Their work was awarded a Nobel Prize in 2000.

Experiments showed that a light touch stimulation of the siphon of *Aplysia* resulted in the gills being withdrawn (Figure 8.32). However, the extent of the withdrawal lessens with repeated stimulation (a case of habituation). Then the research team simulated a violent attack using a small electrical shock (applied between siphon stimulations 13 and 14 – the arrow in Figure 8.32). The outcome was a complete gill withdrawal.

Figure 8.32 Stimulations of *Aplysia* that result in gill withdrawal.

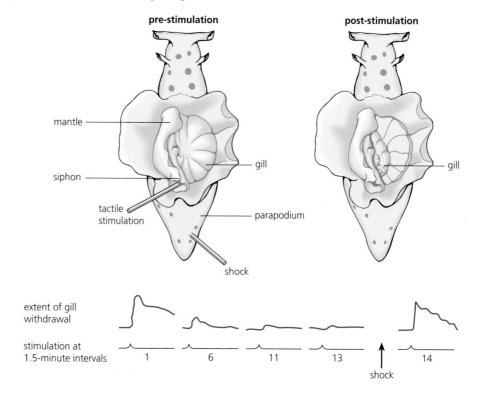

In the subsequent, detailed investigation of the neurones involved, Kendel's team uncovered the physical basis for the habituation observed.

■ During habituation, the pre-synaptic terminals of the sensory neurones are the sites of the events responsible for the behavioural modification that we recognise as basic learning. The repeated arrival of impulses as a result of ongoing stimulation of the siphon leads to a gradual inactivation of the Ca^{2+} channels there. This is followed by a reduction in the quantity of neurotransmitter released by the pre-synaptic membranes with each action potential, and therefore by the progressive diminution in gill withdrawals that is observed (Figure 8.32). This is the chemical basis of habituation.

- When an intense shock (a laboratory simulation of a predator attack) is applied to the tail, the response to gentle stimulation of the siphon, diminished by habituation, is reactivated (Figure 8.32). This is due to the release of another neurotransmitter by the interneurones (Figure 8.31). This transmitter (**serotonin**) triggers a cascade of changes in the pre-synaptic neurones, resulting in enhanced uptake of Ca^{2+}. As a result, more neurotransmitter is released, greater depolarisation of the post-synaptic membrane results, a higher frequency of action potentials is generated, and enhanced gill withdrawals are observed. This phenomenon is known as **sensitisation**.

- When mild stimulations were repeatedly applied to the mantle, paired with the noxious stimulation of the tail (electric shock), the animal started to respond far more vigorously to mantle stimulation. (This response is comparable to the conditioning of reflexes demonstrated by Pavlov in a vertebrate.) This form of learning endured only briefly (short-term memory). However, other programmes of conditioning resulted in the acquisition of a more long-term memory – lasting for more than three weeks. Long-term memory occurred not from transient metabolic changes, but rather as a result of structural changes. It was observed that the number and size of synapses, together with the number of synaptic vesicles formed, was substantially increased.

17 Draw up a table summarising what can be concluded about the process of memory, based on the experimental evidence discussed here.

Animals in research – an ethical conundrum

You may have noted the conditions under which a dog was held in Pavlov's experiments on the control of digestion. Also, that the experiments on 'memory' in the sea slug, discussed above, involved somewhat stressful laboratory conditions and the application of essentially unpleasant stimuli.

Today, the involvement of laboratory animals in research is extensive (Figure 8.33). It is estimated that a total of three million animals are used annually in the UK; in the USA the figure is possibly in excess of 20 million, and globally the estimate is that 50 million animals are used worldwide, every year. About 90% of the animals are rodents.

The idea of carrying out an experiment that is expected to cause pain to an animal is unacceptable to most people. This revulsion has lead to the introduction of laws that attempt to eliminate any unnecessary suffering. Even so, some people believe that no experimentation on animals can ever be justified.

Are there circumstances in which we should accept the need for experiments on animals, even though these may include the possibility of stressful or unpleasant conditions for them, at times?

Figure 8.33 Animals in scientific research.

What are the ethical issues relating to the use of animals in medical research, for example? To tackle this issue, first remind yourself of the discussion of the nature of ethics and the listing of ethical standards in *Biology for AS*, pages 95–96. These were:

■ rights
■ justice
■ utilitarianism
■ common good
■ virtue.

Activity 8.16: Should we involve animals in research? If so, why, and how? (HSW Criterion 10)

There are websites that it may be helpful to consult (Activity 8.16).

Another conundrum is presented in SAQ 19. You may care to take more time over resolving your own response to this. In view of the extent and harm brought about be malaria (admittedly not in this country) we might hope this conundrum becomes a practical issue in our life-time.

18 **The challenge:** The needs and rights of the non-human animal world are virtually impossible to reconcile with the advantages to be gained from their selective, supervised use in medical research in certain circumstances. The opposing arguments are more-or-less impossible to resolve. Instead, tabulate the essential contrasting points you feel that an 'animal rights' supporter and an 'animal welfare' supporter would make.

19 Imagine a (highly plausible) situation in which approval was needed for the use of animals (say rodents, and primates, too) in a programme to test the safety and efficacy of a particular experimental vaccine against malaria – caused by a parasite (*Plasmodium*) – which kills more children around the world than any other disease. Could you approve this – and why?

Neurotransmitter of the brain – in health and disease

About 100 metabolites are known to be, or suspected of being, neurotransmitters – but in many circumstances it is hard to establish their precise roles. This is because neurones, their cell bodies, dendrites and axons, mostly occur tightly packed together, particularly in the brain. Furthermore, the amount of neurotransmitter liberated at a synapse is tiny, as are the synaptic clefts where neurotransmitters operate (Figure 8.7, page 145). Nevertheless, several neurotransmitters have well-established roles.

Acetylcholine is the neurotransmitter you are already familiar with – it operates at very many of the excitatory synapses throughout the body. Within the autonomic nervous system, acetylcholine occurs in PNS synapses but we have noted that noradrenaline occurs in the SNS synapses.

Within the brain, the amino acid glutamate has a powerful excitatory effect – about 50% of the synapses there communicate via glutamate. Similarly, gamma aminobutyric acid (GABA) is an inhibitory neurotransmitter found to operate *only* in the brain. GABA occurs at about one-third of synapses. Other classes of chemicals active at synapses include a family of neuropeptides called endorphines – these are the body's natural painkillers. Also, the amines dopamine and serotonin have important roles in the brain, of which more shortly.

■ Extension: Nitric oxide

The gas nitric oxide (NO) has widespread effects throughout the body that have been discovered recently. Unlike other neurotransmitters, NO is not synthesised in advanced and stored in vesicles. Rather, it is formed as required, immediately active, and rapidly removed. In fact, NO is a potentially harmful molecule, quickly converted to nitrites and nitrates. Endothelial cells in the walls of the blood vessels (*Biology for AS*, page 14) release NO, which causes the smooth muscles there to relax, so enhancing blood flow. Thus it has a role in lowering blood pressure. It plays a part in erection of the penis, too.

Brain neurotransmitters and ill-health

We can illustrate the role of neurotransmitters of the brain in health and disease, first by reference to two important diseases, namely Parkinson's disease and depression.

Figure 8.34 The impacts of Parkinson's disease and depression.

Parkinson's disease

forward tilt of trunk

reduced arm swinging

shuffling gate with short steps

rigidity and trembling of head

rigidity and trembling of extremities

Depression
This painting by Vincent van Gogh (1890) represents the despair felt by a sufferer of depression.

Parkinson's disease

Parkinson's disease is a chronic, progressive disease that affects body movement (Figure 8.34). Its victims are typically of age 50–60 years, but only 1–2% of the population are affected. Parkinson's is not an inherited disease – only approximately 5% of cases arise where there is a family history of the condition. Consequently, some environmental factor is suspected. The chief symptoms are:

- a tremor in the arms and hands, at a maximum when the limbs are at rest
- rigidity and stiffness of skeletal muscles, together with impaired balance
- slowness of movements with shuffling gait, stooped posture and short steps
- difficulties with speech and swallowing.

Within the brain, this condition is triggered when particular neurones degenerate. These neurones extend from a structure in the midbrain called the substantia nigra to the basal ganglia in the cerebral hemispheres – where they release the neurotransmitter dopamine (DA). Also in the basal ganglia are neurones that release acetylcholine (ACh), and these are unaffected. So, in Parkinson's disease, the level of DA declines but ACh remains the same. It is this imbalance in neurotransmitters that triggers the symptoms.

Treatment of the symptoms of Parkinson's involves the prescription of:

- the drug selegiline – a selective, irreversible inhibitor of monoamine oxidase (MAO); MAO is an enzyme that naturally breaks down dopamine present in the brain tissue
- the drug L-dopa, which is a precursor of dopamine – once in the blood stream, it crosses the blood–brain barrier (page 157), is absorbed in the brain, and converted into dopamine (dopamine itself is unable to cross the blood–brain barrier and so is valueless against Parkinson's disease, if administered directly)
- drugs that are dopamine agonists (they work by stimulating the dopamine receptors) – however, these cause the dopamine receptors to become progressively less sensitive, thereby exacerbating the symptoms, over time.

DL
www
Activity 8.17:
Observing the effect of treatment with L-dopa

In addition, surgeons have attempted to transplant fetal tissues rich in dopamine into the basal ganglia region of patients with particularly severe symptoms. To be successful, the introduced tissue needs to develop a permanent presence. However, only a few of these patients experienced improvements, in the early stages of this approach.

Depression

Diagnosis of depression has to be based on the patient's own reported experiences together with observations of their behaviour (Figure 8.34). As a consequence, it is probably significantly under-reported, particularly by young people – the onset is usually early to mid-adulthood. The symptoms exhibited by an affected person include:

- marked changes in mood including periods of profound sadness
- a persisting loss of interest and pleasure in activities once enjoyed
- feelings of worthlessness, helplessness, and pessimism, accompanied by difficulty in concentrating or making decisions.

In the developed world, somewhere between 5 and 10% of people suffer from one or more episodes of depression, at some time in their lives. A significant number of these patients have a family history of the condition – suggesting there may be a genetic basis for this disease.

The neurotransmitter serotonin is believed to play a part in determining mood, but the precise relationship between serotonin and depression is not known. It has been claimed that an oversimplified connection has been presented to the public. Neurones that manufacture serotonin occur in the brain stem, and axons from their cell bodies serve areas of the hind-, mid- and forebrain, including the cerebral hemispheres.

Treatments for depression may include the following.

- **Medication** – prescription of anti-depressant drugs. These are substances that increase the extracellular levels of serotonin by inhibiting its re-uptake into the pre-synaptic neurones where this neurotransmitter is metabolised and secreted. The effect is to raise the levels of serotonin available to bind to post-synaptic receptors. An example of an anti-depressant drug is Prozac.
- **Psychotherapy** – provided to individuals or groups. Psychotherapy means treatment by psychological means – by approaches that seek to sympathetically explore the patient's state of mind, possibly by discussion. This is designed to identify experiential causes, and ideally leads to a self-cure.
- **Electroconvulsive therapy** – ECT or electroshock treatment. In this treatment, which is an approach sometimes proposed in cases of severe depression that do not respond to alternatives, a 'seizure' is electrically induced in an anaesthetised patient – for proven therapeutic effect.

Development of new drugs to treat brain disease

Existing drug treatments for Alzheimer's disease (page 167) do not provide a cure, but do temporarily slow down the development of the symptoms of this form of dementia. Research has established that the brains of people with Alzheimer's are deficient in acetylcholine. Existing, approved drugs may belong to a group that inhibits acetylchoholinesterase (the enzyme that breaks down acetylcholine, page 145). Other drugs stimulate the release of acetylcholine in the brain. Another approach is to block the action of glutamate, for this neurotransmitter is present in excess in the brain of people with Alzheimer's.

In the brain of an Alzheimer's patient, there is a progressive build up of an abnormal protein which is believed to be responsible for the symptoms. Pharmaceutical companies seek to tackle this possible root cause (Activity 8.18).

DL
www
Activity 8.18: Research raises hopes of new drugs for Alzheimer's

Effect of psychoactive drugs on synaptic transmission

A **psychoactive drug** is one that affects the mind. These drugs have their effects on synapses in the brain, the performance of which may be profoundly altered (Figure 8.35). Some drugs amplify the processes of synaptic transmission – in effect, they increase post-synaptic stimulation. We describe them as agonists. Nicotine has this effect. Other drugs inhibit the processes of synaptic transmission, in effect decreasing post-synaptic stimulation. We describe them as antagonists. β-blocker drugs have these effects.

Why may psychoactive drugs affect personality?

We have noted the significance of synaptic transmission in brain function, together with the brain's central role in the co-ordination of memory, emotions, and creative and abstract reasoning powers. For these reasons, the use of drugs may have a profound effect on behaviour – and possibly on personality.

Figure 8.35 Drugs may increase or decrease synaptic transmission.

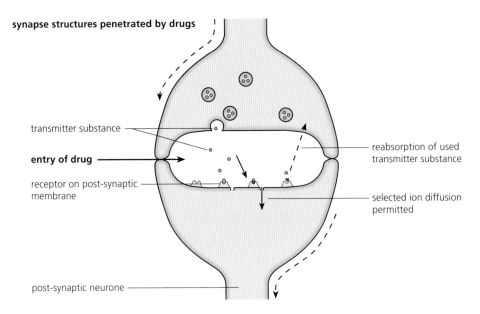

synapse structures penetrated by drugs

transmitter substance

entry of drug

receptor on post-synaptic membrane

reabsorption of used transmitter substance

selected ion diffusion permitted

post-synaptic neurone

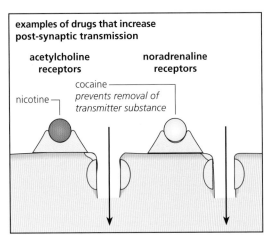

examples of drugs that increase post-synaptic transmission

acetylcholine receptors

noradrenaline receptors

cocaine
prevents removal of transmitter substance

nicotine

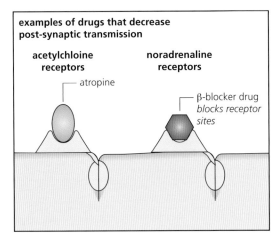

examples of drugs that decrease post-synaptic transmission

acetylchloine receptors

noradrenaline receptors

atropine

β-blocker drug
blocks receptor sites

The use of psychoactive drugs in a social and recreational context is popular with many people in diverse societies all over the world. However, their uses often have dangerous or tragic consequences. Examples of such drugs are well known. We can illustrate the affect of such a drug by reference to 'ecstasy'.

MDMA – its impact on synaptic transmission

The psychoactive drug known as ecstasy is a semisynthetic organic chemical, a member of the amphetamine group of drugs, whose full biochemical name is methylenedioxy-N-methamphetamine (generally abbreviated to MDMA). This is a very widely used, illicit drug.

The immediate effect of taking MDMA is the creation of a sense of euphoria, a sense of intimacy, and a diminished feeling of anxiety and fear. It also creates a feeling of thirst, a raised heart beat, and a tendency for hyperthermia, for ecstasy also disrupts the ability of the brain to regulate body temperature. The long-term psychological effects include depression and severe anxiety.

MDMA exerts its effect on synapses where the neurotransmitter serotonin operates. Serotonin molecules, on release into the synaptic cleft and binding to receptors on the post-synaptic membrane, are transported back across the pre-synaptic membrane. However, MDMA binds to the serotonin transport molecules, preventing the neurotransmitter's removal. The result is an enhanced or prolonged supply of this neurotransmitter – known to bring about mood changes.

20 Identify the health dangers of alcohol abuse, including effects on the liver. You might use as your sources recent articles in *Biological Science Review, New Scientist, Scientific American,* or appropriate websites, for example. Acknowledge your sources.

A review – mechanisms of co-ordination in animals

Control and communication within the body of an animal involve both the nervous system and hormones. **Hormones** are chemical substances produced and secreted from the cells of the ductless or **endocrine** glands. In effect, hormones carry messages about the body – but in a totally different way from the nervous system. Hormones are transported indiscriminately in the blood stream, but they act only at specific sites, called target organs. Although present in small quantities, hormones are extremely effective messengers, helping to control and co-ordinate body activities. Once released, hormones typically cause changes to specific metabolic reactions of their target organs. However, hormones circulate in the blood stream only briefly. In the liver, they are broken down and the breakdown products are excreted at the kidneys. So, long-acting hormones must be secreted continuously to be effective.

Examples of hormones include insulin, released from the islets of Langerhans in the pancreas, which regulates blood glucose, and the sex hormones released by the gonads. The positions of all the endocrine glands of the human body are shown in Figure 8.36.

The endocrine system and the nervous system work in distinctive and different ways in the control and co-ordination of body activities (Table 8.5). However, the activities of the nervous and endocrine systems are co-ordinated by the **pituitary gland**, the master gland of the endocrine system working in tandem with the hypothalamus of the brain. The hypothalamus secretes hormones that regulate the functioning of the pituitary. The hypothalamus also monitors the level of hormones in the blood and regulates secretion by negative feedback control.

Figure 8.36 The human endocrine system.

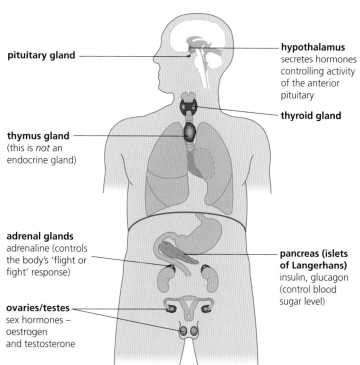

Table 8.5 Endocrine and nervous systems compared.

Endocrine system	Nervous system
communication is by chemical messengers transmitted in the blood stream	communication is by electrochemical action potentials (impulses) transmitted via nerve fibres
hormones are 'broadcast' all over the body but influence only target cells and tissues	action potentials are targeted on specific cells
causes changes in metabolic activity	causes muscles to contract or glands to secrete
hormones have their effects over many minutes, several hours or longer	produces effects within milliseconds
effects tend to be long-lasting	effects tend to be short-lived and reversible

8.3 Plants and sensitivity

Sensitivity is a characteristic of all living things, but the responses of organisms can be very different. In contrast to the responses of animals, plant responses are mostly growth movements. For example, young stems grow towards the light, and the main roots of plants grow towards gravity. These responses, while quite slow and unspectacular, are essential to plant growth, development and nutrition. We shall see that they are also quite precise and carefully regulated responses.

The investigation of plant responses to the external stimulus light, led to the discovery of plant hormones, better known as **growth regulators**. The list of plant growth regulators now includes five groups of substances, all chemically very different. The first to be discovered were the auxins – the others are the gibberellins, cytokinins, abscisic acid and ethane (a gas). They are called growth regulators rather than hormones because they bear little resemblance to the hormones of animals (Table 8.6).

Table 8.6 Differences between plant growth regulators and animal hormones.

Plant growth regulators	Animal hormones
produced in a region of plant structure, e.g. stem or root tips, in unspecialised cells	produced in specific glands in specialised cells e.g. islets of Langerhans in the pancreas (producing insulin)
not necessarily transported widely or at all, and some are active at sites of production	transported to all parts of body by the blood stream
not particularly specific – tend to influence different tissues and organs, sometimes in contrasting ways	effects are mostly highly specific to a particular tissue or organ, and without effects in other parts or on different processes

Plant stems and light

The response of green plants to light is shown in Figure 8.37. The photograph shows that the relationship between the growth of a green plant shoot and light is complex – and perhaps rather surprising.

In the dark, plant stems grow thin and weak, and they bear tiny, undeveloped leaves, yellow in colour. The shoots of plants in the dark are said to be **etiolated**.

By contrast, shoots grown in full light are short, with sturdy stems. The leaves are fully expanded and dark green in colour.

We already know that sunlight is essential for photosynthesis (page 8), to sustain plant nutrition. But we cannot also say that light is essential for plant growth in length. Quite the contrary in fact – light *inhibits* plant stem growth. The shoots grown in unilateral light confirm this. (Unilateral light is a beam of light coming from one direction.) Here the stems grow towards the light. We explain this on the basis that growth on the illuminated side of the stem is inhibited by light, but stem growth is unchecked on the dark side, so a growth curvature results. So, light does inhibit plant stem growth in length. On the other hand, light is essential for chlorophyll formation and leaf expansion.

To investigate this response, growing stems can be marked at regular intervals, using a felt-tip marker pen. Some of marked stems are then exposed to unilateral light and others to normal illumination. We are able to see that the region where elongation of the stem occurs is also the region of growth curvature in unilateral light. So we conclude that the response of the plant stem to unilateral light is a *growth* response. Growth movements of plant organs in response to an external stimulus, and in which the direction of the stimulus determines the direction of the response, are called tropic movements or **tropisms**. For example, when the stem tip responds by growing towards the light, it is positively phototropic.

21 Make a list of the various effects of light on plant growth and development.

Figure 8.37 Seedling growth and light.

the effects of light on plant growth

seedlings grown in total darkness – long, weak stems and small, yellow leaves

seedlings grown in even illumination – short, strong stems and large, green leaves

pea seedlings in unilateral light – the stems have grown towards the light, showing positive phototropism

the region of stem growth

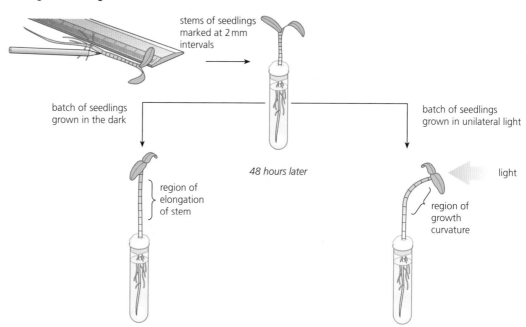

stems of seedlings marked at 2 mm intervals

batch of seedlings grown in the dark

batch of seedlings grown in unilateral light

48 hours later

region of elongation of stem

light

region of growth curvature

the phototropic response of the stem is a growth response

Using coleoptiles to investigate phototropism

The **coleoptile** is a sheath of tissue, unique to the grass family, which encloses the shoot of a germinating grass seedling, but only as long as it grows up through the soil. The coleoptile grows rather like a stem does, but it is uncluttered by leaves or buds, so its growth is easily observed. Experiments have been conducted with oat seedling coleoptiles, the plant organ first used to investigate phototropism (Figure 8.38, overleaf). In fact, experiments on the responses of oat coleoptiles to unilateral light led to the discovery of the plant growth substance named 'auxin', later shown to be a substance called indoleacetic acid (IAA – Figure 8.41, page 184).

Auxin is manufactured by cells undergoing repeated cell division, such as those found at the stem and root tips (and at the tip of coleoptiles). Consequently, the concentration of auxin is highest there. Auxin is then transported to the region of growth behind the tip, where it causes cells to elongate. In the process, the auxin is used up and inactivated.

In one experiment, the tip of the stem or coleoptile is cut off and stood on a gelatin block for a short while. Then the block is placed on a cut stump of stem or coleoptile. Growth in length is found to continue. The explanation is that auxin passes into the gelatin block, so when the gelatin is placed on the stump, the auxin passes down into the tissue and stimulates elongation of the cells. This technique has been used to investigate auxin actions further, as follows.

Figure 8.38 The coleoptile as an experimental organ, and the discovery of auxin.

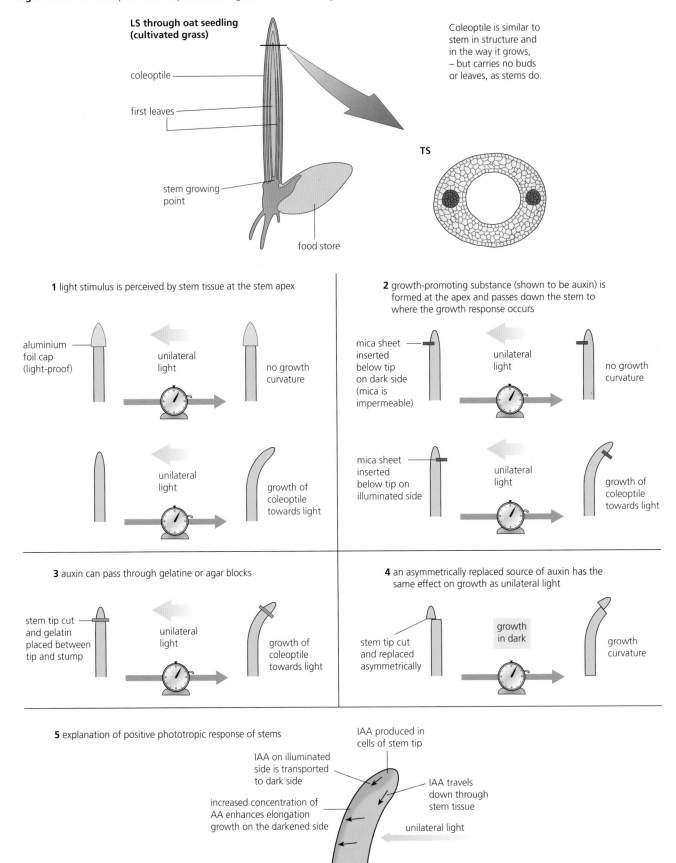

LS through oat seedling (cultivated grass)

coleoptile

first leaves

stem growing point

food store

Coleoptile is similar to stem in structure and in the way it grows, – but carries no buds or leaves, as stems do.

TS

1 light stimulus is perceived by stem tissue at the stem apex

aluminium foil cap (light-proof)

unilateral light

no growth curvature

unilateral light

growth of coleoptile towards light

2 growth-promoting substance (shown to be auxin) is formed at the apex and passes down the stem to where the growth response occurs

mica sheet inserted below tip on dark side (mica is impermeable)

unilateral light

no growth curvature

mica sheet inserted below tip on illuminated side

unilateral light

growth of coleoptile towards light

3 auxin can pass through gelatine or agar blocks

stem tip cut and gelatin placed between tip and stump

unilateral light

growth of coleoptile towards light

4 an asymmetrically replaced source of auxin has the same effect on growth as unilateral light

stem tip cut and replaced asymmetrically

growth in dark

growth curvature

5 explanation of positive phototropic response of stems

IAA produced in cells of stem tip

IAA on illuminated side is transported to dark side

IAA travels down through stem tissue

increased concentration of AA enhances elongation growth on the darkened side

unilateral light

The effect of light on auxin distribution

In stems and coleoptiles exposed to unilateral light, it is the auxin passing down the stem that is redistributed to the darkened side, causing differential growth and the curvature of the stem. The degree of curvature is proportional to the amount of auxin, up to a certain concentration. Above this, additional auxin inhibits growth.

This discovery was used to estimate the concentration of auxin in samples from plant tissues by a biological test. A cut tip of a coleoptile or a gelatin block with auxin was placed asymmetrically on a freshly decapitated oat seedling coleoptile, and the resulting curvature was found to be proportional to the amount of auxin present. Consequently, the degree of curvature caused by an unknown sample can be measured and compared with the curvature produced by samples of known concentration of auxin (IAA). This is an example of a biological measurement, called a **bioassay** (Figure 8.39).

An explanation of how auxin (IAA) affects coleoptile growth is shown in Figure 8.40. The range of effects of auxin on plant growth is summarised in Figure 8.41, overleaf.

Figure 8.39 The oat coleoptile curvature test.

tip then discarded

coleoptile tip stood on gelatin block for 2 hours

tip discarded

fresh coleoptile stump (tip removed)

curvature due to asymmetric growth of coleoptile

2 hours

measurement of the angle of curvature taken from a photograph of curved coleoptile

angle of curvature

Degree of curvature was found to be proportional to the number of coleoptile tips stood on the gelatin block.

increasing number of coleoptile tips

After auxin was found to be IAA, the curvature test was repeated with IAA in gelatin, at a range of concentrations.

higher concentrations of IAA inhibit growth

IAA concentration in gelatin block/mg dm^{-3}

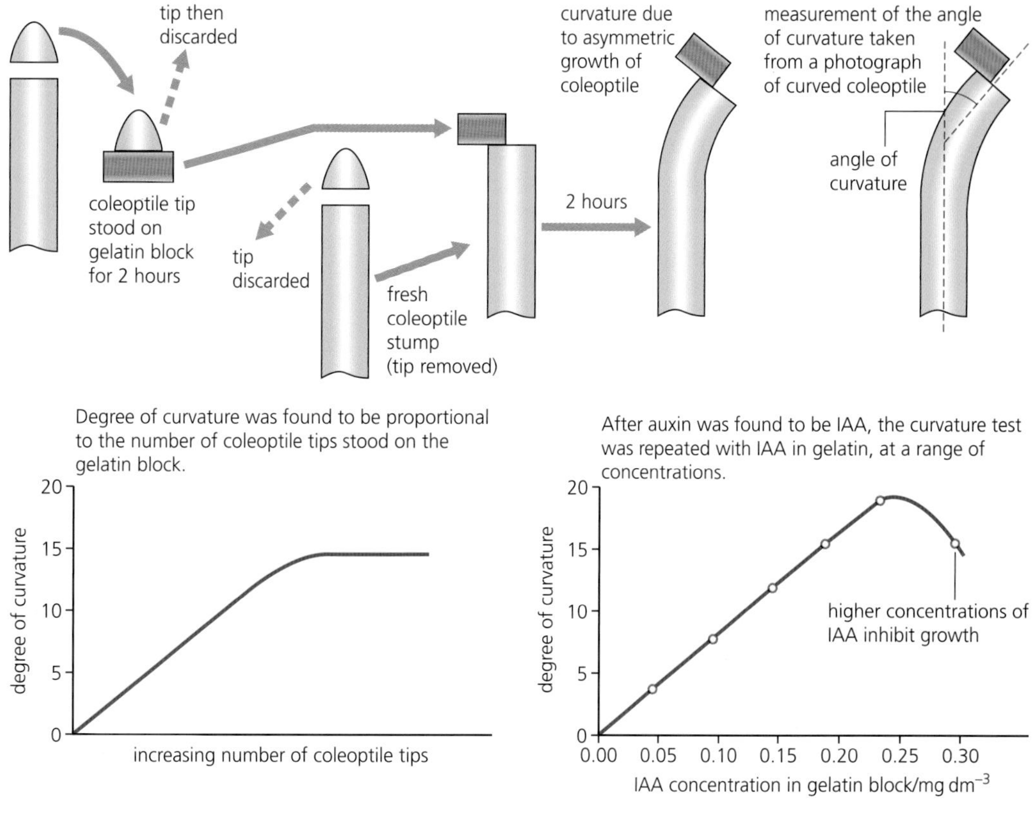

Figure 8.40 Auxin and positive phototropism in coleoptiles.

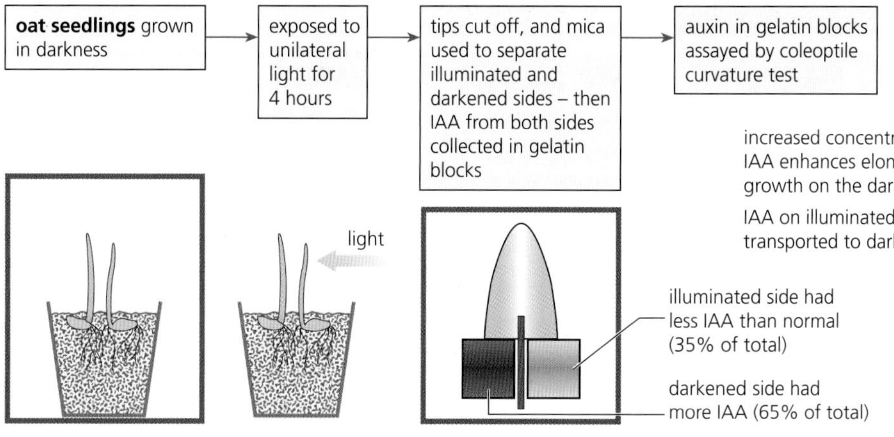

| oat seedlings grown in darkness | exposed to unilateral light for 4 hours | tips cut off, and mica used to separate illuminated and darkened sides – then IAA from both sides collected in gelatin blocks | auxin in gelatin blocks assayed by coleoptile curvature test |

explanation of positive phototropic response of stems

IAA produced in cells of stem tip

IAA travels down through stem tissue

unilateral light

increased concentration of IAA enhances elongation growth on the darkened side

IAA on illuminated side is transported to dark side

illuminated side had less IAA than normal (35% of total)

darkened side had more IAA (65% of total)

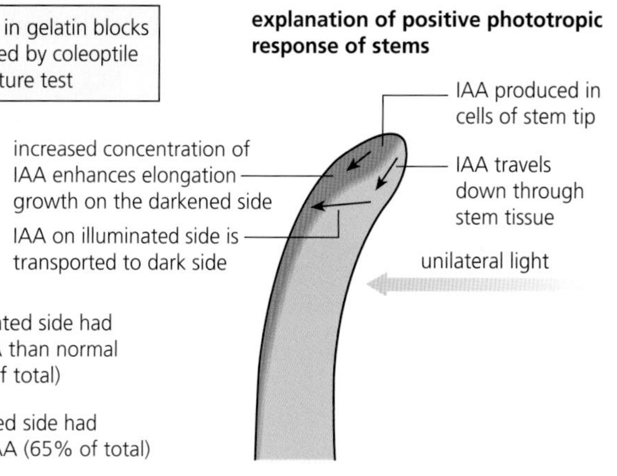

light

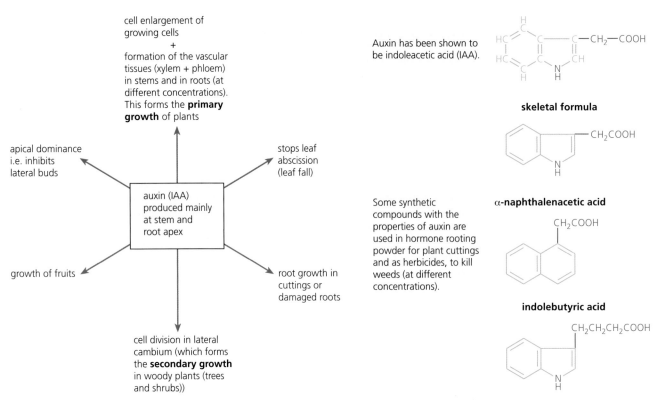

Figure 8.41 The roles of auxin (IAA) in plant growth, and the structure of natural auxin, and synthetic alternatives.

■ Extension: Day length and the control of flowering

Another effect of light on plant growth and development is its role in determining the switch from vegetative growth to the production of flowers (reproductive growth). You will be well aware that most plants flower at different and particular times of the year. In fact, most species have a precise season when flowers are produced. How is flowering switched on by this environmental condition? The answer is that day length provides important signals and these are mediated by a special pigment (Figure 8.42). *We need to examine this pigment first.*

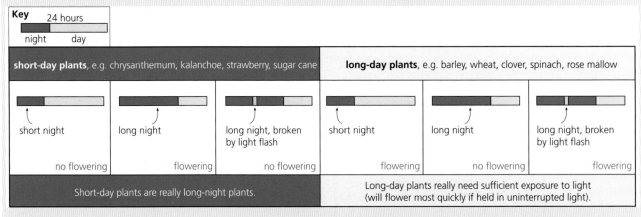

Figure 8.42 Flowering related to day length.

■ Extension: Plant development and phytochrome

A blue–green pigment called **phytochrome** is present in green plants in very low concentrations. The amount of phytochrome is not sufficient to mask chlorophyll, and it has been difficult to isolate and purify the substance from plant tissue, although this has been done. Phytochrome is a very large conjugated protein (protein molecule and pigment molecule, combined), and it is a highly reactive molecule. It is not a plant growth substance, but it is a photoreceptor pigment, able to absorb light of particular wavelength, and change its structure as a consequence. It is likely to react with different molecules around it, according to its structure.

We know that phytochrome exists in two inter-convertible forms. One form, referred to as P_R, is a blue pigment that absorbs mainly red light of wavelength 660 nm (this is what 'R' stands for). The other form is P_{FR}, a blue–green pigment that absorbs mainly far-red light of wavelength 730 nm. When P_R is exposed to light (or red light on its own), it is converted to P_{FR}. In the dark (or if exposed to far-red light alone), it is converted back to P_R.

$$P_R \underset{\text{(slow) darkness (or far-red light alone) (fast)}}{\overset{\text{(slow)   light (or red light alone)   (fast)}}{\rightleftharpoons}} P_{FR},$$

The influence of light on plant growth and development is known as **photomorphogenesis.** Phytochrome is the pigment system involved in photomorphogenesis. We know this because the red/far-red **absorption spectrum** of phytochrome corresponds to the **action spectrum** of some specific effects of light on development. (The terms 'absorption spectrum' and 'action spectrum' are often referred to in photosynthesis, concerning the pigment chlorophyll – you may have come across them in that connection. However, they are explained here in Activity 8.19.)

It appears that it is P_{FR} that is the active form of phytochrome in photomorphogenesis, stimulating some effects in plant development and inhibiting others. In particular, there are examples in the phenomenon of the control of the onset of flowering (Figure 8.43) (A* Extension 8.10).

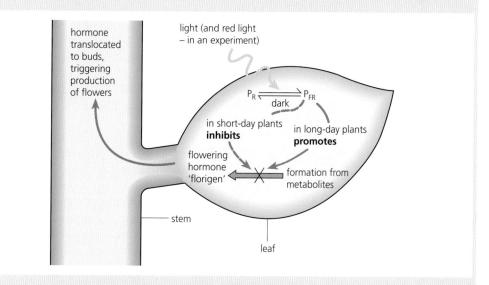

Figure 8.43 Phytochrome and flowering, a suggested hypothesis.

Activity 8.20:
Wellcome Trust Human
Genome website

Activity 8.21: Wider
reading – 'Genomics'

22 What do you
   understand by
   'proteomics'?

8.4 Developments in modern genetics

The Human Genome Project (HGP) was introduced in *Biology for AS* (page 94). There, the issue was related to the search for the gene for cystic fibrosis (CF), and the attempts being made to treat that inherited disorder by gene therapy. We return to the HGP now, in order to discuss the opportunities it is providing for the development of targeted drugs.

Outcomes of the HGP

Ultimately, most if not all aspects of biological investigation will be enhanced by the outcomes of this project. Initially it has been applied specifically to certain issues, including how many individual genes we have and how they work, and the locating of genes that cause genetic disease. The latter discovery has generated the possibility of fundamental cures by means of gene therapy. Here we will illustrate just one other development – that of targeted drugs.

Development of 'targeted drugs'

With the advances made by and from the HGP and the science of proteomics, new disciplines within the field of applied genetics have developed. These include:

■ **bioinformatics** – based upon the use of computers to store and analyse the huge amount of data that is generated as the sequence of bases in different genomes is discovered; this facilitates, among other things, the discovery of comparable gene sequences in different organisms, for example
■ **pharmacogenomics** – analysis of the responses of organisms to drugs, based on their genetic make-up; this process is dependent upon the identification of genes involved in a disease, understanding of how the products of these genes (in their 'healthy' and mutated forms) may be 'active' within cell metabolism, as well as knowledge of how these genes and their products are affected by various potential drugs.

These two disciplines facilitate understanding of disease processes at the molecular level and are leading to the development of new therapeutic procedures. On the horizon, so to speak, is an era of molecular medicine; examples of gene-targeted drug development will help us to understand this innovation.

RNA interference (antisense technology – RNAi), and the suppression of cardiovascular restenosis
In **antisense technology**, tiny RNA molecules are produced that are complementary to part of the base sequence of a messenger RNA (mRNA) copy of a particular target gene. Thus the RNAi, once in position on the mRNA, will block production of the protein the mRNA codes for. This would otherwise have occurred in ribosomes. In this way, a disease gene can indirectly be 'silenced', for example.

We have seen how stenosis of a cardiac artery can be treated by coronary angioplasty and the insertion of a stent (*Biology for AS*, page 31). The term restenosis simply refers to the reoccurrence of stenosis – the formation of a new blockage at the site of the angioplasty or stent placement. It is an unfortunate fact that, within 3–6 months of a stent being inserted, the endothelial cells that line all blood vessels may proliferate around the stent, leading again to a narrowed lumen of the artery at that point. A promising approach to this problem is the coating of a stent, before insertion. Various substances have been experimented with. One successful trial has involved an antisense drug – a specific length of RNAi that works by blocking the action of the gene responsible for the proliferation events in the endothelium there. Trials of this 'drug' have proved successful.

Selective attack on cancer cells

Cancers are diseases of specific somatic cells due to the excessive genetic changes that have been triggered in them. An effectively targeted treatment for cancer needs to selectively attack these cells but leave the surrounding healthy cells entirely alone. Developments arising from the HGP make this possible, in cases where the genes involved have been identified, for it raises the possibility of identifying substances that will interfere with gene expression there. This might be done very precisely by terminating gene transcription into mRNA (or translation of mRNA into a protein). Alternatively, it may be done by killing the mutant cell altogether.

We can illustrate this approach in the disease of colon cancer. Here the cancer cells contain a mutant form of a gene known as *K-Ras*. This mutation disrupts normal signalling in the cell and leads to uncontrolled growth. In a healthy cell, the *K-Ras* gene, known as an oncogene, is transcribed into mRNA, the code of which is translated into a protein that regulates cell division. It instructs the cell to grow and divide or to mature into a specialised function. But in mutated form, this gene has the potential to switch normal growth into uncontrolled, cancerous growth.

In the search for new drugs that will target oncogenes with the mutated *K-Ras* gene, research teams use paired cell colonies (known as cell lines) that differ in only a single mutated gene – the *K-Ras* gene. Both cell lines originated in a colon cancer patient. Using the cell colonies, thousands of drug compounds have been screened. So far, four compounds have been identified that distinguish mutant cells from normal, healthy cells. One of these compounds inhibits the growth of tumours in mice, so it is the subject of further, thorough investigations.

23 The potential development of new drugs by exploiting our growing knowledge of the human genome may raise issues for the community as a whole. Identify key social and ethical issues that you feel are raised, tabulate them, and indicate whether they underpin or undermine such research work.

The production of drugs using genetically modified organisms

Very many organisms have been genetically modified by humans, most of them by means of artificial selection. The majority of the animals and plants used in agriculture, horticulture, transport and leisure pursuits have been bred from wild animals and plants in this way. Artificial selection involves taking the largest and best or the most useful of the offspring for a particular purpose, and using them for the next generation of parents. At the same time, the rest of the offspring are prevented from breeding. The effect of this selection process is the relative speedy and deliberate genetic change of local populations of plants or animals into new varieties, useful to humans.

Today a new type of genetic modification is also in use, known as **genetic engineering**. Genes from one organism are transferred to the set of genes (the genome) of another unrelated organism. The process is also known as **recombinant DNA technology**. The outcomes are new varieties of organisms, mostly but not exclusively of micro-organisms. Micro-organisms are preferred simply because they are easier to modify (SAQ 24). Gene technology has important applications in biotechnology, medicinal drug production (pharmaceuticals industry), gene therapy, agriculture and horticulture. Genetic engineering generates many potential benefits for humans, but there are potential hazards, too. The economic advantages may be out-weighed by environmental and ethical drawbacks or dangers. The issues require balanced and informed judgements (page 191).

24 Explain why a micro-organism may be significantly easier to genetically modify than cells of eukaryotes.

Using a micro-organism

One of the earliest applications of the techniques of genetic engineering was in the production of bacteria containing a gene taken from a eukaryote. For example, the human genes for insulin production were transferred to a strain of the bacterium *Escherichia coli* (Figure 6.14, page 71). Insulin consists of two short proteins (polypeptides) liked together by sulphide bridges (–S–S–). This hormone enables body cells to regulate blood sugar levels, and a supply is needed in the treatment of diabetes. Cultures of *E. coli* have been 'engineered' to secrete insulin, when cultured in a bulk fermenter with appropriate nutrients (Figure 8.44, overleaf).

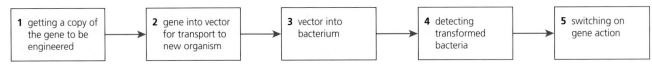

Figure 8.44 The steps involved in genetic engineering of *E. coli* for insulin production.

A strategy for obtaining a copy of the genes for insulin free of the introns that eukaryotic genes contain (page 59) involves starting with messenger RNA, rather than searching for the genes among the chromosomes.

Where is mRNA for insulin to be found?

The human pancreas contains patches of cells (islets of Langerhans) where insulin is produced. The relevant genes in the nuclei of these cells are transcribed to produce messenger RNA. This messenger RNA passes out to the ribosomes in the cytoplasm. Here the base sequence of the RNA is translated into a linear sequence of amino acids of the insulin proteins. In the laboratory, messenger RNA for insulin can be isolated from a sample of human pancreas tissue. Using this RNA and the enzyme reverse transcriptase (itself obtained from a type of virus called a retrovirus, page 79), a copy of the gene can be synthesis, as shown in Figure 8.45.

Figure 8.45 Using reverse transcriptase to build the gene for insulin.

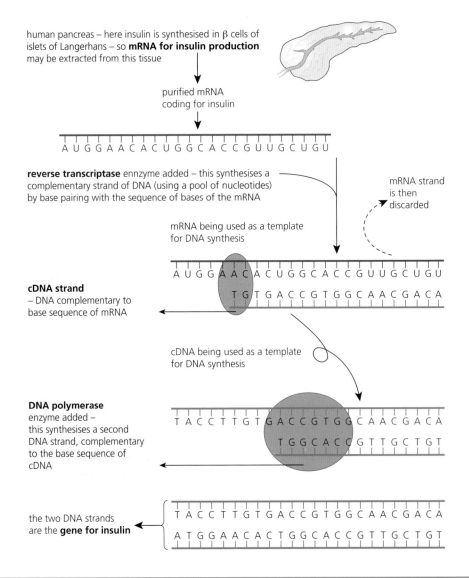

It is a mutant form of *E. coli* that is used in genetic engineering, because in this form it is only able to survive in special laboratory conditions. This is an obvious safety precaution, since otherwise an 'engineered' bacterium might escape at some time in the future, and exchange its genes with gut populations, and cause harm to humans.

Transformed bacteria were cultured in fermenters (vessels used for the growth of micro-organisms in liquid culture) with the transferred gene 'switched on', and there produced proteins of value, in significant quantities. These were extracted and purified from the medium.

Using transformed animals

'Transgenic' organisms have genetic material introduced artificially from another organism. Actually, manipulating genes in eukaryotes is a more difficult process than in prokaryotes. The reasons for this include:

- plasmids, the most useful vehicle for moving genes, do not occur in eukaryotes (except in yeasts) and, if introduced, may not survive and be replicated there
- eukaryotes are diploid organisms, so two forms (alleles) for every gene must be engineered into the nucleus – prokaryotes have a single, circular 'chromosome', so only one copy of a gene has to be engineered into the chromosome
- transcription of eukaryotic DNA to mRNA is more complex than in prokaryotes, where it involves removal of short lengths of 'non-informative' DNA sequences – the introns
- machinery for triggering gene expression in bacteria is known – in eukaryotes the machinery is more complex and is only partially understood.

Despite these difficulties of 'engineering' eukaryotic cells, several varieties of transgenic animal have been produced. Transferred genes may be directly injected into cells, or alternatively they may be incorporated into tiny particles and 'bombarded' into cells at high speed, or introduced through temporary, tiny holes in a cell's plasma membrane that are induced by rapid, brief electrical pulses applied to the cell membrane (known as electroporation). Occasionally, a gene introduced by these methods becomes attached to a chromosome and is then replicated in every cell of the organism that is formed. Success rates can be quite low.

Transgenic sheep have been successfully engineered to yield rare and expensive human proteins in their milk that may be useful as medicines. One example of this type of genetic engineering is the production of a special human blood protein, known as AAT. Production of AAT in our bodies enables us to maintain our vital lung elasticity. Patients with a rare genetic disease are unable to manufacture AAT at all, and they develop emphysema (a disease of the air sacs of the lungs). The chemical industry is unable to manufacture AAT in the laboratory on a practical scale. However, the human gene for AAT production has been identified and isolated, and it has been cloned into sheep, together with a promoter gene (a sheep's milk protein promoter) attached to it. Consequently the sheep's mammary glands produce the human protein and secrete it in their milk, during lactations (Figure 8.46, overleaf). AAT is made available for use with patients.

25 Why is it that a gene which becomes inserted in the nucleus of a fertilised egg cell is also passed to the progeny of the animal that grows from that cell?

Using transformed plants

Vaccines for animals and humans have traditionally been produced by growing the disease-causing organism in culture and then producing dead or 'attenuated' forms to inject into healthy people to induce immunity. The vaccine contains one (or more) proteins from the outer surface of the pathogen that are recognised by the human immune system on entry (that is, they are antigens). Protective antibodies are then produced against the antigen, and the ability to produce them in future (memory cells, pages 85 and 87) is set up.

An alternative approach currently being researched involves the use of a plant and a specific virus that infects it. By genetic engineering, an antigen from the animal pathogen can be added to the plant virus protein coat. If this GM plant virus is used as a vaccine, it will trigger the formation of antibodies against the pathogen's antigen, thereby conferring future immunity against invasion by the actual living pathogen. The plant virus chosen must be chemically robust, and harmless to all organisms except its plant host. This technique is summarised in Figure 8.47 (page 191).

Figure 8.46 The cloning of transgenic sheep to secrete human AAT protein.

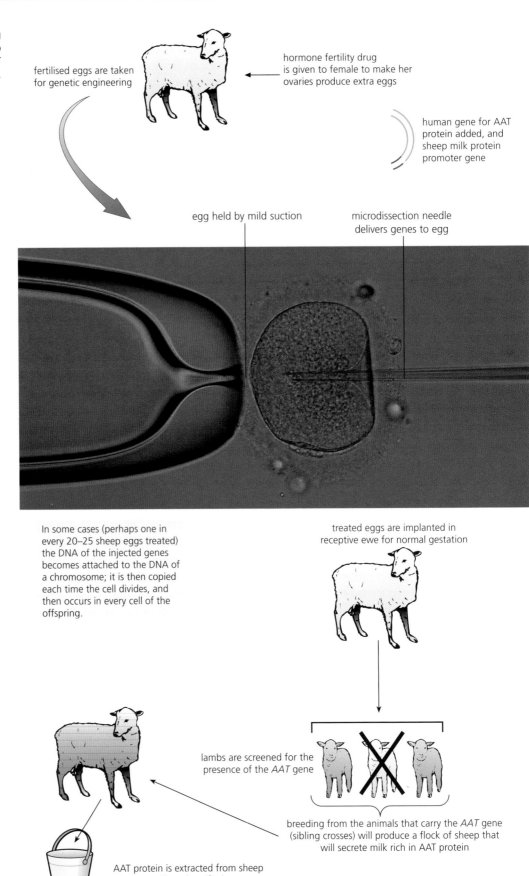

fertilised eggs are taken for genetic engineering

hormone fertility drug is given to female to make her ovaries produce extra eggs

human gene for AAT protein added, and sheep milk protein promoter gene

egg held by mild suction

microdissection needle delivers genes to egg

In some cases (perhaps one in every 20–25 sheep eggs treated) the DNA of the injected genes becomes attached to the DNA of a chromosome; it is then copied each time the cell divides, and then occurs in every cell of the offspring.

treated eggs are implanted in receptive ewe for normal gestation

lambs are screened for the presence of the *AAT* gene

breeding from the animals that carry the *AAT* gene (sibling crosses) will produce a flock of sheep that will secrete milk rich in AAT protein

AAT protein is extracted from sheep milk and purified

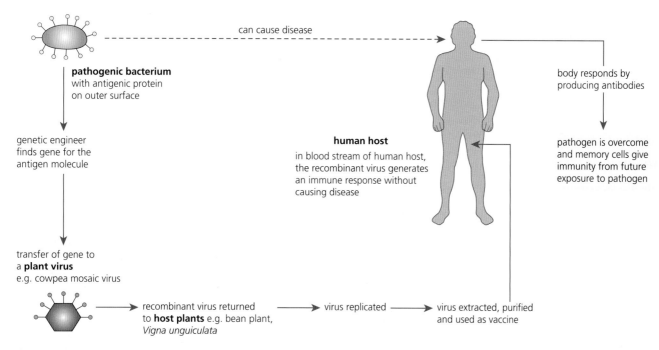

Figure 8.47 Steps to vaccine production using plant viruses.

Environmental and ethical issues of genetic engineering

There are benefits from genetic engineering work illustrated here, but there are also potential dangers. You can learn more about the case *for* GM work with crops from Agricultural Biotechnology Council (2002) *GM Crops: Understanding the Issues* ISBN 0954216504.

You can learn more about the case *against* GM work with crops from:

www.defra.gov.uk/farm/crops/gm/index.htm

www.indsp.org/pshoc.php

In examining the risks and benefits associated with the use of genetically modified organisms, specific ethical issues are raised (Figure 8.48).

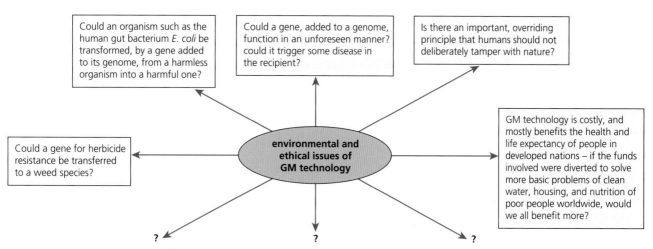

Figure 8.48 Some of the environmental and ethical issues in GM work.

HSW 8.4: HSW Criteria 9, 10 and 12 – Frankenstein foods!

HSW 8.5: Criterion 9 – GM herbicide tolerance in a crop plant such as sugar beet

HSW 8.6: Criterion 9 – A decision to go ahead with a particular GM project may raise ethical or environmental issues

Ethical issues arise for the scientists involved, for legislators and administrators in a position to approve, ban or regulate a development, and for the media when they present issues for public discussion. Ultimately, developments like these need the general support of a majority of the public if they are to come about.

For example, for media people there is the issue of how information is presented (HSW 8.4).

For the scientists involved, there is the need to diligently research any potential dangers in a valuable project, and to appreciate the ethical issues raised by their work. Further, they need to present these to legislators. What ethical issues are raised for them (HSW 8.5)?

For the general public, all applications of GM technology concomitantly raise ethical issues (HSW 8.6).

End-of-topic test

An end-of-topic test is provided as part of the accompanying *Edexcel Biology for A2* Dynamic Learning resources, with (separate) answers.

Sample assessment material produced by Edexcel is available via the Edexcel web site: www.edexcel.org.uk.

Answers to SAQs

1 Lifestyle, health and risk

1 Thin sections of mesophyll cells are necessary because the electron beam travels at high speed but at low energy. Specimens must be thin for electrons to pass through at all. So thin sections are cut and then stained with electron-dense salts to increase contrast. Also, air molecules would deflect this beam, so inside the electron microscope is a vacuum. Consequently, living material must first be killed, 'fixed' in a life-like condition, and dehydrated (water would boil away in a vacuum).

2

Photosystem I	
many accessory pigment molecules	harvest light energy and funnel the energy to a single, key chlorophyll molecule in the reaction centre
reaction centre with chlorophyll a molecule, absorbing light of wavelength 700 nm	has ground-state electrons that are raised to an excited state when light energy is received from the accessory pigments – excited electrons are passed to oxidised NADP$^+$
electron-carrier molecules	receive electrons in excited state and transfer them to NADP$^+$ in the stroma
Photosystem II	
many accessory pigment molecules	harvest light energy and funnel the energy to a single, key chlorophyll molecule in the reaction centre
reaction centre with chlorophyll a molecule, absorbing light of 680 nm wavelength	has ground-state electrons that are raised to an excited state when light energy is received from the accessory pigments – excited electrons are passed to photosystem I
water-splitting enzyme	catalyses the splitting of water into hydrogen ions, electrons and oxygen atoms
electron-carrier molecules	receive excited electrons and pass these on, simultaneous pumping protons from the matrix into the thylakoid compartment

3 Electrons displaced from the reaction centre of photosystem II in an excited state are first passed to reaction centre of photosystem I. Here they are again raised to an excited state and this time they are passed to oxidised NADP (NADP$^+$) to form reduced NADP (NADPH + H$^+$).

4 The important features of ATP, as the universal source of energy for chemical change in cells, tissues and organisms, are that it is able to:
- move easily within cells and organisms, by facilitated diffusion
- take part in many steps in cellular respiration and in very many reactions of metabolism
- transfer energy in relatively small amounts, sufficient to drive individual reactions.

5 NPP of mature rain forest (Puerto Richo) is 54 600 kJ m^{-2} y^{-1}. GPP of lucerne (alfalfa) crop (USA) is 102 480 kJ m^{-2} y^{-1})

6 Humans who eat food of plant origin only are at trophic level 2, as primary consumers. Humans who eat a diverse range of foods, such as hunter-gatherers, are at all 'consumer' trophic levels (level 2 and higher).

7 (1600/14 000) $\times$ 100% = 11.4%

8 a 3050 – (1025 + 1900) = 125 kJ m^{-2}y^{-1}
125 $\times$ 100/3050 = 4.1%
b 3050 $\times$ 100/21 250 = 14.4%

9 For example, in the hypothetical ecosystem illustrated in Activity 5.9 (the bottle ecosystem):
a temperature, light
b predation of flies by spiders and carnivorous plants, herbivory by fruit flies.

10 a high-water plant: channelled wrack
high-water animal: rough winkle
b low water plant: oar weed
low-water animal: acorn barnacle

11 The estimated population size would be halved: 40 ÷ 2 = 20

12 a primary succession
b Decreasing soil density (increasing humus content) with increasing biota; decreasing wind speed with increased density of vegetation (decreased amount of bare ground).

13 a carbon dioxide
b hydrogen carbonate ion
c carbonates e.g. calcium carbonate

14 Atmospheric methane comes from anaerobic decay of organic matter (in bogs, lakes, paddy fields, sewage works, farm slurry pits and landfill sites). Also, it is a waste product of digestion, particularly from ruminants (e.g. cattle) and it escapes when fossil fuels are pumped out or mined, and when their subsequent combustion is incomplete.

15 See The Linnean Society of London: www.linnean.org.

16 There should be no shortage of contentious press reports to record and discuss.

17 The optima of the enzymes of marine plankton will be close to the mean sea water temperature, whereas the optima of the enzymes of an endothermic mammal will be close to its normal body temperature (therefore, much higher than those of the plankton).

18 The extinction of dinosaurs is probably linked with periods of prolonged 'Arctic winter', associated with violent impacts on the Earth's surface of matter from space. TSD would not deliver breeding pairs in these conditions.

19 Table: the arguments of the *Origin of Species* presented as statements (**S**) and deductions (**D**).

S₁	organisms produce a far greater number of offspring than survive to be mature individuals
S₂	the number of individuals in species remain more or less constant
D₁	therefore, many organisms die before they can reproduce
S₃	the individuals in a species are not identical, but show variations in their characteristics
D₂	therefore, some individuals are more successful than others in the competition for survival – so the parents for the next generation will be selected from among those members of the species better adapted to the conditions of the environment
S₄	hereditary resemblance between parents and offspring is a fact
D₃	therefore, subsequent generations will maintain and improve in the degree of adaptation of their parents, by gradual change

20 See **The Hardy–Weinberg principle and disturbing factors**, page 41.

21 Sedimentary rocks are usually laid down under water, often under anaerobic conditions, from sediments washed in from dry land. Objects that fall to the bottom (for example, from dead organisms) are covered and compressed, and their molecules may eventually react with or be replaced by mineral ions.

22

RNA involved in transcription	messenger RNA (mRNA)	A complementary copy of the code of a specific gene (part of the coding strand of DNA of a chromosome)
RNA involved in translation	messenger RNA (mRNA)	mRNA is a linear molecule in the cytoplasm along which ribosomes move, 'reading' the code and transcribing the information into a linear sequence of amino acid residues.
	transfer RNA (tRNA)	In the cytoplasm amino acids available for incorporation into protein are activated by combining with short lengths of transfer RNA (tRNA). The special significance of tRNA is that it permits the translation a three-base sequence into an amino acid sequence.
	ribosomal RNA	RNA is a major component of the ribosomes – the organelles found in the cytoplasm and attached in rough endoplasmic reticulum (RER). Here the mRNA is 'read' and the protein molecules are formed.

6 Infections, immunity and forensics

1 Francis Crick was referring to the realisation that base pairing would ensure accurate ('word perfect') copies of the information in nucleic acids (whether in DNA replication or RNA transcription, as here).

2 See **Extension: Direction in the DNA molecule** and **Figure 6.2**, pages 57–8.

3 See **Peptide linkages** and **Figure 2.22**, in *Edexcel Biology for AS*, page 62.

4 The sequence of changes is illustrated in **Figure 6.2**, page 58.

5 'gact'; on maternal chromosome, it is repeated ×8; on the paternal chromosome it is repeated ×5.

6 Proteins are hydrolysed to shorter chain polypeptides and finally to amino acids by protease enzymes. Here, as a result, the DNA of the chromosomes is freed from its protein component.

7 1.4 mm = 1400 μm; 660 nm = 0.660 μm.

8 You may wish to draw up a table of the differences, focusing on prokaryotic cell structure (the bacterium) contrasted with the 'crystalline' structure of nucleic acid 'core' surrounded by a protein coat (virus).

9 Plants build up the complex organic molecules they require from sugar with the addition of mineral elements absorbed as ions from the soil solution (autotrophic nutrition). Animals, on the other hand, require complex organic molecules of food, which they digest (heterotrophic nutrition). These organic molecules come directly or indirectly from plants (as food chains establish). The supply of nutrients that plants use is limited. When organisms die their bodies become broken down and decomposed, mainly by (saprotrophic) bacteria and fungi. In the process, nutrients are released, passed to the soil solution, and then re-used continuously. This recycling activity is essential for the survival of all living things.

10 Hydrogencarbonate ion → phytoplankton → non-vertebrate, shelled animal → sedimentary rock (later exposed to atmosphere) → weathering of carbonate rock → carbon dioxide of atmosphere.

11 The ciliated epithelium that lines the trachea and bronchi removes any dust particles from the incoming air, because they are trapped in the copious mucus secreted by the numerous goblet cells in the epithelium. In this way, dust particles are prevented from reaching the delicate alveoli.

12 The issue of antibiotic resistance is of great importance today. Many different antibiotics have been discovered, and new ones are searched for. Some new discoveries are effective – and are not toxic to patients. However, problems arise with antibiotics with time. Sooner or later some pathogenic bacteria in a population develop genes for resistance. Consequently, these bacteria survive exposure to the drug, and once competition with other (non-resistant) bacteria is removed by the antibiotic, the resistant pathogenic bacteria flourish. Resistant genes develop either by mutations, or as a result of gene transfer between bacteria by conjugation. In the longer term, the pharmaceutical industry faces the challenge of producing new antibiotics faster than bacteria develop resistance to them.

13 HIV and AIDS almost exclusively handicap the young adult population at their time of greatest economic activity and family building.

14 See **What recognition of 'self' entails**, page 82, and **Figure 6.27**, page 85.

15 Antigens may be present more-or-less anywhere in the body that becomes contaminated from outside the body. Antibodies exist in the blood and lymph, and may be carried in the plasma solution anywhere that blood 'leaks out' – including at sites of invasions.

16 The parts played by the blood in the protection of the body are tabulated here.

inflammation response	rapid, localised response to cuts, blows or bites – involving vasodilatation of capillaries and increased permeability of blood vessels, bringing phagocytic white cells to site, for example
clotting of blood	sealing of gaps due to local haemorrhage, cuts or breaks in vessels – see **The blood clotting mechanism**, *Biology for AS*, page 16
immune response	production of specific antibodies – see **Lymphocytes and the antigen–antibody reaction**, page 82

17 The existence of memory cells avoids the steps involving the production of activated T-cells. The particular memory cell, once re-activated by the re-invading antigen, switches into production of an excess of appropriate plasma cells and helper T-cells.

18 Immunity is resistance to the onset of disease after infection by harmful micro-organisms or internal parasites. Long-lived specific immunity is a result of the action of the immune system, and may be acquired naturally by previous infection, but can also be induced by vaccination. See **In summary – types of immunity**, page 87.

19 An epidemic disease is one of widespread occurrence in a community at a particular time. A pandemic disease is one that is prevalent over a whole country, continent, or the world.

20 Antibiotics are added to the feed of intensively reared livestock such as chicken and pigs. Here they reduce or prevent the incidence of many diseases, and the animals are found to grow better with them. Possible dangers arise from the over-exposure of bacteria to antibiotics.

21

1 Isolation of patients	Because of the possibility of the direct transmission of the disease-causing agent as living cells or spores by contacts, or via airborne transmission of spores.
2 Hand washing by staff and visitors	
3 Gloves and aprons worn	
4 Screening of patients for 'superbug' infections on arrival	Because of the possibility of 'pools' of resistant strains of microorganisms existing in the community the patients come from.
5 Longer term measures	Because resistance to the adverse actions of antibiotics develops more speedily where the microorganisms are exposed to sub-lethal doses.
6 Parallel development	Because resistance to the adverse actions of antibiotics develops more speedily where the microorganisms are exposed to them regularly.

22 $200 - 100 = 100$ hours

23 $7\frac{1}{2}$ days

7 Run for your life

1 The functions of the mammalian skeleton are outlined in the second paragraph on page 99.

2 See **Figures 7.3, 7.4** and **7.5** (pages 103–4).

3 a leg muscles (the 'drumsticks') are predominantly slow-twitch fibres (myoglobin-rich, giving 'dark meat')
  b the flight muscles ('chicken breast meat') are mainly fast-twitch fibres (pale-coloured, 'white meat').

4 The following are produced during glycolysis: NADH; ATP; pyruvate.

5 a Dehydrogenases
  In respiration, all the hydrogen atoms are gradually removed from glucose, catalysed by dehydrogenase enzymes. They are added to hydrogen acceptors, usually NAD (nicotinamide adenine dinucleotide), which itself is reduced. We can write this addition of hydrogen to its carrier as:
  $NAD + 2H \rightarrow NADH_2$
  But what actually happens is:
  $NAD^+ + 2H \rightarrow NADH + H^+$.
  So NAD is a coenzyme that works with specific dehydrogenase enzymes in the oxidation of substrate molecules by the removal of hydrogen.

  b Decarboxylases
  Decarboxylation is the removal of carbon from organic compounds by the formation of carbon dioxide. For example, glucose consists of six carbon atoms. All six carbon atoms are removed at different stages of respiration, one at a time, and given off as carbon dioxide. A specific decarboxylase enzyme is involved in each case. The first decarboxylation in aerobic respiration occurs in the reaction linking glycolysis with the Krebs cycle, when pyruvate is converted to a two-carbon molecule. The other decarboxylation reactions of aerobic respiration occur in steps in the Krebs cycle.

6 In the absence of oxygen, reduced NAD ($NADH_2$) accumulates, and oxidised NAD^+ reserves are used up. In the absence of NAD^+, pyruvate production by glycolysis slows and stops, so subsequent steps in respiration stop too.

7 See **Figure 7.17** page 114. Protons move from the inter-membrane space to the matrix (the interior) of the mitochondrion.

8 a substrate = molecule that is the starting point for a biochemical reaction; it forms a complex with a specific enzyme
  intermediate = metabolite formed as a component of a metabolic pathway
  b see **1 Glycolysis**, page 110, and **2 The link reaction and the Krebs cycle**, page 111
  c see the appendix **Background Chemistry for Biologists**, in the Dynamic Learning resources

9 In effect, the respiratory chamber (in use) is a thermo-barometer. It will reflect changes in atmospheric pressure and temperature during the experiment – as well as oxygen uptake. Are changes in temperature likely to arise from the contact with the hands of the experimenter, as living material is added, for example?

10 lactate and ATP

11 The structure of globular proteins is affected by pH (why?). The activity of enzymes (typically globular proteins) is dependent upon their shape and the structure of their active site. Body pH is held constant at about 7.35–7.45.
  Oxygen partial pressure around respiring cells must be maintained at a high level, and carbon dioxide there must be at a minimum partial pressure (why?). However, the tissue demands for oxygen and production of carbon dioxide vary widely between those of resting tissues and (for example) those of actively contracting skeletal muscle during violent activity. Therefore, the blood circulation (and consequently blood pressure) has to be closely regulated to achieve these levels.

12 Body temperature falls significantly during sleep, but rises above normal during periods of physical activity.

13 Endergonic reactions require energy input, because the products have more potential energy than the reactants. Note: the alternative type of reaction is one in which the products have less potential energy than the reactants, and these reactions transfer energy as heat and work. They are called exergonic reactions.

14 The body is a compact structure. From the body 'core', heat is effectively lost only as it is conducted to the skin, particularly of the extremities.

Heat production by chemical reactions of metabolism (much of which occurs in organs deep inside the body) will be accelerated as temperature rises. Such heat production in an overheated body will be accelerated by positive feedback.

15 a tidal volume = 0.5 dm^3; rate of breathing = 14 breaths per minute

   b rate of oxygen consumption
   = volume of oxygen used (dm^3) ÷ time (s)
   = (3.75 − 2.25 dm^3) ÷ 60 s
   = (1.5 ÷ 60) dm^3 s^{-1}
   = 0.025 dm^3 s^{-1}

(Note that the volume measurements are taken at the same point in the breathing cycle at the start and finish of the time period.)

16 Adrenaline is secreted in 'flight or fight' situations, when the individual is suddenly startled or attacked, or otherwise believes itself to be in danger. Adrenaline prepares the body for exertion and high physical and mental performance.

17 See **Control of cardiac output**, page 126.

18

	Heart rate	Stroke volume	Cardiac output
trained athlete at rest	slower than that of an untrained person – typically 50 bpm (rather than 70 bpm)	greater than that of an untrained person – typically 100 cm^3 (rather than 70 cm^3)	about 5 dm^3 min^{-1} – whether or not a person is trained
trained athlete during exercise	rises to 195 bpm (whether or not a person is trained)	rises, typically to 180 cm^3 (rather than 110 cm^3 in an untrained person)	about 35 dm^3 min^{-1} (compared with 22 dm^3 min^{-1} in an untrained person)

19 Bone is a living tissue. The specialised bone cells, called osteocytes, are surrounded by a hard matrix (ground substance). The cells occur in tiny cavities (lacunae) in the matrix, with cytoplasmic connections in tiny tubes. Chemically, bone is approximately 70% mineral matter, a form of calcium phosphate, and 30% organic matter, mainly collagen fibres. Bone cells both secrete and maintain (or repair) this matrix. The matrix is impervious to tissue fluid, but blood vessels run into the bone and blood delivers essential nutrients and removes waste products.

Bone is a very strong tissue, and especially able to resist compression. There are two types of bone tissue, compact bone and spongy bone. Compact bone makes up the greater part of the bones of the body. It has osteocytes arranged in concentric rings around a central canal, known as Haversian systems. The spaces within spongy bone contain bone marrow tissue.

It is the activities if these living cells in bones that bring about repairs, given a supply of nutrients, delivered by blood capillaries.

20 Oedema arises when an excess of tissue fluid is formed and not re-absorbed. The organs and tissues of the body swell up. EPO will trigger oedema by increasing capillary blood pressure – the flow of blood being impeded by its raised viscosity.

8 Grey matter

1 In **negative feedback**, the effect of a deviation from the normal or set conditions is to create a tendency to eliminate the deviation. Negative feedback is a part of almost all control systems in living things. The effect of negative feedback is to reduce further corrective action of the control system once the set-point value is reached (page 118).

In **positive feedback**, the effect of a deviation from the normal or set condition is to create a tendency to reinforce the deviation. Positive feedback intensifies the corrective action taken by a control system, so leading to a 'vicious circle' situation. Imagine a car in which the driver's seat was set on rollers (not secured to the floor), being driven at speed. The slightest application of the foot brake causes the driver to slide and to press harder on the brake as the car starts to slow, with an extreme outcome.

Biological examples of positive feedback are rare, but one can be identified in a nerve fibre during transmission of an impulse. When a wave of depolarisation takes effect in the post-synaptic membrane, the entry of sodium ions triggers the entry of further sodium ions at a greater rate. This is a case of positive feedback – after the depolarised state is established, it triggers the accelerated movement of the action potential along the post-synaptic membrane.

Another example is in the process of birth and its hormonal control. Stretching of the cervix triggers release of the hormone oxytocin from the posterior pituitary gland at the base of the brain. Oxytocin causes muscles of the uterus wall to contract, pushing the baby against the enlarging cervix, stretching it further. As stretching increases, so more oxytocin is released.

2 a See **The resting potential**, page 141.
   b See **The action potential**, page 142.

3 See **Speed of conduction of the action potential**, page 144.

4 a See **Synapses – the junctions between neurones**, page 145.
   b See **Figures 8.7** and **8.8**, pages 145 and 146.

5 The blind spot is where the nerve fibres from the retina meet and become the optic nerve. The fovea is the point of most accurate vision.

6 See **Neurones – structure and function** page 139, and **Figure 8.13**, page 152.

7

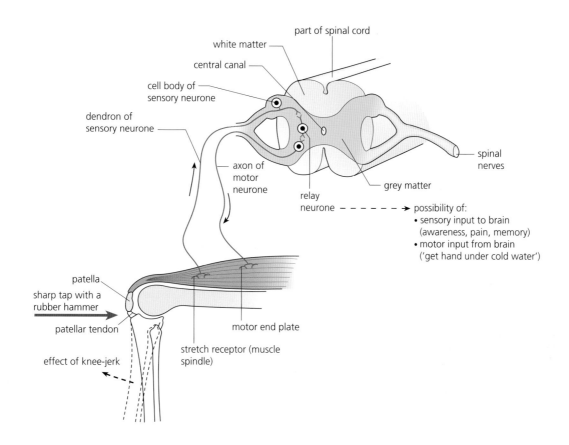

part of spinal cord

white matter

central canal

cell body of
sensory neurone

dendron of
sensory neurone

axon of
motor
neurone

relay
neurone

grey matter

spinal
nerves

possibility of:
• sensory input to brain
  (awareness, pain, memory)
• motor input from brain
  ('get hand under cold water')

patella

sharp tap with a
rubber hammer

patellar tendon

effect of knee-jerk

motor end plate

stretch receptor (muscle
spindle)

8 See Chapter 7, **Control of cardiac output**, page 126..

9 See **Figure 8.18**, page 156.

10 A reduction in the size of the pupil (equivalent to the iris diaphragm of a camera) increases the depth of focus.

11 See **Extension: The brain and decision making – an introduction**, page 159.

12 The critical period falls within the period from week 4 to the week preceding the three-month stage of development.

13 Your explanation should centre on the ideas that 'nature' means genetically determined, and that 'nurture' means based upon life experiences and environmental influences.

14 'Hard-wired' responses are due to patterns of neurones and synaptic connections laid down during embryological development and therefore present at birth, rather than forming in response to stimulation from the external environment.

15 Examples include:
  ■ becoming unaware of road noises after living within close proximity to a busy motorway for some time
  ■ lack of awareness of clothes touching your skin, soon after dressing.

16

	Myelinated	Non-myelinated
Structure	see **Figure 8.1**, page 140	similar, but without the presence of any Schwann cells and myelin sheath
Function	identical, but differing in the speed of conduction – see **Speed of conduction of an action potential**, page 144	

17

Short-term memory	Long-term memory
The repeated activation of neurone pathways without any associated disturbance or adverse effect leads to gradual inactivation of Ca^{2+} channels in pre-synaptic membranes. That is, short-term memory has a chemical, physiological basis at the level of neurones.	The repeated activation of neurone pathways together with an associated disturbance or adverse effect leads to the formation of additional synapses within the neurone pathways concerned, together with the formation of more synaptic vesicles containing transmitter substances. That is, long-term memory has a structural basis together with a chemical, physiological basis at the level of neurones.

18 The table below lists a number of points contrasting ethical standpoints on the use of animals in medical research – virtually contradictory – which you may have raised in response to this issue.

'Animal rights' case	'Animal welfare' rather than rights
Questions the assumption that humans have the automatic right to make decisions for other animals.	Animals are unable to enter into a social contract or make moral choices – so cannot be regarded as having 'rights'. Only human beings have duties and 'rights'.
Animals should no longer be regarded as property, or used as food, clothing, research subjects or for entertainment.	There is nothing inherently wrong with using animals as a resource for human purposes – a cost–benefit analysis should be applied to justify certain types of research whilst prohibiting others.
Before medical procedures are performed on humans, informed consent is required. All other sentient beings should be treated similarly.	There are pragmatic decisions to be made, weighing the benefits to society against any pain, suffering or death of animals.
The total abolition of animal research is the only acceptable response to this practise, which otherwise is an abuse of our position.	Humans have an obligation to ensure that animals do not suffer unnecessarily. We should work to replace the use of animals with alternatives where possible, so as to reduce the occasions they are required.
Animals should be regarded as members of the moral community. The legal 'thinghood' of animals should now be recognised.	Where issues such as the effectiveness of a cure for a cancer, the development of a vaccine for malaria, or the protection of people against devastating side effects of a new drug are at stake, the controlled, regulated use of animals is not inherently wrong.

Are there other arguments or points that should be stated?

19 An even more intractable issue – or a straightforward example of essential animal experimentation?

20 A concise presentation your research could be added to a 'wall newspaper', to which all your peers contribute on this issue. This provides the opportunity to identify the points that generate the most concern to your peer group, at this point in time. Remember, when clean water was not available – for example, in the time of John Snow (the first epidemiologist, 1813–58) – beers were consumed by adults and children to avoid exposure to diseases like cholera. (This beer was much weaker than is usual today – perhaps 2% alcohol.)

21 Light has diverse effects on plants, including:
- it is required for the manufacture of sugar in photosynthesis
- it inhibits extension growth in length of stems (so plants growing in the dark 'bolt', whereas plants in full light are short and sturdy)
- it causes positive phototropic growth and 'sun-tracking'
- it promotes expansion of leaf blades
- it is a requirement for the formation of chlorophyll (so plants in the dark are yellow)
- it triggers the switch from vegetative growth to flowering in many species, in response to some particular regime of light and dark (day and night) cycles
- it triggers germination in a few species.

22 The study of proteins. The term is reminiscent of 'genomics' – the study of genes. Perhaps this term recognises the parallel importance of 'proteins' and 'genes'?

23 One personal response to this challenge is as follows.

Social issues

cost	Is the community getting 'value for money'?
availability	Are the benefits available to all?
diversional effects	Would the money be better invested in different initiatives – such as … ?

Ethical issues

rights and justice	Responses here will depend upon the views expressed regarding the 'social issues' above, as well as upon personal values and standards.
utilitarianism	
common good / virtue	

24 Manipulating genes in prokaryotes is easier than in eukaryotes because:
- plasmids, the most useful vehicle (vector) for moving genes, occur in prokaryotes, and are absent in eukaryotes (except in yeasts)
- prokaryotes have a single, circular 'chromosome', so only one of a gene has to be engineered into their chromosome – in eukaryotes (diploid organisms), two forms (alleles) for every gene must be engineered into the nucleus
- transcription of DNA to mRNA does not have the complexities it has in eukaryotes (where it involves removal of short lengths of 'non-informative' DNA sequences within the mRNA)
- the machinery for triggering gene expression in bacteria is known and understood and is less complex than it is in eukaryotes.

25 All the cells of the organism formed from a zygote have the same genome – including any gene inserted into a chromosome of the egg cell by a genetic engineer.

Index